A Most Unladylike Occupation

Lisa Wright

The Book Guild Ltd

First published in Great Britain in 2018 by
The Book Guild Ltd
9 Priory Business Park
Wistow Road, Kibworth
Leicestershire, LE8 0RX
Freephone: 0800 999 2982
www.bookguild.co.uk
Email: info@bookguild.co.uk
Twitter: @bookguild

Typeset in Aldine BT 401

Printed and bound in Great Britain by CPI Group (UK) Ltd, Croydon, CR0 4YY

ISBN 978 1912362 929

British Library Cataloguing in Publication Data.
A catalogue record for this book is available from the British Library.

With love for Martin, who always aids and abets me

Prologue

The French windows were open onto the lawn on a glorious early September morning at the Boyce Court in Gloucestershire. Though the dew was fading it remained glistening on the grass. Most of the family was at the breakfast table but Mary, in riding habit, was pulling on her riding boots and lifting her skirts to the knees before she set off round the house to the stables.

Ginny the maid came in with a packet of letters and handed them to Squire George.

"Anything for me?" said Mary.

"No," said the Squire, riffling through the pile. "Two for me, two for Mother, three for Horace, one for Evelyn from Lucy."

Ethel, the oldest sister, rarely received any letter, and went on eating toast, but looked expectant.

The maid took the letters round the table to Mrs Deane.

"Thank you, Ginny, just another five minutes, then you can clear away," said Mrs Deane.

"Yes Madam," said Ginny. Five minutes meant she had to go all the way back to the kitchen and then back again. Nothing useful could be done in five minutes, not enough time to make a bed or do any dusting. She pressed her lips together and left the room.

Ethel watched the others opening their letters as she chewed her toast.

Evelyn made a clucking noise as she read.

"What has she done this time?" said Ethel.

"Nothing yet," said Evelyn, "She's busy giving her lectures for the Health Society. Says she doesn't get home till half past ten. BUT – she says they like her talks – says her first lecture got twenty-eight people, but the one last week had forty-one. She says she's made quite a hit."

"Well, she would say that wouldn't she?" said Ethel. "She always tells us when she's made a hit."

"Why do you have to be so catty, Ethel? She is really good at giving the health talks; the women do really listen. She makes it interesting for them and she doesn't talk down to them. I was caught up in it all myself when I went to listen to her."

"Yes, but you've got the do-gooder streak yourself – you just don't blow your own trumpet so much!"

Mrs Deane sighed. "Girls, girls, stop it. Lucy is admirable, and Hyacinth too, in her own way, and they both have to make their own way in the world."

Evelyn was triumphant. "Well, Lucy certainly will. She says here she is going to apply for the post of a Female Sanitary Inspector in Kensington!"

A bombshell could not have caused more effect.

Ethel stood up. "A SANITARY INSPECTOR!"

Squire Deane's mouth fell open.

Mrs Deane blenched. "Oh dear! Oh dear!"

She rang the bell for the maid.

Harry and Becky Porter lived in one of the alleys between Fenchurch Street and the River Thames. The alleys were narrow and dark, but the Porters' top floor window, their only window, faced east, and in summer mornings the sun's rays brightened their room for a few hours at the beginning of the day.

This morning brought them a September sunrise that gave promise of a truly warm day. Even this early, with the church clock just striking six, the beams crept across the floorboards and warmed the faces of the man and woman sleeping on the mattress on the floor under the window. The woman stirred. "Six's struck, 'arry." She shook him gently and then looked into the old wooden drawer beside her. It was padded with rough strips of blanket, and a very small baby lay swaddled inside. She picked it up and cradled it. It stirred a little and half opened its eyes, gazing at her.

"There, Lily love, 'allo, Lily." She put the baby to her breast, but little Lily turned her face away. "Come on, Lily, I ain't got much, you need to get all there is." Lily gave a sad listless mew, and wrinkled her face. Her mother inspected the wrappings.

"She's no better, Harry, she's hardly wet, and she won't suck."

Harry stood up and looked at his daughter as he pulled on a pair of threadbare trousers. "Hallo, little Lil. The kids can take 'er out today. A bit of sun might do 'er good. What can I eat?"

"There's bread, enough for all of us, and I saved you a potato from last night. I can light the fire if you'd like a cup of tea."

"Don't bother, water'll do. It's going to be a hot day. I'd best be off." He had landed a job as a casual labourer on a new building site across the river, and last night the family had enjoyed a thick stew with a few bits of pork sausage in it. This week he was earning 2s 6d a day, good wages. He was off, whistling, before the church clock had struck the half past.

Becky rocked her inert baby and put her to the breast again, but Lily seemed to have dozed off, so she laid her down and put on her skirt and blouse. She stirred her older three children with her foot as they slept on the other mattress in the corner. "Wake up, you lazy lot, it's a lovely day. Up you get Ida, we need the water. NOW!"

Ida was a thin child with the same wide, gap toothed smiling face as her father. She sat up at once. "'Ow's Lily?"

"She's ill. She still won't drink. I'll try 'er with some boiled water when you've got it."

Ida scrambled into her skirt and bodice and laced up her boots and set off with the water bucket for the pump at the entrance to the alley. Several women and children were there before her with buckets and kettles. Two women asked after Lily and shook their heads and looked grave.

As she hauled the bucket, step by step up the rickety staircase, the door to their room was open and she saw Job and three year old Mina sitting on their pots in a ray of sunshine; they were blowing the hundreds of fur particles floating around them like bubbles, and laughing, spitting them out as they wafted into their mouths and noses.

"Look at 'em, Ma, ain't they silly!"

Becky straightened up from pulling her mattress onto the one in the corner, shaking out the blankets and folding them neatly. She had built a small fire in the grate and now poured some of the water into the kettle and set it to boil.

"You can't go to school today, Ida. You'll 'ave to stay 'ere with Min and Lily. I'll take Job to school when I go to fetch the fur."

Ida pulled a face but said nothing. She dressed Mina and sat her on the bench at the table, and cut them all a slice of bread, spreading it thinly with jam. She poured some warm water into the mugs, put a spoonful of sugar into each one and stirred it round. When the kettle boiled she made her mother a cup of strong tea with sugar. "Do you want bread, Ma?"

Becky shook her head; she rocked the sick baby gently, holding her close to her, shielding the minute pale head from the rays of the sun.

"I'll have to go in a minute to get the sack of fur. Job will have to wait at school early, until the gate opens, or I shall miss the easiest sacks. Mina, be a good girl for Ida. Keep the sun out of Lil's eyes. Come on, Job. I'll be back as soon as I can."

"She'll be good as good, won't you Min?"

Mina nodded silently.

Left to themselves, Ida settled Mina on the mattress pile with her comfort rag and her peg dolly, wiped the table of crumbs, and rinsed the mugs in the enamel basin.

Job was not the first child waiting outside the school railings, but he was the youngest, and preferred to stay gripping the gates until the teachers arrived at a quarter to eight.

"Ida will fetch you tonight. Don't move till she come." Becky ruffled his hair and hurried off.

The Furrier's Emporium was an imposing edifice towards Holborn. The queue at the back of the building was already into double figures, with women waiting to collect the poorer quality smaller skins, rabbit, fox, beaver, squirrel, hare. The furriers displayed the first class furs on their premises and fashioned the garments with magnificent sable, ermine, mink, astrakhan, but farmed out the cheaper skins to home workers to be brushed, scraped, cut, combed, and rubbed clean and smooth. The skins smelt and their hairs were matted with scabs and scars and scratches, and the homes of the workers, where the cooking and eating and sleeping and day-to-day living went on, were thick with the grease, and the particles of fur that hung in the air, and in the lungs and eyes and food of the workers and their families. The cleaned furs were taken back to the furriers who paid a pittance according to the size and quality of each piece.

The golden September sun moved steadily down the alley as Becky carried her canvas sack up the stairs. The door to her room stood open. Ida and Mina were sitting on the bench by the window in the sun; the myriad motes of the fur swinging lazily like cream and white snowflakes from the draught. Ida held the baby; and her large tears dropped silently onto the table. Mina stroked Lily's white cheek.

Lucy Deane woke very early indeed despite her late lecture the evening before. This was the morning she was going to hand in her application form for the post of Female Sanitary Inspector for the Royal Borough of Kensington. The sun streamed into the bedroom window of the little house at 100 Fulham Road as she washed and dressed with great care. It was going to be a perfect September day.

Hyacinth was already up and dressed, making tea and cutting bread. The sisters embraced.

"How did the lecture go last night?"

"I enjoyed it, and so did they, I know. There were at least twenty more there than last week, the village hall was more than half full."

"You must be really tired."

"Not too bad. I was lucky enough to get a carriage to myself, and I dozed until Charing Cross. There were some rough sorts around the station, so I treated myself to a cab home. Thanks for leaving me the soup."

"Well, I'm sorry I didn't stay up for you. I said I would go in to help the new students settle in, so I can't be late. I'm off right now."

"We'll talk tonight."

"Yes. Are you going to wear the brown bowler hat with the wide brim?"

"I thought I would."

"Well, don't. Wear the small black felt with the pheasant feathers. Much more business-like." And Hyacinth set off.

Lucy obediently wore the black hat. Mrs Casey, their daily servant, arrived just as she was setting out.

"You're looking very smart, Miss Lucy, so bright and early!"

"Thank you, Mrs Casey. I'm off to the Town Hall to hand in my application form. Hyacinth has left you a note for the shopping."

"I'll deal with it, Miss Lucy, don't you worry. You really do look very handsome."

Lucy walked purposefully to the Town Hall and found another young woman there as well. They looked at one another's envelopes and laughed. The elderly clerk who took the letters bowed and then gestured to the steps. "Ah, Dr Dudfield is arriving at this moment." Thomas Orme Dudfield, the redoubtable Medical Officer of Health for Kensington, greeted them as they introduced themselves. Miss Dunbar. Miss Deane.

"Rest assured that we shall look at all the applications with great care and interest," said he. "The Kensington Vestry consider these new posts to be of immense importance, as do I. We are breaking new ground with the Health and Safety Requirements for workers and outworkers in the Borough, particularly women workers. Those of you who will be appointed will be pioneers in this field. Good day to you both." He raised his hat and went up the stairs to his office.

"Mercy," said Miss Dunbar. "I feel quite overcome. Pioneers! I feel us pioneers need a cup of tea."

They took a bus to the Army and Navy Co-operative Society in Victoria Street, and ran into two friends of Miss Dunbar in the refreshment room. There were introductions all round. Miss Hadlow – Miss Deane – Miss Deane – Miss Amberley. Miss Hadlow was to be married next month. Miss Amberley was currently helping with a Girls' Friendly Society Club on Friday nights in Putney.

"We are applying for the posts of Sanitary Inspectors at Kensington Town Hall."

"A paid job?"

"Oh, yes!"

The Misses Hadlow and Amberley looked incredulous.

"Inspectors? That sounds frightfully important. Will we have to curtsey to you?"

"No, no. It's very down to earth. We shall have to inspect laundries, and dressmakers, and milliners!"

"But what FOR?"

"To see if they are overcrowded, and if they have enough light, and to see if they work too many hours."

"And suppose they ARE overcrowded?"

"Then we would have to make a report, and the Medical Officer of Health would require them to make more room."

"And suppose they haven't got any more room."

"They might have to sack some people or even close." said Miss Dunbar.

"That would be TERRIBLE! Poor people! You couldn't do that!"

"Well," said Miss Hadlow, "as long as you don't close down Madame Julius in Queens Gate until after October 15th. They're making my wedding dress, AND the dresses for my six bridesmaids, AND my mother's dress, and lots of things for me and the girls. So don't you dare close them down before that. I don't care what you do after. Come, Rosalie, we shall be late for lunch with Mother."

"Goodbye. Goodbye, Miss Deane. Lovely to have met you. I do think you are both very brave." And they wafted away.

Lucy said to her new ally, "I realised we wouldn't be very popular with the employers – or the employees – I hadn't realised we wouldn't be popular with the customers!"

Miss Dunbar nodded. "Good job we didn't get on to the subject of sanitary conveniences."

Lucy walked on to the offices of the National Health Society off Oxford Street. The receptionist smiled. "Good morning Miss Deane. Miss Lankester is free at this moment. Do go up…"

Lucy ran up the stairs, knocked at the door and went in.

"Oh, Lucy, how good to see you. Did you decide to apply for the Kensington post?"

"I did. I took in my application myself."

"Well, I wish you good luck. Miss Rose Squire has applied as well. I expect there will be many applications, but I feel you both have a good chance. I have heard excellent reports of your lecture evenings."

"You taught us so well, Miss Lankester."

"We teach everyone well, Lucy, but they don't all turn out as accomplished as you."

"I truly enjoy the lecturing."

"That's obvious from the remarks from Erith and Chatham. It will be a pity for us if you do get the Inspector's post. You won't be able to continue the health lecturing."

Lucy looked downcast.

"Never mind. Dr Dudfield is determined that there shall be qualified Female Sanitary Inspectors – not just in London, but nationwide, and he is a force in the land. To be the first would be a true prize!"

On the evening of the interviews at Kensington Town Hall Lucy felt sick with nerves. Hyacinth put her arms around her. "Don't be silly, Lucy. I know you're better than all those others."

"Oh, Hye, how can you know?"

"I just do."

Faithful Mrs Casey had waited to go home after work until Lucy had set off. She brushed a hair from Lucy's shoulder.

Lucy pulled herself together. "We're both in the same boat. You must be anxious about your final cookery exams."

Hye shook her head. "No, I'm not. I know I have at least passed them. I can't not have. So I shall find a post somewhere – not ground breaking like you, of course. Off you go."

She pinned a tiny posy to Lucy's coat, kissed her, waved her off and crossed all her fingers.

Mrs Casey crossed her fingers as well, and set off home. She watched until Lucy had crossed the road towards Sydney Street; then she took a swig from her hip flask, slid it back into her pocket, patted the pocket, and set off in the opposite direction.

There were four short-listed candidates for the post of Sanitary Inspector, and Lucy was the first to be interviewed. The elderly gentlemen of the Kensington Vestry were courteous, but were clearly bemused by the whole situation, and it was left to Dr Dudfield to ask the probing, and sometimes awkward, questions. Lucy did not know whether she had given a good account of herself or not. Then she had to wait while the three other candidates went in and out. Miss Squire was there but no sign of Miss Dunbar. Finally the door to the interview room opened, and a flustered woman came out. She had a set smile on her face but it was clear that tears were not far away.

Out came the elderly clerk. "Thank you very much, ladies, that concludes our interviews for this evening. The Vestry will send you their reports by post in the morning. I hope you all have comfortable journeys home. May we call a cab for any of you?"

They gathered up their belongings and shook hands with each other. As they reached the top of the stairs Lucy and Rose Squire stopped for a few words with each other, and the clerk beckoned them. "Ladies, Dr Dudfield and the Chairman of the Vestry would like to see you for a moment."

Hye opened the door for her. "I was watching for you. How did it go?"

"I got the post, Hye, and so did a woman called Rose Squire. Both of us have a six month probationary period. They asked me all the easy questions, I was lucky, one poor woman got asked real posers. I would have been hard put to it to answer any of hers. Dr Dudfield and Mr Braye from the Kensington Vestry really worked hard for me, I'm convinced. At the end they called me in and then asked my age! I said, 'I think it more honest to leave that to your judgement, gentlemen.' And they laughed."

"Wonderful," said Hye, and waved a piece of paper under Lucy's nose, "so now I can tell you. I passed too! TOP! FIRST in Plain Cooking – FIRST in Haute Cuisine – all the other sections I got a first or a second class. The letter came by the evening post just after you'd gone."

"Oh, Hye, what a night!" And they hugged and danced round the living room.

"Have we got anything to toast ourselves with?"

"Nothing alcoholic. Cocoa will do."

At Boyce Court Evelyn ran into the morning room. "Lucy has got the post as Sanitary Inspector."

"My goodness!" said Mrs Deane, looking up from her desk.

"Oh, for heaven's sake!" said Ethel.

"That'll put a damper on our social activities," said Mary, busy sketching ivy and robins for a watercolour. "You can imagine at our next dance – May I introduce our cousin, the Sanitary Inspector – all the young men will FLOCK to dance with her! And our other cousin, the Good Plain Cook!"

"You are impossible, hateful," cried Evelyn, "They are first rate. If I can help them in any way, I will."

"We all will, Evelyn," soothed Mrs Deane. "And I shall write to congratulate them at once. AND invite them for Christmas."

1

First steps

Miss Lankester rejoices; Lucy meets Eliza Orme; Rose Squire; Aunt Augusta; Miss Lankester's plans; Mrs Casey hits the bottle; Lucy meets May Abraham; Lucy's first conference speeches.

Miss Lankester was ecstatic next day when Lucy went to tell her the good news. "Both of you! Tremendous! And tremendous for us too – and for the honour of our National Health Society." She indicated a lady sitting beside her desk. "May I introduce Miss Bateson of the *Queen Magazine*?"

Miss Bateson seemed very enthusiastic. "May I interview you and Miss Squire on your appointments? Have you photographs we could insert in the article?"

Lucy had not thought of photographs.

"Oh, do," said Miss Bateson. "I am sure your faces will be in great demand in the future."

Lucy laughed. "I'll leave you to your meeting. It's a great day for us. My younger sister has passed her final Cookery College exams with Distinction too."

"Lucy, before you go. There is a Conference of Women in Trade and Industry in Leeds next month. The Duchess of Bedford is President. Would you read a paper on woman inspectors and their expected roles?"

"I – yes, Miss Lankester, if you think it would be useful."

"It would be momentous. And I shall arrange for you to meet Miss Eliza Orme. She can give you good advice."

"Goodness. The first woman lawyer."

"She was vastly influential in her quiet way on the Commission into the state of women in workshops and dangerous trades."

"Thank you, Miss Lankester. I should be honoured to meet her."

A few days later Lucy arrived at Eliza Orme's room in Bedford Square. Miss Orme was a true pioneer, graduating in Law in 1888. She came from a Liberal family, supported women's suffrage, women's education, and reforms of women's labour conditions; she had opened the first women's law office and served as the senior woman representative on Asquith's Commission on Women's Labour in 1891.

Lucy was expecting a fierce, terrier like female, but not so. She was shown into a feminine room, with a cheerful fire burning, pretty ornaments on the shelves. The room was lined with files and books, but the desk was polished. Comfortable chairs with soft cushions were by the fire. Small, dumpy, with soft wispy hair, Miss Orme came to greet her.

"My dear Miss Deane, welcome. I am delighted to meet a fellow fighter for the Women's Cause. Miss Lankester writes in glowing terms."

"She has been more than kind and helpful. I am so grateful."

"Sit in the warm, dear, by the fire. Well it won't be plain sailing, I assure you, but you will find many in Government WILL give you real help and backing. Dr Dudfield is a precious ally. He has worked for twenty years in Kensington – knows the problems inside out – though many of them have come from the Kensington Vestry themselves, a sadly complacent lot. It was Thom Dudfield who first got Asquith interested in women workers, and collected us women onto the Commission."

She began to walk about the room and speak very fast and fluently. "What can I tell you? Have you met May Abraham yet? Wonderful young woman, razor sharp, very persuasive. You must meet her. And Lady Dilke – very down to earth, despite her title – very influential – head screwed on for all her arts and crafts ways. Never sentimental about the women she sets out to help. Nor must you be. MUST be highly organised – daily notes – record every letter received or sent. Or someone will trip you up. Keep TABULATED reports, who you see, what they say, where you are. I'll show you some of mine.

"And don't expect conditions in workshops to be much higher than the girls' own homes. They share one privy between three or four families.

But the privy the workplace provides has GOT to be clean. There MUST be enough ventilation – and it must be permanently open. You must make sure it's fixed at the top of the window, or they'll just pull the sash down if it's cold and get no air at all.

"Don't believe ANYTHING without seeing the evidence for yourself. Women and girls lie awfully, just as bad as men. Examine and inspect thoroughly, girls and managers both. Women shop workers are different from men, men want MONEY, women want comfortable quarters. They'll go for a position where there's a choice of 'tea or cocoa' and shorter hours, and a chair they can loll in for ten minutes.

"Oh, and keep clear of public speaking, or sympathy with ANYTHING political, or TRADES UNIONS, because government and civil servants CANNOT be linked to any cause or bias shown by a Factory Inspector facing problems between employers and employees. – Oh! Are you taking notes? Am I going too fast?"

Lucy laughed. "Perhaps. I've been hard put to it to keep up."

"I'm sorry. But you were right to try. I can't stress how important it is to keep notes of everything, and every letter you write. Don't buy smart looking report books. Buy cheap little exercise books that will slip into your hand bag, and an indelible pencil, then you can write notes on the bus or the train before you forget as you go from place to place."

The next day she met Rose Squire on the steps of the Town Hall and they clasped hands.

"I shall never find out all the things I need to know before we begin," said Lucy.

"Nor me, but I've made a start. Yesterday I went to Hornsey Sanitary Museum Department, AND the sewage works, AND the isolation hospital."

"Mercy! What did you think of them all?"

"Well, the Sanitary Museum was dirty, and the sewage works didn't smell, and the isolation hospital was full of people. It was all very odd."

Dr Dudfield's office was a hive of activity, filing clerks and record books and office boys carrying letters.

Lucy told him of Miss Lankester's request for her to go to the conference in Leeds for four days. He assented. He thought they should begin their work on November 13th. "You will have to organise your own work. I shall supply you both with a map of Kensington, a directory of work places to be inspected – not up to date – and a set of credentials that will give you the right to enter any workplace, when and where you please. Then you shall proceed as you please."

"But HOW are we to proceed?" said Rose Squire as they came out of the Town Hall.

"I've a good way to start. Yesterday, while you went to the sewage works, I went to meet Miss Eliza Orme."

"Heavens!"

"Miss Lankester sent me. She talked so fast and I tried to write it all down. She was extraordinarily helpful."

Rose Squire looked impressed. "Shall we go to a Lyons shop and you tell me?"

"I can't, I'm having lunch with my Aunt Florrie. Could we meet at the Charing Cross Lyons for tea?"

"Four o'clock then. Then I can catch the train home from there."

Aunt Florrie, the Honourable Florence Boscawen, was small and bony, with a soft wool long black fitted jacket and soft black wool skirt, a sable fur stole and a large black velvet wide brimmed hat with vivid purple feathers. She sat on a thin chair in the entrance hall of the Grand Hotel in Northumberland Avenue, completely dwarfing it with her personality. Lucy felt like a small plain sparrow.

"Lucy, darling! What a clever girl you are! We are all so proud. Your father and mother will be rejoicing in heaven."

"Dear Aunt Florrie!"

"Lunch, darling?" Aunt Florrie entered the hotel restaurant. The head waiter was by her side in an instant and placed them in a quiet corner and produced large menus. Aunt Florrie paid them no attention. "Last time I came you had some very good dover sole, have we got it today?"

"We have, Madam."

"That's what we'll have, both of us, delicious. NO soup. No meat course – JUST the sole and some small potatoes. Then we can be devils and have a really nice pudding – can't we? JUST water, thank you, nothing else."

The head waiter and his minion withdrew.

"So where do you begin, Lucy, and where will you be based?"

"I begin on November 13th, based in Kensington Town Hall. But I'm off to a Women's Conference in Leeds on Nov 7th for four days. I'm to read a paper on What Women Inspectors Do."

Aunt Florrie chuckled. "Are you indeed? You haven't the faintest idea what they do. Nobody's been one yet. Leeds, eh – is the Duchess of Devonshire heading it up?"

"Yes."

"Oh, good, her mother and I played together when we were children. I'll introduce you to her and Lady Fred Cavendish. Next week?"

"That's amazing, Aunt Florrie. I'm doing well for introductions. Miss Jones is taking me to Octavia Hill on Friday, and Miss Waters has promised me an introduction to Miss Brandreth and Mrs Borrowfield."

"Who are they?"

"They're the Poor Law Guardians for South Kensington."

"Good for Miss Waters. We're all behind you Lucy, we may not be the working classes, but we have our uses."

"Oh, Aunt Florrie, you know we couldn't do without you, Hye and me. Where would we have been without you and Bossie?"

"You would both have got by, dear Lucy. But I'm glad you didn't have to." And Aunt Florrie raised her glass of water in salute.

Lucy considered buying a new hat for the winter on the strength of the new post, but there was no time to shop around the next morning. However, she stole an hour and got off the omnibus in Regent Street and looked in all the shop windows on her way to Miss Lankester's offices in Berners Street, just to get ideas, in readiness for a shopping spree to come.

Miss Lankester was delighted to see her and sent one of her secretaries scurrying to collect papers and scribbled notes for Lucy. "I have seen Mr Asquith since I saw you last, and I have been to the Local Government Board, and I have picked up some VERY interesting snippets we could use for you."

"Oh?" said Lucy.

"Now then, sit down, Lucy. We'll talk about Leeds in a minute. I have heard from Mr Asquith's private secretary himself that Mr Asquith is thinking of adding two women to the team of Factory Inspectors in the spring – one in the Midlands and one in Yorkshire. They would be peripatetic, dealing with inspections and complaints relating specially to women workers, but based in London, immediately under the supervision of the Chief Inspector, Mr Sprague Oram."

"Why not under the Yorkshire inspectors? Or the Midland ones?"

"Mr Sprague Oram thinks they would be eaten alive. The Men Inspectors would delegate them to the far corners of their Departments. Nobody would ever see them again."

"It sounds as if they would be thoroughly disliked."

"Oh, yes, they would, thoroughly – to begin with. But if they had brains, AND tact, AND knowledge, AND the personal protection of the Chief Inspector, THINK what they could accomplish!"

Lucy looked at her.

"You would be admirable, Lucy."

"Miss Lankester, I have only just been appointed as a Sanitary Inspector – on six months' probation – in ONE London Borough. I haven't even begun it, Miss Lankester!"

"Well, this is only an idea in Asquith's head so far. But think of the boost to our National Health Society's reputation. A Health lecturer trained by US as a Senior Factory Inspector."

"I'm speechless, Miss Lankester."

"Being speechless won't further anyone's cause, Lucy. I shall speak to Mr Asquith and to Mrs Sidney Webb about you for the Midlands Inspector when your six month trial period is up."

"Meanwhile, Miss Lankester, I am going to have to give up nearly all my Health Society Lecturing from November on."

"Yes, of course, and my staff are already choosing other lecturers to take over from you. We are lucky in that we have plenty of really competent people."

"I'll finish giving the Erith course. But I'll have to stop the Chatham course."

"From next week, yes. I'll get Mrs Dixon to take over from you. They'll all be sorry to lose you."

"May I come sometime in the next few days and read my two little speeches for Leeds? One is on the work of the National Health Society and one is on the work of Sanitary Inspectors."

"Definitely, go and arrange to read them to Miss Brown. She always gives good advice. Then, what are you going to do today?"

"Over lunchtime I am going to the Parkes Institute to a lecture on Sewage Disposal; and then I'm going to buy a new hat."

"Enjoy them both," said Miss Lankester, shaking hands.

★★★

Lucy let herself into the house carrying her new hat box and picked up a pile of letters from the hall table. She took out the hat, a wide brimmed grey felt hat with a broad band of grey grosgrain swathed around it and put it on, gazing at herself approvingly in the hall mirror. Turning, she saw Hye in the doorway to the living room, looking woebegone. Hye put her finger to her lips and pointed to the kitchen door. Lucy went through to see Mrs Casey slumped in a chair at the table, her head down, snoring gently.

"She's been there all afternoon," whispered Hye, "she came this morning and said she didn't feel well, her stomach felt bad. But she scrubbed the floor and cleaned the kitchen and said she would go home early. So I went off shopping and when I came in about teatime, she was sitting there asleep. And she won't wake up. I've shaken her and she just mutters and groans."

Lucy bent over Mrs Casey and shook her gently. Mrs Casey half woke, and muttered and growled and went back to sleep. Lucy sniffed and then shook her hard. "Wake up, Mrs Casey, you must go home. Wake up!"

Mrs Casey stirred and opened her eyes and groaned.

"Go home!" said Lucy sternly. "Your daughter will be anxious about you."

"Oh, Lucy don't be rough, she is ill."

"She is drunk," said Lucy.

"Oh no, she said she didn't feel well this morning."

Mrs Casey had staggered to her feet. "Oh, Miss Deane, I'm not well." She swayed.

"Do you want me to fetch your daughter?" said Lucy.

"No, no, I feel better now. Oh, my head, oh, my stomach."

"Can you get home on your own?"

"I think so."

"Let me help you on with your coat." Something clinked in the pocket. "I'll keep this bottle, shall I? It's empty."

"Oh, oh, Miss Deane, I'm sorry, oh, oh, my head."

"I'll come round tomorrow afternoon when your daughter has come home. Then I can see you both. Goodnight, Mrs Casey."

Hye opened the door and Lucy propelled Mrs Casey out. Mrs Casey stumbled down the street holding on to the railings, holding her hat. She put it shakily on her head.

They closed the door and went into the sitting room and plopped down. "Are you sure she was drunk?"

"Of course. You could smell it from the hall. What a fright! And everything was going so well!"

"Yes," said Hye. She looked at Lucy. "I like the hat," she said.

★★★

One of the letters Lucy had picked up from the hall table was from May Abraham. She had been Lady Dilke's private secretary before she had been selected as one of the four women appointed to the Royal Commission on Labour as a Woman Assistant Commissioner, and she had written the report on Laundresses and Laundries. The letter congratulated Lucy on her appointment and invited her to tea at her apartment in Tite Street.

Lucy arrived on the appointed afternoon and began to climb, up, and up, and up, to the top floor. As she reached it, out of breath, May Abraham was leaning over the banisters. "I saw you out of the window," she said, "and came out to encourage you. But you came up nearly as fast as I do. Come in and have a rest."

Lucy sat in a chair and looked around the bright, simply furnished room. A small fire warmed it. The round table in the corner of the room and the bookcases behind it were full of record books and files, but there were some women's magazines and novels on the stool by her chair, and gay cushions scattered around, and some pretty ornaments on the mantelpiece. May brought in a tea tray, silver teapot and jug and cakes. "Only shop cakes," she said. "We don't do much cooking here."

She was a bright, handsome looking young woman with dark hair and eyes. She came from Dublin, she said as they chatted, her father had been a doctor, and when he had died she needed to earn her own living and his connections had brought her to London. She loved horse riding and rode as often as she could manage in Hyde Park. She had come over to be Lady Dilke's secretary, and was straightway in her element, immersed in all the women's organisations, women's better working conditions that Lady Dilke was supporting. "Just up my street! My parents were always interested in working conditions and health issues. I suppose it's in my blood. So I was so proud when I was appointed one of the Assistant Commissioners on the Royal Commission. How did you come into this field?"

"In some ways like you. My father was a military man, killed in the Battle of Landors Nek in the Seventies, so my mother and my younger sister and I came to live with my uncle and aunts in Kent, and Hye and I grew up there. My mother's friends were all very interested in various girls' clubs and small hospitals and women's welfare charities – and I got interested too – and so when my mother died, in 1886, and it was clear that Hye and I were going to have to provide for ourselves it seemed the obvious path to take. So I did a six months' nursing course at the Chelsea Infirmary with Miss de Pledge, the Matron there, and then trained on a lecturer's course at the National Health Society. I've been with them for a while and now through Miss Lankester I've got the job as Woman Sanitary Inspector with Doctor Dudfield in Kensington."

"First rate," said May. "I'm sure we can work a good deal in each other's hands."

"I'd be really grateful for any tips you can give me on inspecting. I shall be mostly with outworkers, and small workshops, dressmakers and laundries – there seem to be thousands and thousands of laundries."

"The main thing with dressmakers is to insist – well if you can't insist, to strongly recommend employers to establish some PERMANENT means of ventilating their workrooms. If the women CAN shut all the doors and windows they DO. They positively loathe fresh air. The vents need to be high enough up so that they can't reach them. That'll do you for a start. Laundresses are desperate for some proper working conditions. I'm in favour of bringing laundries under the Factory Act. It won't drive women out of them in favour of men. It's so nasty that men don't want to do it!"

The door bell rang. "Oh, goodness, that'll be Miss Dunn. She's come down from Liverpool," and she scurried to the front door. Miss Dunn came in, rather red in the face because of the stairs, and also a tall extremely pretty girl, with a pork pie hat and an armful of shopping bags. She collapsed on the door mat.

"Do come in, Miss Dunn. Get up Gertrude, it's not that bad. Miss Dunn isn't making a fuss."

"She's got to be polite. I don't have to. This shopping is heavy. How do you do, Miss Dunn, you'll feel better in a minute, so they tell me."

"This is Miss Lucy Deane, Miss Dunn, and this is Miss Gertrude Tuckwell. She shares the flat with me. She likes it really. She's just out of condition."

"Oh, Miss Tuckwell," said Miss Dunn, "Is it you I write to at Lady Dilke's office. How do you do?" She tugged off her gloves.

"That's me," said Miss Tuckwell, handing the shopping bags to May who bore them away to the kitchen. "And you must be lecturing in the Liverpool Sanitary Institute."

Miss Dunn nodded, pleased.

"She has come to find out about the new Factory Inspector's posts for next spring."

"Are you interested in them?" said Lucy curiously.

"In the one to be based in Yorkshire, certainly," said Miss Dunn.

"What about you?" enquired Miss Tuckwell, taking off her hat.

"Oh, I've only just got the post of Sanitary Inspector in Kensington. I haven't even started there yet until tomorrow."

"Hmmm!" said Miss Tuckwell in a non-committal tone.

At the Town Hall the next morning Lucy and Rose Squires went through the registers and report forms. Shelves and shelves of dusty brown bound books gazed balefully down upon them.

"I don't believe they're up to date at all," said Lucy. "I've found my end of the Fulham Road and the laundry across the road isn't mentioned and I'm sure it's been there years. And the one in the next street is mentioned, but under another name entirely."

"Mmm, and I'm looking at the report forms that have been made out for dressmakers, and they are very scrappy. I'd want to update them and make them easier to fill in. Nothing about underage workers, or hours for meals."

"But how would we know what was to go on the forms?"

"Well, I was planning to inspect a few today, on a trial run. I'll jot down some notes. Dr Dudfield says take it easy to start with. He's very cross."

"With us?"

"No, no. There's an outbreak of smallpox in North Kensington. He's gone there already. Mr Braye says he always gets in a terrible temper when that happens there. He's been fighting it for years, Mr Braye says. I'll give you my ideas on the report forms when I next see you. When I come back from the Leeds Conference. Saturday night."

"Oh yes. Monday then. Hope the talks go well. Oh, did you know Miss Lankester says the National Health Society is going to put us both forward for the Factory Inspectorships in the spring?"

"I didn't know you were trying for it."

"Might as well."

"Goodness," said Lucy. "It's all going too fast for me."

The Conference of Women Workers at Leeds went by in a bewildering blur of hats, papers, applause, noddings, shaking of heads, introductions, tubthumpings.

Lucy, very nervous, made her speech about the work of the National Health Society, an organisation she knew well. Very few women in the room. Very little applause. No questions.

She sat in one audience listening to a woman with a strong Birmingham accent who held the audience in the palm of her hand, tremendous applause and excitement, watched the roused faces, and heard the remarks of the hearers, accents from all parts of the country as the hall emptied.

She gave her second talk on the importance of Female Sanitary Inspectors, about which she knew nothing, in a small hall filled with enquirers. It was a great success, many questions, and enthusiastic applause.

She shook hands with Lady Fred Cavendish, sensible and unsentimental.

She sat and chatted with Mrs Talbot Baines, handsome and clever.

She was introduced to two very old, encyclopaedic ladies, Poor Law guardians in Winchester.

She shook hands with Deaconess Gilmore and fell in love with Miss Clifford of Bristol.

Listened to Lady Henrietta Somerset; a most lovely voice and intonation, but rather a romantic and high faluting talk on American immigrants in Chicago.

Nodded off in the train carriage on the way home with phrases such as 'Lady rent collectors a most splendid and most useful opening', 'Matrons of work houses – much needed', '£100 a year AND rations', 'The Horticultural College in Swanley is an opening, but expensive to train.'

Finally went to sleep.

2

Beating an orderly advance

Dust and disorder; the very first dressmakers' inspection; carving out a Workshop Directory; meeting a 'Trotter'; beautiful Alice Ravenhill comes to call; bogged down by sewage matters; the Sanitary Inspectors Examination.

On Monday 13th November, 1893, Lucy arrived at Kensington Town Hall early. Neither Rose Squire nor Dr Dudfield were there; but on her desk in their small office was a neat folder from Dr Dudfield, a street map and an Inspection Register Book; and there were drafts of a possible Report Form from Miss Squire. In Rose Squire's large neat handwriting there was a letter which said:

'There is NO convenient Directory of workshop establishments for our purposes. I have amended it for the streets around North End Road and Lillie Road. Please copy into this new book. I will see you tomorrow. Rose Squire.'

Lucy's heart sank. She sat down and began to write.

She wrote all Tuesday as well. Rose Squire came from inspecting on Wednesday and wrote with her.

On Thursday she went to see Miss Lankester at the Women's National Health Society, and told her of the conversations she had had at the Leeds Conference about the Society's lecturing courses.

"I do feel the moment has come, Miss Lankester, for the Health Society to push to be acknowledged by the Education Department, to train lecturers in hygiene and safety. Then, when we were acknowledged, we could set up training schemes all over the country, not just in London and the South."

"Yes, we feel the same. I have been able to speak with Mr Asquith, and I have visited several local government boards, and all of them seem very favourably disposed to us."

"In Leeds I was talking to the Co-operative Societies ladies, and they have plans to have examinations for inspectors in the future. Our Health Society ought to have examinations for future inspectors as well."

Miss Lankester nodded. "I'll follow that up. And, Lucy, I did speak to Mr Asquith about you and the Midlands Factory Inspectorship. And I spoke to Mrs Sidney Webb about you. For when your six months' trial at Kensington is over, of course."

"But my probationary period has hardly started yet, Miss Lankester. Tomorrow Dr Dudfield will give me my credentials. I do my first inspection tomorrow. Only then shall I feel like a Sanitary Inspector. And I have decided that I am going to apply to take the Final Government Examination for Sanitary Inspectors. I hope you will feel able to sign my application."

"Of course. Who will you ask to write you a testimonial for the exam application?"

"I thought Mrs Celine Seymour. And Colonel Bircham, a friend of my father."

"Excellent. Most suitable, Lucy. Good luck with the application."

Madame Renaude's establishment in Sussex Place had already been visited by May Abraham for the Royal Commission Enquiry. The shop front was extremely smart, a bottle-green door and a sparkling bay window with a single mannequin wearing a sage-green silk tea gown trimmed with narrow dark-grey ribbons at the throat and the cuffs. A smart young woman in brown wool, with her hair dressed prettily and plainly, came smiling forward, gave Lucy a chair and took her card through to the workroom. There was a short pause.

Madame Renaude came out and greeted her. Lucy showed her credentials and Madame Renaude read them politely and enquired chattily about Lucy's new appointment. Lucy wondered whether she was playing for time. She asked to be shown over the premises. Madame Renaude said "Of course," but as two ladies were being fitted in the two fitting rooms upstairs, it would not be possible to go there. Lucy said that was acceptable.

Madame Renaude led the way through to a smart, square hall, with a highly polished staircase and some substantial potted plants on each side of the banisters. Then they went through to the two workrooms behind the stairs; in one there was a vast table taking up most of the room where three women were cutting various fabrics and marking them with tailors' chalk. It was very clean and the November sun shone wanly through the window. The other room was crammed with narrow tables and long benches, some with treadle sewing machines, and about eighteen to twenty women in linen aprons bent over their work. It was stuffy in the room, but it appeared in good order, and the requirements of the Factory Act, with the Abstracts for this particular business, were clearly pinned up on the wall.

Lucy made some notes on Rose's new interim form and then went into the back room. Here, the walls were very dingy, the wallpaper worn and peeling, and crammed with hooks and pegs for the women's hats and coats. There was an old range with three large black kettles steaming gently, and a collection of old cracked cups and mugs, all very stained and dirty, in an even dirtier stained sink. 'The WC' wrote Lucy, 'Shocking. As full as it could hold despite only mid-morning'. It was out in the yard outside, and with no shutter and the door half off its hinge. Madame Renaude said no more, watching Lucy as she made her notes.

"Who is responsible for the sink and for the refreshments?" asked Lucy.

"The women take it in turns, two each day."

"And the sanitary conveniences?"

"It is emptied once a week. The council men come round once a week on a Friday evening – this evening, in fact, very late."

"Once a week with only one convenience is not enough," said Lucy. Madame Renaude shrugged.

The girl in the brown wool dress came into the yard to say that one of the ladies who was being fitted was leaving. Madame Renaude excused herself, and a pleasant middle-aged forewoman came out to Lucy.

"Tain't too bad, is it?" she said.

"It's very stuffy in your workrooms," said Lucy.

"Oh, terrible," said the woman cheerfully. "But it's their own fault.

They WON'T 'ave the windows open. Madame put a vent in when your last man came round, but the girls just stuffed it up. Suffocatin'."

Lucy had sent for the syllabus for the Sanitary and Factory Inspectors examination and it arrived by the early post. She skimmed through it while she was dressing and came down to breakfast holding it in her teeth while she put the last hairpins into her neat bun. Hye saw her scared eyes and poured out a cup of tea.

Lucy put the papers down on the cloth. "It's hopeless, Hye. I'm appalled. There's no hope of my passing."

"Why ever not?"

"I don't know any of it. Legal stuff, Factory Acts from way back – even to Shaftesbury."

"You can swot that up."

"Given time I could. But then there's Machinery and Mechanics, and APPLIED Mechanics. I can't learn those in the time."

"You could learn enough to get by and learn the rest on the job."

"But how? And who from?"

Hye looked sympathetic.

"And then I've got to work full-time – more than full-time – at Kensington. I've NO idea how that works either. This whole Factory Inspector idea is stupid. It's too much for me."

Hye took a deep breath. "Nonsense. You are made for it. Of course you can do it. I won't hear any more. You'll be fine."

Lucy looked amazed. "Goodness Hye. You are determined."

"I'm only saying what you keep saying to ME."

At the Town Hall the two young women completed, with no little difficulty, the new draft of the Register of Dressmakers, with the help of a very small thin office boy, who almost buckled under the weight of the old volumes.

"Half past one – finished. Hurrah!" said Rose Squire.

"Now all that remains is to inspect every one," said Lucy.

"Not until after lunch."

They went together to registers numbers 10 and 12, Lucy to No.14, and Rose to Nos. 16 and 18. At five o'clock they met at the Town Hall to compare notes.

"Well, none of them were BAD. And all the employers were civil," said Lucy.

"My last two were on the defensive, though. And all the buildings were so airless and cramped."

"But the employees insist on it. Even in the WC they stuff up the vent."

"The women seemed very ignorant and scared in my last one, although their hours seem reasonable and the regulations were all displayed."

"Nine until half past two on Saturday afternoons, though. That's not much of a half-holiday."

"Goodnight Miss Deane. Sleep well."

"Goodnight Miss Squire. Off we go again tomorrow."

The next few days were dry and fine. The two women walked from establishment to establishment.

In establishment 22 there were too many people crammed together. The owner said there was no way she could alter the space, and with so much work she needed every employee she had got.

No. 24 said she would turn one of her own living rooms into another space.

No. 26 was a huge establishment, and the owner, Mr Humphreys, was a horrid and truculent man, but the forewomen, each in charge of two workrooms, were friendly; and though several rooms were overcrowded, they were well ventilated, and the women were chatting pleasantly amongst themselves.

Lucy noticed that a small, square girl with a cheerful smile and crooked teeth seemed to be in much demand.

"Trotter! Over here, love."

"Trotter! Take this to Mrs Peasley's table."

"Trotter! These skirts to the bodice room!"

"Trotter! These cuffs have got to be pressed again!"

"Miss Trotter is having a busy morning," said Lucy.

The forewoman laughed. "Her name's Myrtle, Madam. Trotter's her job. She trots about. She's the new apprentice. Gets her used to the set up."

"How much does she get paid?"

"Oh, she don't get paid for the first three months. Then she gets eight pence a week for the next three months learning to use the machines, and sewing skirt hems. Then the apprentices get 2s 6d a week for the next couple of years. We're a good firm. An apprentice like her can earn a good wage when she's finished."

"How much would that be?"

"Well, a skirt hand would get 14s a week, maybe 16s, a bodice hand 18s–21s, an improver the same. But a cutter can get 25s, and a GOOD cutter – an employer would pay any money; but they have terrible tempers – and airs – you've no idea the tantrums we get from cutters."

A woman came and called the forewoman away.

Instantly two girls put down their sewing and sprang up to close a window which had been an inch open. All the others grinned and clapped silently.

As usual the WC was foul.

At the end of the day Lucy went to the Parkes Institute to a lecture on Offensive Trades and was pleased that she knew most of what was being explained. She blessed the National Health Society for its good grounding. She came home jubilant because the young man sitting next to her explained the principles of ballcocks to her.

On Sunday it was cold and showery. "I shan't go to church," said Lucy. "The hems of both my heavy skirts are solid with mud. I must sponge them and press them. And clean all my shoes." Hye was busy planning a 'really nice' dinner. "It's nice not to have Mrs Casey here at the weekends," she said. "She never cleans up properly in the kitchen these days, and if I'm in during the week she tells me what she's going to do – the stairs, or the bedrooms – and then comes and leans on the door post to the sitting room and talks, about the other women in her boarding house, and all their illnesses. Awful. And you know, Lucy, she smells bad, sometimes. I have to tell her I'm busy preparing my lessons and writing my notes, and she doesn't like it and looks offended."

"Oh dear!" said Lucy. "But she's honest, and we've been Her Girls for so long now. It must be three years since Matron first found her for us. I'll have a word with Matron when I see her – and I must see her – I haven't been for ages. Maybe she'll have a word with Mrs Casey's daughter. She's a much tougher character."

"Oh, do, Lucy. I don't feel comfortable with Mrs Casey around these days." Lucy sighed. The door bell rang. Lucy had just set out her shoes on the floor in the back kitchen.

"It's Miss Alice Ravenhill," said Hye, "Just dropped by. Do come in, Miss Ravenhill. Let me take your umbrella."

"Bless you, just blown in for a moment. I won't keep you. I can see you are in the midst of a hundred little tasks." She stood in the midst of the Little Tasks, soignée, slim, shining, her tiny brown velvet toque perched above her smooth gleaming chignon, and an even tinier glowing turquoise bird nestling among the veiling.

"I just came in to say two things. First, I heard you were applying for the Factory Inspector post TOO! Isn't it exciting? National Health Society are backing me, Miss Lankester says they think SO much of me – of us – they have sent in your name to Asquith too. Have you sent in your Testimonies yet?"

"Not all of them."

"Best be quick. I've managed to get Dr Thorne Thorne, and the Duchess of Albany, and Lady Collins."

"I say!"

"I know, aren't I lucky? I hear you've given up your lecturing work for the Society."

"Well, you see, I—"

"Of course, with your new post, something has to go. I've got a full load of lecturing now, couldn't fit one more lecture in. It's a great success and I seem to be very popular."

"Oh, good—"

"Oh, and I saw Matron at the Chelsea Hospital – I gave up the idea of registrar at St. Bartholomew's – and Matron said to tell you she is VERY vexed you haven't called on her recently."

"Yes, I must really—"

"But the other thing I wanted to see you about was this application the National Health Society want us to draft out for them. Do you think we could draft it out NOW, possibly, and then we could both sign it? Then they can send it off to the London Government Board."

"Application?" said Hye.

"Yes, Miss Lankester thinks your sister and I would be the perfect people to draft her an application form. She wants the London Examining Board to include the Health Society in the examining body that is being formed for the Sanitary Institute."

"Very well, as good a time as any," said Lucy, and began to clear the table and set out paper and ink.

"I'll put the kettle on for tea. You'll need sustenance," said Hye and went resignedly into the kitchen, to put the preparations for the 'really nice dinner' on hold.

Lucy had to acknowledge that Alice was certainly very capable; the application draft was completed in an hour and a half, and the two sisters waved her off as she gaily opened her umbrella and stepped out into the November drizzle.

"She's exhausting. And she's overdressed," said Hye.

"But I have to admit she's very capable," said Lucy. "She'll probably get the Factory Inspector job."

"She's not THAT capable. Anyone really capable would have bought a bigger umbrella. That one won't even keep the bird dry."

The following evening Lucy went with Miss Dunbar to a lecture on Metallic Trades at the Parkes Institute. Lucy was fascinated and took copious notes on the awful and unnecessary mortality rates from lung diseases and lead poisoning. Tile cutters and grinders seemed particularly prone to sickness. Overcrowding and, as usual, poor ventilation seemed rife. The lecturer was a young redheaded doctor from Sheffield, very keen and energetic. He thought that the workmen were very lax about keeping to their own safety regulations, although the workshop owners were always held responsible. Lucy's head came up. "That's unfair," she muttered to Miss Dunbar. "Workmen should be made to do what they can in their own interest."

Miss Dunbar introduced her to the Chief Sanitary Inspector, who had written Miss Dunbar's references for the exams. He was very affable and promised to coach them for two sessions on sanitary matters for the exam and to take them over a building site to see drains being laid.

Lucy was delighted and Miss Dunbar was amused. "You make it sound exhilarating, Miss Deane."

The final days of November were a repetitive pattern of walking from one dressmaker's shop to another in the daytime, scuttling to lectures on Drains, Sewage and Dangerous Practices in the early evening and writing reports on sempstresses and cubic space until late at night. One night Lucy shut her notebooks and laid her head on the table. "There is no way I can pass this, Hye."

"You passed the last one with flying colours," said Hye. "Don't be silly. You always batter me that I'm going to pass tests."

"Yes, and you always do," said Lucy. "But this is going to beat me. Sewage matters? Drains? Cubic space? Ventilation?"

"You know EVERYTHING about cubic space and ventilation. You are a BORE about cubic space and ventilation. I know all about cubic space because of you. I could pass that exam myself. I'd help if I could, but I'm out the next three evenings organising the final year students for their exam banqueting menus. Get Evelyn to come and help test you. She'd love it."

Evelyn was indeed thrilled to help and arrived on Friday evening as enthusiastic as if she was going to a society house party. "We'll soak ourselves in sewage matters!" she cried gaily.

The morning of December the first was dark and foggy. A great crowd of young men were waiting outside the Medicine Hall on the Victoria Embankment, trying to look nonchalant. Lucy saw Miss Dunbar by the railings peering at a small marbled exercise book and went to her. Very soon Miss Moffatt, a nurse lecturer, and Miss Dunn came up. On the stroke of nine the door was opened. "Candidates for the Sanitary Inspectors Examination, Part Two. Please go to the Hall on your right." The ranks of men parted to let the women go first. All the eyes watched them walk up the steps. A fifth young woman scuttled up after them. Then the men flowed in like a river. Lucy thought there must have been about sixty.

As she read the questions, she could not believe they were so easy. "Don't be misled," she thought to herself as she wrote, "There's bound to be a catch in it. What have I missed?" In fact she wrote herself into misery, worrying about the Viva Voce the next day.

Hyacinth and Evelyn simply laughed at her. Hye had cooked a fish pie for supper. Evelyn refused to think up any more questions. "You know more than any of them. Just go to bed early." But Lucy was too wound up to sleep and sat up until the small hours writing up the official Kensington inspection reports and her diary.

She wore her new grey wide brimmed hat to the Viva Voce and sat with the rows of young men waiting to be called to one of the several small rooms for her interview. She saw Miss Moffatt several lines away, looking stoic, but no sign of the other women. The examiners were courteous, but

21

pressing; Lucy enjoyed herself and felt at ease. I really think I might have passed, she thought; and so it proved when the results came through the letterbox, some days later. Miss Dunbar and Miss Moffatt had passed as well.

3

Mangles and Applied Mechanics

Lucy takes her references to the Home Office; a sore throat; Lady Howard's cheque; Lucy meets Sir Charles and Lady Emilia Dilke; Applied Mechanics; 4 dozen bottles of claret; the Tailors Union meeting; Miss George comes to see Hyacinth; Mechanics is a hopeless case; Mr Pitt's laundry; Dr Dudfield is most displeased; Mr Elliott coaches Lucy; Evelyn hurls herself at Applied Mechanics; Mathematics, Mechanics and Cam Shafts.

On December the 6th, Alice Ravenhill came to dinner at 100 Fulham Road, looking elegant and beautiful. Hye cooked the meal, and Alice Ravenhill talked and talked, all about Alice Ravenhill and her plans and schemes for trying to get the Factory Inspectorship. Lucy held her tongue and so did Hye, though she was longing to mention Lucy's plans. Alice's hopes were built on Doctor Thorne Thorne at the London Government Board – to whom she had explained that Lucy and Rose Squire 'were only Assistant Sanitary Inspectors' – and also Mr Oram, Chief Inspector of Factories, and Sir Richard Collins, "Oh, he's the Duchess of Albany's Equerry or something." When she had swept off into the night, a hansom cab trotting past at the precise moment the front door was opened, Lucy and Hye looked at each other and laughed.

At Kensington Town Hall the next day Rose Squire and Lucy decided that Lucy must get on with presenting her testimonials and references for the Inspectorship as soon as possible. She took the reference from Lord

Medway, very short and cold, very disappointing, she thought, round to Miss Lankester, and found the forms had already been sent in to the Home Office. Miss Lankester advised her to call directly on Mr Asquith's secretary, Mr Tennant, at the Home Office with her other references.

Meanwhile the Kensington Sanitary Inspectors must keep on inspecting. Lucy walked from one firm to the other along the Brompton Road, each one more depressing and dirtier than the next. One of the dirtiest set of workrooms belonged to old Mr Wheeler, a vestryman, who had been very supportive to Lucy and very influential in choosing her. What was she to do?

There was a persistent cold drizzle and the fog was creeping through the afternoon into the evening. When she arrived home the house was dark, only a tiny gas lamp in the hall, Mrs Casey nowhere to be seen and the fire in the kitchen range almost out. Hye was away for the week in Cumbria, examining. Lucy rescued the fire and made herself a large bowl of bread and milk, and wrote up the day's reports sitting as close as she could get to the range. She hung her winter coat on the airer above the range to dry. By ten o'clock she had filled the stone hot water bottle, wrapped it in its blanket and gone to bed.

In the morning there were a pile of letters, all wanting immediate attention, and one for Hyacinth with the Cookery College crest on it marked Urgent. She opened it. 'Would Miss Hyacinth Deane appear for a Cookery interview the day after tomorrow?' Another letter contained a Complaint about conditions in the Dressmaking Department at Derry and Toms. Two others told of overcrowding complaints and 'bad smells' endured by the inhabitants of adjoining neighbours to the dressmaker's yard.

Lucy's head ached and her throat was sore, but she put on her coat and hat and trailed round to the Cookery College, near to the Temple, inspecting twice en route. When she got there and explained about Hyacinth being in the North of England, the secretary first looked blank and then told her that the appointment interview was not until the next week. The typist had made a mistake. Lucy could have bitten them!

She caught the omnibus to the Town Hall, where Rose Squire was anxious for them to complete drawing up the new forms for the Official Diary, and they managed to do this by teatime. She tramped home through the ubiquitous drizzle, which did seem to have driven away the fog, to find a note on the mat from Mrs Casey.

'Dear Miss deane, I as ad a turn, my stomach and dizy. There is soup. And enough cole. See you Monday god wiling. Mrs C.'

Lucy made up the fire and cried a little. There was soup, quite good soup, but her throat was too sore to cope with the lumps. A note from Hye said the week was being most successful and she would be home on Saturday, but SO tired and looking forward to a good rest!

In the morning the sky was clear, the rain had stopped and a stiff breeze was blowing hats off in the street. Lucy ate a boiled egg and drank sweet tea and enjoyed it. She had a good hot wash by the kitchen range, polished her shoes and her handbag, did her hair with great care and set off at eight o'clock to inspect the Complaint at Derry and Toms.

There was nothing warranting a Complaint at all in the store that she could see. She said so, and the floor manager, a Mr Hooper, offered to tip her! "We have evidently got a nasty person among our employees who writes anonymous notes."

Then she went to the Home Office with Miss Lankester's letter of introduction and her references. Mr Tennant greeted her, a very small, unassuming, gentleman-like, fair haired, unattractive young man. Lucy decided he was probably not clever, but kindly, and he was no doubt discreet and painstaking. He was officially cautious and even said it had not been decided whether ANY Female Inspectors should be appointed; but she managed to worm out of him that, if there were, he thought there would be two, one for the Midlands and one for London, and both peripatetic. "I should prefer the latter," said Lucy. Mr Tennant nodded gravely, took her folder and said he would lay her qualifications before Mr Asquith. He did not ask her if she had any other questions, and he did not give her any other information. He smiled vaguely and the meeting was at an end.

As she came out of the Home Office her sore throat returned with a vengeance. She made herself go to the Town Hall and listen to Rose Squire who had been cheerfully busying herself with the niceties of laundry inspections, their pay structures and their prodigious hours of work. Lucy felt guilty that her mind had been so little involved with her work there. Whilst she had been concerned with exams and references and Factory Inspectors, Rose Squire had been sensibly and systematically forming their methods of procedure with every sign of enjoyment. "She is a dear," thought Lucy. "And I have not been pulling my weight. And she has been quietly collecting her own testimonials. I hope we both get interviews. But oh help, if we do, what will poor Dr Dudfield think of us?"

"Go home," said Rose. "You can hardly speak. You've had a bad week. You look all in. Don't come in Saturday morning. Have a lie in. See you on Monday."

"Oh, Rose, what wonderful words," said Lucy.

She bought milk and eggs and stayed in bed all day on Saturday, writing up papers and her diary and the reports of the Complaints.

"Happy New Year, Lucy."

"Happy New Year Hye, darling."

"There's a letter from Lady Howard."

"Oho! I hope it has a cheque inside it."

"Well, hurry up, then."

"Oh! Hye! Hye! Look! TWO cheques! One for £60.0.0 – and one for £200!"

"Oh, my goodness!"

"She says, 'My dear girls, A very happy New Year to you both and the very best of wishes for all your activities and plans for the coming year. I am filled with admiration for the brave way you are both making your way in the world. Your parents would be so proud of their daughters and their achievements. Well done. Please find enclosed two cheques. The first for £60.0.0 continues our quarterly agreement, and is to be spent on looking smart and having fun, both essential for professional women. The second is to be invested with your own saved capital. I know Bossie will give you sound advice. Affectionately Constance. Lady Howard de Walden.'"

"Well! Let me see it. Isn't she wonderful?"

"I'll write to Bossie right away. And I'll send the bank books to be made up. Oh, and Hye, there's a note from Matron. She's going to take me to meet Sir Charles and Lady Dilke. She says they are very interested in the appointment of Lady Factory Inspectors and want to see me."

"Ho! They're all going to be looking you over. You'd better buy a new coat with some of that Professional Woman's money!"

And so, on the following Saturday afternoon Miss de Pledge, Matron of the Chelsea Hospital and Workhouse, and Miss Lucy Deane went up the steps of 76 Sloane Street, and rang the bell. A smiling maid opened the door and admitted them into a wide hall, with a black and white marbled floor and a plethora of Roman busts, statues, hunting prints, large potted plants, an inlaid table with several labelled letter trays upon it, and various leather bags and boxes around it.

The maid took their umbrellas and Miss de Pledge's mackintosh cape. But before she could lead them up the polished curved stairs, May Abraham came running down to greet them.

"I have been looking out of the window for you ever since I knew you had been invited. Thank you for bringing her, Miss de Pledge. I am May Abraham, Lady Dilke's secretary. Do come up into the warm. Lady Dilke and Sir Charles are both here."

The drawing room was very grand, stretching the whole width of the house, but quite different from the dark and cluttered hall downstairs. It was light and very pretty; the ornaments of china and silver and the paintings were a mixture of styles and periods, some very modern indeed. Two or three pictures by the windows were clearly in the new strange Impressionist style, very rough, thought Lucy, and yet they seemed to blend effortlessly with the sumptuous browns and pink of the Persian carpet.

Lady Emilia Dilke was standing by the roaring fire and stretched out her hands to them. "Come and get warm, welcome to you both," she said. "How are you, dear friend?" she said to Matron, and, "I'm so happy to meet you, Miss Deane, I have heard great things of you from Doctor Dudfield. May I introduce you to my husband, Sir Charles?"

Lucy shook hands and bowed her head lightly. "I hope you are both well."

"She is always well," said Sir Charles. "But I am very sleepy. I have been up all night in the House wrangling over the Local Government Bill. A lot of hot air and we are very little further forward. Please sit down, ladies. May, let me bring that chair further forward."

Lady Dilke rang the bell and ordered tea to be brought up. She was a striking middle-aged woman, her dark hair with strands of silver grey piled on the top of her head, and wearing a simple pale brown, softly draped, woollen dress and a rust and red Paisley shawl around her shoulders. Her fingers were bare except for her wedding ring, but the two large single diamonds in her ears glinted and sparkled in the firelight.

She asked about Lucy's training and was amused by her preparation for the Sanitary Inspectors Examination. "Drains and Sewage! Well done!"

"And they mentioned Applied Mechanics," said Lucy, "But that would have been my Waterloo!"

Lady Dilke threw up her hands in sympathy. "It would be a challenge, certainly."

Miss de Pledge said she thought it was well within Lucy's capabilities.

Lady Dilke said it was surprising how interested one became in subjects once they became relevant to one's life. Tradesmen were craftsmen, if they were given the chance, and good factory environments could only benefit society. Skimping on good working facilities was bad practice for everyone. She spoke about 'Bad' Factories. She was collecting evidence of specific Factories for the Royal Commission on Labour. "I hoped I could assist May in her work as Assistant Lady Commissioner."

May laughed. "It's the other way round, Lady Emilia, isn't it?" She turned to Matron. "I came over from Dublin to be Lady Emilia's secretary and found she was already steeped in the world of factory reforms and fearful conditions. Everything I learnt I learnt from her. If the tide is turning she began to turn it!" Lady Dilke shook her head gently and nodded at her husband. "Oh, of course, without Sir Charles none of us could proceed at all."

He wagged his finger at her. "The Report will be out this spring, Miss Deane, and it will show a terrible state of affairs – dirty and dangerous, for men and women. But mostly for women. Work shouldn't make women sick, Miss Deane. But it does. So we must have women to inspect it and make it wholesome and good."

"I agree completely," said Lucy. "I am so new to inspecting in Kensington, and wherever I go – mostly laundries and dressmaking establishments – I have only met one so far that complied with all the regulations. And the regulations themselves are hardly demanding. Everything needs tightening up."

"Hurrah!" said Sir Charles, "A woman after my own heart. Someone who can see beyond the present evils and set the standards for the future."

"Of course, there are some outstanding working women in the factories, very prominent in their unions, and very capable of putting their case. And several of the District Factory Inspectors would be happy to have them in their 'team' – under their control, of course," said Lady Dilke. "I have had one or two to stay with me down in the West Country, in the constituency. Very…" She stopped, searching for the right phrase.

Lucy waited.

"Very clever women! VERY clever! Very CLEVER! But – utterly lacking in tact! No discretion, no powers of self-control, no knowledge of how to take the initiative, or to organise, or to grapple on their own responsibility with work, and no practice in writing reports or any office work."

"Hardly surprising!" said Miss de Pledge.

"EXACTLY!! I want Lady Inspectors to be appointed and then I want them to be paid EXTRA to train these working women gradually to manage, to do the official work, first as Assistant Inspectors and then as full Inspectors."

"That's a very tall order," said Lucy. "And a very exciting order."

"It is," said May, "and we are all agog to see how the Home Office plans to set it up. We gather from Miss Lankester that you may be interested."

"I am certainly interested," said Lucy. "But I have only been in my Sanitary Inspector's post for two months! And in Kensington the work is having to be organised from scratch! There are four thousand laundries and dressmaking establishments alone in Dr Dudfield's district, not counting the factories."

"And how many Female Inspectors?"

"Only two. Miss Squire and me."

Sir Charles held his head and groaned.

"Well," said May, "The Female Factory Inspectors would have the whole country to inspect. And there wouldn't be many more than two of them – to start with."

"None of us can do any more until Mr Asquith has decided on the matter anyway. So we shall just get on with our own work for the time being, certainly until mid-April. The Kensington Vestry need not know or worry about any of this until then." Sir Charles smiled at Lucy and looked at his watch. "I must ask you to excuse me. I am expecting a visitor in my study." He shook hands with both the visitors and as he went towards the door he said, "There would of course be the Civil Service exam for any applicants; and if I were you, I would feel more confident of facing the District Inspectors around the country if I HAD boned up on the Applied Mechanics!"

"Applied Mechanics? He couldn't mean it!" Hye's mouth fell open.

"They were all very gracious. But really they were very reticent. Still, they asked me to come again before they leave town. He goes for blocks of time to his constituency."

"Applied Mechanics!"

"I know, I know. Let's not think of it. Hye, I think we should ask Bossie to invest £500 for us. Mr Child at the bank says we have enough in the savings account."

"Just as you think best. But look what's in the kitchen. It came today while I was out. Mrs Casey took it in."

Stacked in the kitchen were four dozen claret bottles and two dozen Amontillado bottles and a note from Lady Howard. 'With best wishes. Must be drunk in two years or will go bad. Affectionately Constance, Lady Howard.'

"Where are we to store it?"

"Heaven knows! Under the beds?"

"Good idea, you can swig it while you're swotting up on Applied Mechanics."

The next week Lucy and Rose worked for three days on putting into geographical order the lists of laundry workshops and steam laundries in the borough. The Registers grew larger and larger and their eyes, and arms, and backs ached and their fingers were black with ink. No workshop anywhere had any lists of workers. Dr Dudfield was dismissive. "You can write to the owners if you want to." They decided to ask at each place they visited.

On the Friday after work Lucy went to a meeting called by the Amalgamated Tailors Union about the strike of the tailors at Whiteleys Department store. The weather was cold but clear with a full moon and Lucy enjoyed her ride on the top of the omnibus up Park Lane looking out over Hyde Park in the early evening. The streets were full with people going home from work, and with lights in shop windows and richly dressed people alighting from cabs and carriages outside the great hotels.

When she arrived at the Victoria Hall Bayswater she found to her pleasure Lady Dilke and her maid Miriam, alighting from a hansom at the door. She enveloped Lucy in her fur cape and bore her into the large room, overfilled with small dapper men.

"How lovely to see you," said Lady Dilke, "I'm here in my capacity of Leader of the Women's Trade Union League. I'm not here for the platform, so sit with us." They were ushered to seats in the front row, together with a small contingent of women tailors, all in their smartest coats and neatest hats. Lady Dilke greeted them and asked their names. "They have never been on strike before," she said. "But this time ten of the stores' women have come out in sympathy. It's an important step forward for them. Normally the department stores women are never included in the union's strike actions, so the women became blacklegs involuntarily, because they were given the men's work. And so, when wages were reduced to pay for the strike, the women's wages were always reduced first and they were the first to be laid off."

Half the audience was composed of Yiddish tailors from the East End of London. Two of them were called upon to speak which they did capably and humorously, and there was much chuckling and quick-fire repartee from the rows of listeners. Lucy lost most of the jokes, the accent was so difficult to follow. Sounds like Dutch, bad Dutch and bad English, she thought. The meeting was orderly. Two years ago the men had agreed to work for Whiteleys for 6d an hour on condition they brought up the rates of pay of fourteen other employers in the district who could have competed with Whiteleys. Now Whiteleys had reneged on the deal.

"Since then," said a Whiteleys foreman, "Whiteleys has had its work done in sweating dens, and one of our men has caught smallpox by having the clothes brought to him by one of those places." Lady Dilke spoke from the floor, splendidly, extempore, for four minutes, giving advice of how the meeting should require the Union to proceed.

She insisted Lucy should ride in their hansom home. It was exhilarating bowling through the frosty moonlit Hyde Park, down the Exhibition Road to Sloane Street. She began to get out, but Lady Dilke said, "No, no, my dear," and instructed the driver to take her all the way to Fulham Road.

As she stepped down she noticed another cab parked outside number 100, and while she was opening her handbag for her key a lady put her head out of the second cab.

"Miss Deane?"

"Yes, Miss Lucy Deane."

"Oh! I am sorry to bother you, but I have come in hopes of seeing Miss

Hyacinth Deane. I sent a note earlier in the day. My name is Miss George. I am the secretary of the Technical Education Department for the London County Council. I hope she might be able to take an unexpected class for us."

"Do come in," said Lucy, praying fervently that the fire was in and that Mrs Casey had left a little supper and a tidy living room. "She should be home by now, but she is racing all over London this week on Cookery College examining. And I have been at an evening meeting."

The living room was tidy and bright and the fire behind its guard had burnt down but still gleamed warmly. Miss George looked approvingly. "I thought it was worth waiting for ten minutes, I admit I was on the point of giving up. It is an imposition to come so late, but your sister is so resourceful in an emergency." Lucy glowed.

They talked of County Council work and pay scales. Lucy said she had heard it was very low. "I think £90 a year for a lecturer on Nursing and several other subjects is ridiculously little. I heard it from Miss Lankester at the National Health Society."

"Then they have misled you there," said Miss George drily. "We offer £100 a year for a Nursing Lecturer, only two lectures a day, five days a week, and two months, holiday. The nursing profession are boycotting us. But it is as much as a high school teacher gets if university-educated and more than a Cookery teacher who works far harder."

Lucy thought it was certainly enough for a permanent income, and agreed she would have accepted such an offer.

Hyacinth came in very soon after. "I'm all in!" she said, throwing her hat across the table. "Oh! It's Miss George, isn't it? I beg your pardon!"

Miss George explained her errand and apologised. Hyacinth apologised too, and in spite of the extra evenings, accepted gratefully. Lucy took Miss George to the cab rank on the corner, and finally the sisters drank cocoa by the fire before falling into bed. "She said you were always so resourceful in an emergency."

"Did she?" Hyacinth looked surprised. "I always feel anything but." She smiled. "I might catch you up Lucy, one of these days."

"Darling Hye! You are just right. Goodnight."

"Oh by the way, Lucy, can you write to Mr Rorke two doors down? The smoke from his wash house comes into our back windows. Mrs Casey says it makes her retch and it puts smuts on our kitchen."

"Thanks SO much, darling Hye. Just what I really enjoy!! I'll do it. Good night."

Lucy came into the Town Hall pink faced and very cross. "I've inspected in the north of my district, laundries and dyers. They were a very rude lot. I'm not sure I acted for the best about Tisdal the Dyers. He was out and the forewoman RUDE. I think I ought to have gone away and gone over it with Mr Tisdal later. If she makes up a story and he complains to the Vestry they will say I have no tact. And another laundry was VERY rude!" Miss Squire put down her pen and made sympathetic noises. "I really think I kept my temper splendidly in both cases, but then that's what I'm paid to do! Only, isn't it rather undignified for official people to stand at the door of a place they are appointed to enter and wait silently while their occupants shout abuse and hold them up to each other to ridicule?"

Miss Squire nodded sadly. "It's not a good day altogether," she said. "Well actually it could be worse. Dr Dudfield tells me that at the last meeting the Vestry empowered us to sign written intimations, and he is going to propose at the next meeting that we are empowered to authenticate Statutory Notices with our signatures."

"That's good. At least someone in authority has confidence in us."

"Yes, it is. But he's been looking through the forms we designed for the new Registers, and he doesn't approve of the order or the way we have filled them in. So we have to change the order and do them all over again!"

On Saturday morning Lucy went to the Polytechnic to enquire about classes in Applied Mechanics. A Mr Spooner, Head of the Mechanical Dept, was charming, but told her the classes had begun in October; however, she was welcome to join and do what she could. He gave her an introduction to the Chief Engineer of Workshops to go and look at the exhibits there whenever she liked. He sent her to the South Kensington Institute to see Dr Willis, the Instructor in Mechanics, but when she met him he pursed up his lips and said that as she was a complete beginner it was a waste of time to join the class so late in the syllabus. "Read Blackie's Dynamics, Miss Deane, that's the basic handbook, and spend as much time as you can in the Elementary Mechanics section of the Western Galleries. Take the catalogue with you. You can see all the parts of different machines there and take your own time over it." Lucy thanked him and went home, aware he thought her a hopeless case and inwardly agreeing with him.

She made better progress on Monday morning when she visited Mr Pitts' laundry in Ifield Road. He too at first persisted in refusal to admit her, asking "What Authorisation?" and declining to even look at her Authorisation card, or the Section 116 of the Public Health Act she showed him. Finally, after a good deal of cajoling and explanation he grudgingly allowed her to enter, saying he actually did need a Sanitary Inspector, but that she was no use to him, as his water supply was out of order and his laundry could only operate at half capacity. Lucy went through and inspected his workrooms, and after half an hour sympathising with him over his sanitary woes, saw a typical cottage laundry trying to operate in premises not built for it. The place was in a disgraceful state, dirty ceilings flaking and falling down because of the steam and the weight of the drying laundry, the traffic and the constant banging door in a jerry-built house. His water supply and his drain pipes were out of order. "Have been for several days! I've reported it! I've complained! Nothing doing!"

The wash house was only meant for three or four women, but there were seven there when Lucy went in. "There's seven because it's Monday and Tuesday. The rest of the week only four. We're the only laundry in this area. Always extra busy washing Monday and Tuesday. They have to work overtime hours, but they like that, and yes, we are overcrowded, but that don't matter, as we aren't under the Factory Law."

"Hmm," thought Lucy, "Roll on the Royal Commission findings." The washerwomen regarded her impassively. They were hot and wet and sweaty with raw red hands, but they looked strong and healthy.

In fact, Pitts' was a reasonable establishment when set against Mrs Brown's laundry. She was the wife of a labourer who, so his wife said, "was more often out of work than not." She did the wash with two neighbours whom she hired for several days in the week. Her front room was turned into an ironing room, also used as a drying room and the family's sleeping room. There was one wash tub in the back kitchen. The living room ceilings and walls were fairly clean, but the premises otherwise were in a filthy condition. There was a minute wash house in the yard which had a huge copper and two tubs. Swarms of children were evidently supporting her in the task, it was a truly family affair. In contrast to the Pitts' laundry, the water supply was good.

"Now what are you doing, Lucy?"

"I'm composing a circular letter to go to all the firms in the district who employ outworkers, asking for their lists. I can get them printed very reasonably. I'll take them in tomorrow and with luck I can have posted them all this weekend."

"I thought you were going to Alberta's charity dance at the weekend."

"I was tempted. But it's too expensive. I should have to get another evening cape, and then the cab there and back. And I really need to go to the lecture on Mechanics."

"Oh, well, of course, obviously the dance can't compete with a Mechanics lecture. Look out Lucy, you'll turn into a bore. What will the Boyce Court family think?"

Rose Squire and Lucy were hard at work recompiling the Registers when Dr Dudfield strode into the room, red-faced and in a towering temper. He waved the outworkers circular around. "What's this? What's this? Which of you is responsible for sending all these out?"

"I did it," said Lucy.

"You had no authority to write for the lists. I give the authority for specific cases only. I've had Brydon the Blind Maker in my office, very angry. I shall have plenty of others, no doubt."

"I'm sorry," said Lucy.

"And anyway, it's badly worded, it's unofficial – it's – it's tart, and you should have submitted it to me before sending it out." He swept out of the room leaving the door open and went stamping up the stairs to his room.

"Oh, dear me," murmured Miss Squire.

Lucy banged her head on the desk. "Stupid me! Memo to myself. Never do anything in future, or take any step unless forced to an initiative. Never even avail myself of the permission to do anything. He distinctly permitted my writing—"

"He did?" said Rose Squire.

"He DID. You heard him. Well don't YOU ever take any initiative! You'll get no thanks for it."

That evening she went to her first lecture about Applied Mechanics and it dampened her spirits even further, Mr Spooner was a splendid teacher, very kind and very clear but Lucy was completely at sea, the only woman's hat among the serried ranks of earnest young apprentices, not understanding the elements and frightened of the mathematical equations. She walked home depressed and then found a letter from Miss Lankester, meaning to be helpful, saying that she had heard that a nomination for the new post was not necessary, as if there was to be an examination it would probably be one of the open ones; and that her informant's private opinion was that the Inspectors would be selected from those engaged in County Council work if they satisfied the examiners; Miss Lankester asked that the letter would be considered strictly confidential.

"It's already slipping away from me," said Lucy sadly.

February the first was a bright morning and a stiff breeze blew the fog over towards the East of London. Lucy went to inspect a large laundry in the Earls Court Road and found a friend. Mr Elliott was welcoming and forthcoming, a spare balding man with a grey moustache and twinkling eyes. His laundry was an orderly hive of activity, the women lively and cheerful in the wash houses and the hot damp steam; even the piles of shirts seemed co-operative and pleased to be being washed. When she had finished her inspection he took her into his office where his two women book keepers were busy with bills and wages packets. He was an intelligent man, sharp and thrifty. "I expect you would like to hear about the different rates of pay for each job," he remarked.

"I would, very much," said Lucy, "But unless there has been a Complaint it is not in my remit to enquire."

"I thought not. But each task has a different pay. I pay most of my workers by piecework, because mine is a large 'Shirt and Collar' trade and all shirt and collar work is paid by piece. The women don't 'scamp' because I look over each article myself and if it is not perfect they have to do it again or pay me the price of rewashing. I had an ironer yesterday who got seven out of her dozen shirts returned to do again unpaid. That makes them careful. Returned work is very rare here. The shirt ironers get 1s 6d a dozen. I had one woman who could do 21 shirts between 8a.m. and 1p.m. She WAS a quick worker. That was 2s 9d just for one morning!

"A collar ironer is better paid than a shirt ironer, they are more difficult. They get 3d a dozen and can make 4s to 4s 6d a day. That's 22s 6d a week! That's a decent wage in anyone's money.

"Washer women get 2s 6d to 2s 9d a day. A 'Copper woman' gets her heavier work for 2s 8d a day and the Forewoman of the Washers get 3s a day.

"The best worker I have is a widow with two children, she entirely supports herself and gets an average of £1 a week. She has the 'run of the Board' that means she can do plain or fancy ironing, caps and frills and such like.

"The 'preparers' they sort and soak, a nasty job often, they get 3s a day.

"Then there are 'dry scrubbers', generally girls who are learning. They'll get 1s or 1s 6d a day.

"New stuff requires great skill. Those workers are paid from 2s 6d to 4s a dozen dealing with new shirts.

"I don't like learners. I tried them but I now only take on a few. As a rule a learner pays 10s to an old hand who teaches her for three months. The old hand gets the benefit of her help and after a week or two pays her a shilling or two a week pocket money. The old hand will make 5s or 6s a day if she has a quick learner.

"I only pay a few of my hands by the day, chiefly per week, but as it is piecework they can demand their wages at any moment if they like. They are a law unto themselves. If their husbands are out of work they will work hard all the hours they can get, but when the men have work the women are likely to throw up their jobs and go."

One of the clerks got up and went to the door and rang a large hand bell for a long time in a determined fashion.

"That's one o'clock. Mealtime. Their dinner is from 1 to 2p.m. I'm a teetotaller myself, but I allow one pint of beer a day each. They go out for their meals, but as it is piecework they only take a very short time for meals. They get half an hour for tea."

The two women closed their books and left the room for their break. One returned in a few minutes with a pot of tea and a jug of milk and pretty cups and saucers and plates on a tray.

"Time for a break for all of us," said Mr Elliott. He opened a leather bag and brought out two tins containing two small meat pies and some small cakes, beautifully packed and wrapped.

He offered them to Lucy who demurred. "This is your lunch."

"It is, but my dear wife always provides too much." He propped the door open. "I like to see what they're doing, who stays, who goes, what state the rooms are left in. Some don't go out; they prefer to work through. Sometimes I allow it, sometimes I don't. Some just want to sit quiet."

He poured out the tea. Lucy admired the china.

"I like pretty things. I don't see why I can't indulge myself just because the work's steamy and wet. We use Borax starch and soap in this works. Some starch is highly destructive and rots the clothes.

"People say steam laundries tear the clothes. They don't. It isn't the machine, it's the carelessness of the women. They hate a machine because it reduces labour, and if the clothes get caught in the machine, instead of disentangling it gently, they drag and pull, laying half the blame on the machine, whilst when they have to do it themselves they are careful, knowing they must bear the blame themselves."

"Are you in favour of the new Factory Act for Laundries about to be brought in?" asked Lucy.

"Factory Act? I should like it personally. I hate the late hours, they are killing me, but my best piece workers will go where they may work overtime and all the week long. They expect to be employed Monday to Friday, at any rate. Let's go and see what the works looks like while they are away."

He ushered Lucy around the laundry, stopping occasionally to check the work left on ironing boards, by mangles, peering along the narrow shelves of un-ironed handkerchiefs, all in small household piles, checking the laundry marks. In the packing room two neat shop girls were still there, counting and labelling. They nodded pleasantly to Mr Elliott.

"No Factory Act could touch me anyway, for piecework; there is no part of the Act that limits the time, (Lucy made a mental note to check) and if they choose to work 14 hours a day, they may demand 14 hours' wages.

"There are two classes of customers. One is 'the shop connection'. They are the common people who bring their washing to the laundry themselves and collect it away for themselves. Then there is the 'outside' connection' – where we call at the house for the washing weekly and send it back the same week. The 'outside' folk are worth more on the whole.

"A laundry woman's life is hard, but the work is healthier than most, and certainly better paid than most women's work. The laundry worker is a healthy woman on the whole, barring the ones who drink, and I don't pity them in the way of wages as women's work goes."

They had reached the shop door. Lucy thanked Mr Elliott for his time and trouble and his invaluable information. "Ah, well, it was a pleasure for me as well," he replied, "and I wish you well in your new profession. We need inspectors like you and I feel sure in due course with more of you about we shall all be in safer hands. I look forward to meeting you again."

Lucy felt invigorated and hurried down the street to a Lyons tea house to buy more tea and a bun and to write up her notes with her indelible pencil as fast as she could.

She dutifully went to the Western Galleries at the Science Museum but was much puzzled by the machinery models. She only grasped one fact, the method by which the direction of force was changed by means of bevelled cogged wheels, but though she was proud of her achievement she somehow felt this would not give her an automatic entry into the world of the Factory Inspector. So she joined the Kensington Library and took out her first book, *Bell's Applied Mechanics*. She thought the library assistant shot her a startled glance as she stamped it, but she looked nonchalant and dropped it into her bag. Evelyn came to stay for the weekend and she and Hye and Lucy had a happy evening reading extracts to each other and making romances about Miss Piston, and the Honourable Endless Band, and Valve, a trustworthy old butler. On the Saturday afternoon they all went to the Polytechnic workshops with an introduction to the Chief Engineer, Mr Rogers, from Mr Spooner. They were the only women there. It was a splendid place, they decided, and much easier to understand than the Weston Galleries. Even Evelyn could make some sense of the Piston and the Valve, and the Flywheel. The rooms were full of young fellows, gazing and writing notes, some of them were members of Lucy's Mechanics class.

Lucy and Hye saw Evelyn off at Waterloo on Sunday evening, "What WILL they say when you tell them at the Boyce how you spent your Saturday afternoon in Applied Mechanics?"

Evelyn leant out of the carriage window. "I don't think I am even going to mention it to them."

Dr Dudfield was still in a bad mood on Monday morning. Old Mr Beedman, the chief clerk, told the two women he had been at work all

Sunday, so of course he was tired. "But he is still very disagreeable," said Rose Squire. He had good reason, said Mr Beedman, the Vestry Committee had not ratified their authorisation papers – Mr Beedman reckoned they had not even read them – and the smallpox outbreak in North Paddington was not abating, so they could not inspect anywhere there.

Dr Dudfield came in momentarily to cast a fat bundle of letters onto Lucy's desk. "More complaints over outworkers lists. I've dealt with them. 'Tisn't as if I was twiddling my thumbs all day. Organise yourselves this week and don't forget to sign all the Statutory Notices."

"But how best to do it?" Rose Squire worried when he had gone. "I couldn't bring myself to tell him that the printer hasn't got our report sheets ready yet. So it's no good writing them up."

"Let's hope they'll come this afternoon. I've made another mistake." Rose looked alarmed. "Oh, it's not serious, but I – never having been told to the contrary – supposed that ALL Kensington High Street is in Kensington. But part of it is in Westminster! So I have inspected and written to twelve outworkers in Westminster Parish. Just wait till one of those writes to Dr Dudfield."

They decided they would do no good staying at the Town Hall and told Mr Beedman they were leaving for the day. "You do that," said Mr Beedman. "For you'll get no advice from the Doctor today. He's vexed enough with the Vestry Committee delaying him. They're a set of old fools, and I said so, and they're not best pleased with me, either."

"Oh, hear, hear, Mr Beedman," said Lucy fervently. The old man came to the top steps and waved them off in a grandfatherly fashion.

She spent the rest of the morning in South Kensington and the afternoon studying Mathematics and Mechanics at home. One ton of coal came, twenty shillings and sixpence, amounting to nearly everything in her purse. Mrs Casey prepared a tasty thick soup for their evening meal, but there was a distinct alcoholic haze about her, which luckily did not transfer itself to the soup. When she had gone Lucy peered under the beds to see if any of the bottles were missing. All seemed to be in order.

Her spirits were lifted the next evening when, on her way to an incomprehensible lecture on Cams and Camshafts at the Polytechnic, she called in at the National Health Society in reply to a note from Miss Lankester. Three visitors were introduced to her, "Lucy, Dr Schofield you know already, and these gentlemen are journalists come about our application to the London Governing Board to become a training body for Sanitary Inspectors. Why do you think Women Sanitary Inspectors are important?"

Lucy reeled off several reasons and said she would also ask Miss Squire. When the gentlemen had gone Miss Lankester thanked her. "I've seen Dr Dudfield and he says your work is as thorough and efficient and more educated than that of any man he has had. He considers you both a great success and HE will advise the Vestry to reappoint you as bona fide Sanitary Inspectors with a salary of £100."

Lucy survived the Cams and Camshaft lecture. Mr Spooner explained it very clearly and she resolved not to waste any more time in the South Kensington Museum Galleries. She felt much comforted until, as she turned into the gate of 100 Fulham Road, she realised she had left her lizard skin handbag on the bus, with papers marked Private in it.

She asked Miss Squire "Why should there be Women Sanitary Inspectors?" Rose Squire thought for a moment and then said firmly "As educators of women." They discussed the matter and Lucy drew up a tabulated list for Dr Schofield. All afternoon they tramped over the Godison Road district to look for new, defunct, or missing workshops from the old Register and only found one still extant. "It's a waste of time and I'm dead tired," Miss Squire grumbled. "Worse than any other work we have to do!" And she stamped her foot.

Lucy thought that this was the first time she had ever seen Miss Squire other than composed and controlled. She heartily agreed with Miss Squire.

4

Has she? Hasn't she?

A Home Office nomination (but don't tell anybody); A Tea Party at Lady Dilke's; Lunch with Lady Dilke; Mrs Casey has an accident; Lucy sleeps in the waiting room at Stafford; the Model Factory in Leek; Mrs Casey signs the Temperance Pledge; countless workshops; high fashion and foul soap; Lucy takes the Civil Service examinations; May Abrahams is encouraging; Lucy waits and waits.

Rose Squire's first summons case; Hyacinth comforts Lucy; good news but no birth certificates; visiting Miss Canny; Lucy passes her medical exam; meeting Mr Sprague Oram; bad news for Rose; Lucy visits Lady Dilke; goodbye to Sanitary Inspecting.

A telegram arrived on Saturday morning from the National Health Society saying 'News for you – come when convenient. Lankester.' Lucy went round there as soon as she could decently leave her tasks at the Town Hall.

"Oh Lucy, I am glad to see you," said Miss Lankester, "I wanted to tell you, on March the 5th I was sent for by Mr Asquith himself. I went at once and I met with his secretary, Mr Tennant, and HE said – but this is very private, mind you – 'one of the short-listed Factory Inspector candidates was a Girton lady, but the other front runners as candidates are Miss Ravenhill and Miss Deane from your Women's National Health Society. Which do you consider most competent?' I said 'Miss Deane because she has more experience.'

"Oh, thank you Miss Lankester."

"I had to say what I thought, Lucy. And you must understand that this is completely confidential, and I ought not to be telling you. But then he said, 'Miss Ravenhill's father and mine were old friends – the Duchess of Albany has written for her'."

"Hmm," said Lucy.

"And now a letter for you has come HERE this morning from the Home Office. Not to your address. I don't know why that should be. Here it is. Would you like to read it in private?"

"No, no. But how strange. Oh, my goodness."

The letter was very brief. 'Dear Miss Deane, with regard to the post of Female Factory Inspector to be based at the Home Office, Mr Asquith offers you the nomination if you can satisfy the Civil Service Commissioners as to qualifications.'

Miss Lankester clasped her hands together. "Another hurdle cleared. I shall not say anything to Miss Ravenhill. I think my part in this should be kept private. Miss Ravenhill is an extremely competent young woman. She will be a great asset to whatever post she takes. I shall be most happy to recommend her for any other."

"Oh, I quite understand you, Miss Lankester and I can't tell you how grateful I am to have your confidence."

"Go home, Lucy and write your letter of acknowledgment and acceptance and get it in the early evening post."

Hyacinth danced around the sitting room, throwing cushions in the air; but promised to be as silent as the grave for a week or two. "Not even to tell Evelyn?"

"Definitely not Evelyn. So we've got to go to church tomorrow, Hye, this is a very responsible post. I need God's help."

However, Lucy soon realised that somebody had been telling somebody something. On Monday morning Lucy received a letter from Lady Dilke. 'Dear Miss Deane, Today I received a letter from Mr Asquith which gave me much pleasure. My best good wishes, believe me, Emilia Dilke.'

Lucy was astounded by the speed of events. She had had no notion that the wheels of power were so interlocked and ran so fast.

She took the letter to the Town Hall and told Dr Dudfield privately that she had had a private intimation from Lady Dilke that she had been appointed Female Factory Inspector by Mr Asquith, and that therefore she thought it right to let him know; but she asked him not to tell the Vestry Committee until she had taken the Civil Service Examination and been officially notified of the appointment.

Dr Dudfield was genuinely pleased for her and Lucy was touched. "I was just beginning to find my feet here," she said. "I am so sorry that possibly I shall be leaving so soon."

"I had heard bits and pieces of news on the wind," he said, "so I am not completely taken unawares. It just shows what an admirable judge of character and ability I am."

Lucy felt quite overcome, and guilty at not being able to tell Rose Squire. To make up for it she worked hard on the Vestry Subcommittee reports all day and finished them by the middle of the afternoon.

She was expected to tea with Lady Dilke at five and arrived punctually on the doorstep wearing her best hat. This was not to be a cosy fireside occasion though. Various ladies and gentlemen arrived on the doorstep with her and introductions were made all round with perfect aplomb by Lady Dilke.

Lucy tried to fit the names to the faces. Miss Williams, secretary of the Democratic Club, Mr Hudson, MP; Mr Creeland, Editor of the Cosmopolitan Yankee; Miss de Pledge, Matron of the Chelsea Hospital – Lucy was relieved to see her; Miss Monck, Secretary, it seemed, of several Trades Unions. Lucy made her best social efforts, aided by Sir Charles, who moved about, always making a third or fourth in a group and constantly using everyone's name and referring to their positions so that it became easy to remember. "What a good teacher you are in social situations," said Lucy as he guided her to a seat by a small table so that a maid could provide her with a cup of tea and a plate for her scone.

"It's essential for me to repeat it for myself as well as for guests. Oh, look, here's Miss de Pledge. I know you know one another." And he gracefully left them to cross to another group.

Miss de Pledge patted her hand. "I've heard the good news," she said, "but not another word for a while."

"Everyone seems to have heard it before me!" said Lucy. "I wish I was wearing a different hat."

Miss de Pledge scanned the headgear of everyone in the room. "Yours is more than adequate," she said, and moved over to let another lady share the sofa. Lucy relaxed and began to enjoy the afternoon. The conversation was pleasant and Lady Dilke in fine fettle sharing the finer points of the successful issue of her libel case, Dilke versus Berger of the Sheffield factory. She pressed Lucy's hand as she left. "No time to talk now, but come to lunch on Sunday, just us for once, and Gertrude. So much to say then."

That evening Lucy asked Hye, "Would you mind if I left you alone to go to lunch with Lady Dilke on Sunday?"

"Not at all. Tina has invited me to stay with her for Saturday and Sunday. Would you mind if I left YOU alone?"

"Well, that works out well. But we see each other so seldom these days. Ships that pass in the night."

"It's the way it's going to be, I expect. We'll have to put ourselves in our diaries soon."

"Oh, mercy, I hope not. Well, tell Mrs Casey not to bother with any food for the weekend."

Lady Dilke's lunch was delightful. The maid brought a trolley with soup and hot rolls into the breakfast parlour where a small oval table had been set by the fire. The only other guest was Gertrude Tuckwell.

"Gertrude, my niece, shares a flat with May Abraham," said Lady Dilke. "She's staying with me to help out as my secretary until I find a new one."

"We've already met," said Lucy, "when I went to meet Miss Abraham."

Lady Dilke seemed pleased. "Up all those stairs! Now I can really congratulate you," she beamed, clasping Lucy's hands. "If you had failed in this application, I would certainly have asked you to be my secretary!"

"What splendid training that would be," Lucy basked in the affirmation.

"Let us sit at the table by the fire and help ourselves. You won't have an easy task at all. You will have to face enormous opposition to begin with."

"From the other inspectors?"

"Definitely. That's why the Chief Inspector insists on your being based at the Home Office – out in the Districts you would have been subsumed into minor roles in no time. And the Trades Unions will be very angry at your appointment."

"Oh! Why?"

45

"And all the Labour Organisations. Because you are 'Upper Class' in the face of their candidates. You have heard of Miss Heaton, I expect."

"No, Lady Dilke. Miss Heaton?"

"She is the factory girl genius. The Trades Union prodigy, very strong and very talented, certainly, but very conceited and very aggressive. When I met her here I felt she was only working for her own ends."

The soup was delicious. In a little while the maid returned with a bowl of bread and butter pudding and cream.

"I do hope you don't mind nursery food," said Lady Dilke. "I crave for it and I never get it except on rare occasions like this. How are your Mechanics classes progressing?"

"Terrible. Everyone around me in the class knows what they are about. I have no inkling – and a shrewd suspicion that a lot of it is humbug." They laughed.

"However, many of the women you will be serving will have to know about their machines or put their lives at risk," mused Lady Dilke. "It would be useful to you to be taken over a really excellent factory, and shown what good machinery and good practice and good conditions can do for the well being of the employees."

"It would, certainly. Do you know of any?"

"I do, but not in London. Are you going to the Conference in Manchester? You could combine the Conference with a good factory I know of."

"No. I thought of asking Dr Dudfield if I could attend, but as things are it would be inconsiderate. I have been in Kensington so little time as it is."

"A pity; but if you COULD get to Nicholson's factory in Leek in Staffordshire even for one day you would learn a huge amount very quickly!"

They arranged that Lucy should visit the factory on a Saturday morning, and Lady Dilke undertook to write and arrange this visit very soon. "Then perhaps you could stop over in Manchester on the Saturday afternoon and Sunday morning."

When Lucy arrived home the house was dark and cold. She raked out the kitchen range and lit the lamps. Hyacinth came home middle evening and they ate boiled eggs and some hard cake, and drank cocoa. Just as they were going to bed there was a loud knock on the door and Mrs Casey's daughter Etta stood woefully on the step. "Oh, Miss Deane, oh, Miss Hyacinth, Mother's been knocked down by a cart, they've taken her to Matron's hospital, she won't be coming tomorrow. I came round this afternoon but you wasn't in."

They comforted Etta and ascertained Mrs Casey had "probably not broken anything but was terrible confused and bruises all over." They reassured her that Mrs Casey would keep her job, and offered to find Etta a cab to go home, which she refused. Then they went to bed, moaning. "I've invited Miss Dunbar to tea tomorrow, and no time to get the room ready before I go in the morning."

"I've got to be at Stepney by eight o'clock tomorrow to demonstrate how to make pastry." As they turned into their rooms Hyacinth said, "I bet you she was drunk."

Hyacinth laid the sitting room fire, and luckily saved the kitchen range from going out before she washed and set off for Stepney. Lucy rushed around Gloucester Road dressmakers in the morning and was heartened by a first class establishment at No.33. Madame Brunne had been a high school teacher before her marriage and her workrooms were luxurious in their cleanliness and height. She said the chief difficulty in stopping overtime work for dressmakers were the employees themselves, who went home and sat up late at night working, under less healthy conditions than her workrooms, for private customers. She instanced the case of her first hand – to whom she paid £200 per annum – who went home at 7.30p.m. and sat up till 1a.m. making the dresses of the apprentices in the workroom over which she was the forewoman for 10 shillings apiece.

She bought some pretty cakes from a patisserie on the way home for Miss Dunbar's tea. She told Miss Dunbar confidentially that she had probably got the factory appointment, and asked if she would like to slip into her shoes at Kensington. Miss Dunbar went pink and said yes, very much. Lucy promised to use what influence she had.

As soon as Miss Dunbar had left she ran round to the domestic agency and engaged a Mrs Dimmock as a temporary help until Mrs Casey's predicament was sorted out.

After work on Friday she went to the National Health Society to receive instructions for the day in Leek which Lady Dilke had organised for her, as well as the visit to the Manchester and Salford Ladies Health Association. Miss Lankester agreed to press Miss Dunbar's claim to succeed Lucy in Kensington. She also divulged the fact that Miss Ravenhill had decided she was not suited as an Inspector. "She does not like the idea of appearing unpleasant," said Miss Lankester drily, and so she was now trying for an important post with the British Medical Association.

Because of this meeting she missed the 8.30p.m. train to Stafford on the way to Leek, and had to catch the 10p.m. mail train, snoozing all the way by herself in a Ladies Only carriage. The train stopped two or three times and finally drew in to Stafford well after midnight. One other person stepped down from the train and he swung smartly away towards the town. The station was otherwise deserted, and cabs had quit the station rank. Lucy asked a solitary night porter the way to the Station Hotel, nowhere in sight.

"A's now good yow goon thur," said the porter. "A's in a bad why, an it's clowsin down. An shay'm now good innywhy."

"Oh dear!" said Lucy.

"Yow'll 'ave ter walk into town," said the porter.

"The trouble is that I have to be back here by 7a.m." said Lucy, "because I've got to catch the early train to Leek."

"Ow well, sty yur then," said the porter. "Sty in the Lydies room. I'll myke up the fyer."

He not only made up the fire, but provided her with a blanket, two hard railway cushions and an enamel mug of hot sweet tea. Lucy settled down gratefully and slept fitfully as occasional goods trains rumbled through and clanked and banged.

At 6a.m. he battered on her door. "I'm off hoam nah. Master's just come. 'E'll see yur all set for Leek."

At 6.30a.m. the stationmaster knocked politely on the door with another enamel mug of hot sweet tea and a jug of hot water and a towel. Lucy was tremendously touched. "Ave yow got someone meeting yow in Leek?" Lucy assured him she had, hoping devoutly this was true. He escorted her personally to the train at 7.07a.m. and she left him a handsome tip for her Guardian Angel Night Porter.

At 8.41a.m. Mr Nicholson, very dapper and suave, met her at Leek and drove her in a very smart small carriage to his silk factory, a huge square building where thirteen hundred employees were all hard at work making silk thread, cotton twist, and countless different braids and trimmings. Lucy was certainly impressed by the extreme cleanliness of the workrooms and workers alike, and could not possibly fault the ventilation; the machines hummed and clattered. She could not believe the complete absence of dust, or of smell, and the apparent ease of the labour. She was struck too by the delicate look of the working girls, neither rough nor coarse, but resembling high class dressmakers' girls.

"They work fifty-four hours only," he told her. "6.30a.m. till 8a.m. then half an hour for breakfast. Then 8.30 till 12. Dinner 12 till 1. Then on till 5p.m. and half an hour for tea, then 5.30 till 6.30. Saturdays they work from 7.30 till 12.30 with a half-hour break. We pay wages on Friday evenings.

"At present the cottages around provide us with hot water three times a day – we charge the workers 2d a week for tea. So we are about to open a tearoom.

"We employ children over twelve on a part-time basis. They attend school two mornings and five afternoons a week."

The factory worked on a Pathway system mostly used by non-textile workshops, so that the goods began on the looms at one end of the building and finished in the warehouse at the other for packing, boxing and distribution.

She was driven to his home, Highfield Hall, and greeted by Mrs Nicholson, a cousin of Lady Dilke. They were very hospitable and gave her a homely and nourishing lunch. Lucy was ravenously hungry by this time and found it difficult to eat politely. "What I should have done if that porter hadn't put all that sugar in my tea, I can't think," she told Hye the next day. "I should have ripped the roast beef with my fingers."

She caught the 1.14 to Manchester and took a cab to the office of the Manchester and Salford Ladies Health Association. The Secretary, Mrs Harris, was there and gave her valuable information about the various Female Health Visitors in the District – "much more advanced than we are in London, Hye, fancy" – and told her about the two Female Workshop Inspectors, "working exactly on the same lines as us, Hye, and they were appointed by the Corporation in Manchester last autumn too. And I never knew!"

Then she went in a cab to the Trades Union Conference where she met up with Lady Dilke, sat in on a very good lecture about American Trade Unions, but had to fight against yawning and drifting off. Ironically, once she climbed into another gloriously empty Ladies Only compartment on the night mail train at Manchester she became wide awake, and so spent her time writing up her notes about the Nicholson's Silk Mill. On Sunday morning Hye made her go to bed as soon as she had had breakfast, and she was asleep as soon as her head hit the pillow. Two friends called as arranged in the afternoon, but Hyacinth refused to wake her.

Rose and Lucy began visiting workshops never previously mentioned in the Registers, meeting the owners and presenting them with the lists of Abstracts (the list of rules and regulations that bound the employers and employees) and the Codes and Requirements of Employment which had to be pinned up where everybody could see them. To their surprise they were greeted with smiles in nearly every place, and the deficiencies of each laundry, though there always were some deficiencies, were not so great as in others more long established. Rose Squire thought perhaps the new ideas were getting through; Lucy thought it was that the newer laundries hadn't had time to get so dirty yet.

A very nice letter sat at the Town Hall from May Abraham welcoming her as colleague.

In the evening, as Lucy was sitting writing her reports on her Leek and Manchester visits, a very repentant Mrs Casey, accompanied by her daughter, knocked on the door. Matron had sent for her and spoken to her severely, and extracted a promise that she would sign up for Mrs Campbell's Temperance Guilds and take the Pledge. Lucy and Hye decided that they would take her back on trial for a month. When Mrs Casey and Etta had left Lucy and Hye looked at one another. "It might work," said Lucy. "It won't," said Hye. But Mrs Casey joined the Temperance Guild and signed a monthly agreement.

The Civil Service Examination loomed nearer and nearer and Lucy sent in her forms of application. She went on going to the Mechanics Lectures, but knew she would never be confident with mechanical procedures. "I shall just have to know enough about the machines to get me by. I'll just have to learn about each one at the time," she said to Mr Spooner. He was encouraging, "They all look different, but they all work on the same principle. Sewing machines, picking up, moving along, how to start them, how to stop them. Coal engines, picking up, moving along, how to start them, how to stop them. You'll get the hang of it. Soak yourself in the basics. Don't be afraid to ask the stupid question." Lucy was unconvinced but grateful for his confidence and care.

She spent her days inspecting the countless workshops and back street factories in the poorer area of Paddington and the Fulham Road, determined to hand on her time in Kensington in an orderly and positive fashion. She genuinely enjoyed tramping from one place to another; no day, however humdrum, was the same and sometimes the differences were incredible. One day she spent the morning at Gooch's tailors in the Brompton Road, surrounded by beautiful and costly wools, tweeds, velvets, and flannels and was shown around by a charming foreman who had worked in London, Paris and New York. "The American Trades Unions are splendid," he told her. "But the English are stupid and silly. In America, the aim is that a worker should be paid what he is worth; in England the aim is to reduce all pay to a dead level and pay the bad and unskilled worker at the same rate as the skilled and industrious. And of course, women should be paid as fairly as men!"

That same day she spent the afternoon in Knight's Soap Boiling Works. She told Hye, "Horrible! Supposed to be the ideal soap works but FILTHY dirty. They grind rough fat, throw it in large lined vats with sulphuric acid, and leave it for 36 hours. Then it's sluiced with water for 3 days, melted in cauldrons – a foul smell and nuisance, and boiled for more days with salt thrown in. That makes the soap rise to the surface like froth and they skim it off and form it into little cakes. The rough stuff is carbolic soap and the better stuff gets scented. Don't go to a soap factory Hye, you come out feeling greasy and dirty."

She wrote to the folk at the Boyce and to Bossie and the Aunts in Sevenoaks to say she would not go for Easter and worked hard on the Arithmetic and Factory Act Sections for the Civil Service Papers. "I can add up and subtract. It's all this Volume and Cubic Feet and Proportions and Ratios and Algebraic Equations! Why am I so woefully ignorant?"

Her sole recreation was to take Mrs Casey to a picture service at Mrs Casey's Mission Hall (Mr Twitchell, the curate there, appeared to have some influence over Mrs Casey) and to go with her to Holy Communion on Easter Sunday morning. In Easter week her days were inspections, inspections, her evenings were sums, sums, and more sums.

One sunny April morning Lucy set off at 9a.m. to the office of the Civil Service, Common Row, Westminster, for her qualifying examination, and there she met Miss Adelaide Anderson, the other nominee. Miss Anderson was the 'Girton Lady.' They gripped each other's hands and were shown into a small office with two large desks.

Just after seven in the evening she got home. Hyacinth opened the door for her.

"Lucy, are you all right? I've been waiting and waiting – You haven't been writing all day, have you?"

"Oh, yes, I have. All day. Hye, I'm exhausted."

"I've got the Amontillado all ready, come and sit down."

Lucy took off her coat and hat and sank into an arm chair by the fire. Hye knelt and unlaced her boots.

"Oh, wonderful, Hye, thank you, thank you."

"Now tell me all about it. Don't leave anything out."

"We were taken into a small office with a nice fire burning and a desk each and they brought us our papers and checked if we had enough ink and paper and left us to it. The first paper was Arithmetic; I was seized with exam fright and made a fearful hash of it. I finished that one about midday. Miss Anderson only had to do part of the exam because she has already worked for the Commission. I don't think she was doing Arithmetic when I was. After each paper we had half an hour before the next one. So I ran out and had a cup of coffee at midday. Then they gave us the Factory Acts paper, that was fine, I knew that, and then she went home. So I thought I would go and have another coffee but it was raining so hard. And then a nice maid came in to make up the fire and just before the Composition paper she came in with a tray with a pot of tea and biscuits, so kind. And they left me to it. I actually enjoyed the Composition paper, I could have written on several of the topics, and the grammar was a doddle, thank God for good governesses."

Hyacinth laid the table and produced a perfect meat pie and Lucy drowsed in the armchair afterwards in the firelight.

Two days later she had her Viva for the Factory Acts with Mr Jasper Redgrave. Quite satisfactory, she felt. Now there was nothing to do but wait. She went to the Town Hall to report, but Dr Dudfield's wife was very ill and she only saw Rose Squire. They carried on as usual on their own, inspections, reports, registers. Rose Squire told her that Miss Dunbar was very hopeful and would certainly take the Kensington post if it was offered to her. Miss Ravenhill was not trying for it.

At the end of the week she lunched with Lady Dilke and May Abraham and Gertrude Tuckwell, and then climbed the heady heights to May's flat in Tite Street. May was confident. "Oh, you'll both be successful, I can feel it. The wheels turn, occasionally they run backwards, but they'll get there in the end. And they WANT us, you know, in the Home Office, they know they need Women Inspectors. I'm sure they'll keep us all together in the Home Office to start with at least.

"The Chief Inspector of Factories is a dear, he is fair-minded and kindly disposed to the idea of women. He is unpopular with the Men Inspectors because he wants us under his immediate control. He will be retiring in a couple of years so he is anxious to get us appointed and firmly in place before he goes. The Men Inspectors are very jealous of us."

"For that reason I suppose," said Lucy.

"Of course. But frightened of us as well. Many of them have been very lax in their work, no enthusiasm, only going for the appointments as a means of livelihood, friends with the factory owners in the neighbourhood and the local magistrates and so on. Not ALL, naturally. But many. So if a WOMAN or anyone is sent to their district to inspect on a 'Complaint', and by her energy brings to light the bad state that came about through their laziness, they are angry. Well, they will be angry."

"It's like going into the lion's den."

"Worse, I expect. Like a hyena's den. And if she has challenged comparisons unfavourable to themselves by her better inspections, even if unwittingly on her part, they WILL be angry. It amounts to an inspection of their inspecting work."

"Have I got the tact to cope with this?"

"We shall all have to learn it. And definitely we must hold on to the courage of our convictions. And the confidence to bring convictions to court if necessary."

"To prosecute?"

"Definitely. But with great care and only when we are sure no other way will do. Some of the District Inspectors are plain disagreeable. Most will be charming to your face; when a woman is sent to help them they will send her to places they have visited shortly before and already put in order; that just wastes everyone's time and makes her position useless and ridiculous."

"How do you know all this?"

"Found it out while on the Royal Commission," said Miss Abraham shortly. "As to the employers, the small workshop owners are nearly always ruder than the large factory owners."

"I've met that already. The women who run dressmakers are terrors."

"Well, naturally. They're already at the disadvantage of coping in a man's world. They've learnt how to fight their corners. And the skilled woman is in such a minority."

"I suppose that's owing to generations of defective training and education."

"A whole range of social and economic causes. But it will change, it will change. We are beginning to put the machinery in place to change it."

"I can see it's going to be hard for us."

"Oh, it is. And I'll tell you, the clerical load is TREMENDOUS. AND no clerical help in sight. AND the hours and the amount of work is irregular."

"Help!"

"So what do you think?"

"I think it's exciting. I wish they would let me know one way or another. Could you ask Mr Oram if I am officially appointed, because I need to tell the Vestry at the next Monday Committee Meeting, and I don't like to before the official announcement."

"I'll do my best. I'll ask and telegraph you with what I find out."

Armed with this promise Lucy felt able to speak to Mr Braye, the Chairman of the Kensington Vestry when he called at the Town Hall in the middle of the week. He was full of congratulations, "I am sorry we have had you for so short a time, but I think we knew our luck when we appointed you both, you and Miss Squire."

"I certainly hope to be able to tell the Vestry at next Monday's meeting. But I felt I had to let you know privately before then." And then she felt able to speak about Miss Dunbar. He listened with a twinkle. He thinks I am taking too much on myself, she thought, but he nodded at her encouragingly as he left.

That evening Lucy was troubled, as she was certainly not sure of the post. She sent another message to May Abraham begging her to let her know anything she had gleaned; but on Saturday a note came saying the Home Office could not call her on Saturday as the Civil Service Commissioners had not made up their mind. "I will try on Monday and will telegraph you then."

Hyacinth found Lucy impossible on Sunday. She could not settle. She began to tidy some clothes drawers and lost heart and crammed everything back; she began to write to Evelyn and tore it up; she began to polish all her shoes just as supper was ready. Finally Hyacinth sent her out for a walk to get rid of her for an hour.

On Monday morning a telegram came from May Abraham. 'Home Office has been informed Civil Service board is not yet decided.'

Lucy panicked. She took the telegram to Dr Dudfield who said, "I know more about it than I can tell you."

Lucy gazed at him. "Do you mean that I failed the exam? Or that Miss Anderson has failed the exam?" He did not answer, but asked her to describe Miss Anderson, particularly her appearance. "But don't report anything to the Committee tonight."

The members of the Sanitary Committee of the Vestry were patently pleased with them and their work, and particular congratulations were given to Rose Squire who had passed her Sanitary Institute exam with flying colours on Saturday. The Committee decided unanimously to reappoint them both permanently as Sanitary Inspectors. Mr Braye thought the salary should be £80 0s 0d per annum. Lucy felt it should be £100 0s 0d but didn't feel in a strong position to make her views known at the moment.

Rose Squire was elated by her examination results but nervous to find she had her first Summons case, about dirty laundry premises.

"I'll come with you and sit at the back of the court," promised Lucy. However, it turned out that the case was to be heard in the Vestry Committee rooms. "Just as frightening," said Rose. "If not more so."

Three Divisional Justices of the Peace were summoned by the Vestry Committee for Sanitary Matters and chaired by Mr Braye. Miss Squire sat at one end of the long table and the owner of the dirty laundry at the other. The JPs sat one side and the Vestry Committee the other.

Everyone clearly knew each other and nodded and smiled. They'll all be having lunch with each other in an hour or so, surmised Lucy. There was a general feeling of complacency in the room balanced at each end by the aura of nervousness around Rose Squire and the aggressive folded arms of the laundry owner.

Rose Squire read out her reports clearly and concisely. The Bench was not at all conversant with the rules and regulations; on seeing the phrase 'dirty ceiling' made merry over the idea that this should be 'injurious to health'. The owner stated that the laundry had been completely limewashed in the last week. "Oh, well then, there is no doubt the Summons should be withdrawn," said the JPs.

Rose Squire stood up at once. "That is not acceptable. The painting was not done until long after the summons was issued and there has still been no provision of any ventilation." The Vestry Committee conferred among themselves. "We think the defendant should certainly pay the costs of this meeting." The JPs nodded as one. "And we defer the case to this day fortnight for a final report."

Rose and Lucy went to a teashop in Kensington Church Street. Rose's handkerchief was damp where her fist had clenched on it.

"We must remember in future that a bench of JPs is a very ignorant thing," said Lucy, "so we must spell out every little detail of Sanitary Law in future if we want a satisfactory conclusion."

"The law is vague though," said Rose Squire spreading jam on her toast, "because a laundry is not classed as a workshop, and it's clearly not a factory, so they slip through the net of the Factory Act."

"All London workshops do. The Public Health Act doesn't apply, unless it's a work SHOP and not just a work PLACE."

"And then we can only give written intimations in the case of overcrowding."

"So I suppose we shall have to get the law changed, shan't we?"

When they reported the morning's events to Dr Dudfield he commended Rose. He told them he was negotiating with the Vestry for higher salaries for them and that, as the London general rate would not allow a Sanitation Inspector's salary as low as £80, and that as the London Council would pay half the salary, he was proposing a salary of £120.

He also told Lucy privately that the hitch in the appointment was not over her exam but over Miss Anderson's.

Lucy went home with relief and wrote to Miss Dunbar not to let Mr Braye pin her to any fixed salary when she visits but to leave it in the hands of the Vestry.

April 12th and 13th were perfect spring days, exactly the sort of weather to spend at the Boyce. "They'll be getting the boats out ready for the lake and Mr George's lambs will be all over the front field," mourned Hyacinth. "Why don't we go Lucy? No officials are going to be in their offices this weekend."

"You go, dear. I don't want to have to face their sympathetic faces if it all falls through."

"Well, it won't, Lucy, don't be silly. And everyone there wants you to get it."

"Oh no they don't! Uncle George thinks it quite unsuitable and Mary thinks I'm letting the side down terribly going into such rough and filthy places."

"But as she has never been known to do a hand's turn for anyone in her life she is hardly entitled to an opinion."

"Hyacinth! Don't be spiteful! She's great fun, and she's really talented with her drawings and her paintings. She makes us all laugh. She's a great hostess."

"Only because she's got all the maids and grooms to run around for her. She hasn't got a clue how to run a house or hold down a proper job. She doesn't need to. And she'll take care to marry someone who can support her. She won't marry without money."

"Stop, Hye! I don't know how we got on to her. And Ethel and Evelyn don't think like her anyway. Nor Horace. No, I'm just too nervy to be good company this weekend. Do go, darling it would be a shame to waste this lovely weather."

But Hyacinth loyally refused to leave her. And they were tantalised further when they went shopping to buy eggs from Miss Jones' dairy and met Miss Redgraves, who congratulated Lucy warmly. They were nonplussed when she told them she had not received official confirmation. "But Father saw the present Inspector this week – Mr Oram – and he told him PERSONALLY."

"But they haven't told ME," wailed Lucy.

When they got home another consignment of coals arrived. While they were being poured into the coal shed, Mr Philips' young man called to arrange a time for repairing the kitchen drain and quoted a not unreasonable price. In the afternoon they went to Pontings to windowshop and ended up buying plain underlinen.

"Well, what a happy and exciting day we have had, full of incident and gay abandon," said Hyacinth, whisking eggs for an omelette. "And now for a scintillating evening. I'll be writing up my student lesson plans on how to make meat pies with left over meat, and you can study the Factory Act for 1891!"

Lucy promised to do something pleasant the next day if it was fine. It was, and they did, taking the bus to Kew gardens and delighting in the drifts of spring flowers and marvelling at the enormous palm trees in the greenhouses.

At last, at last, the Civil Service broke into a flurry of activity on Monday morning. They sent to ask for Lucy's birth certificate and gave notice she was to attend for a medical examination on the Wednesday at 3 Trafalgar Square (fee, 10s 6d), for the post of Factory Inspector.

"I haven't got my birth certificate. Or yours," said Lucy, "only our baptism certificates from Madras." She telegraphed to Uncle Murray on her way to the Town Hall and he telegraphed back by lunchtime to say she must go to the India Office.

At Kensington Town Hall there were congratulations. "I knew you had it," said Dr Dudfield. "The examiner confused you and Miss Anderson, hence the delay. But I couldn't say so outright." He gave her permission to go to the India Office and, after only a short wait, an official stated they could not procure her a birth certificate but could give her a baptism certificate. As she already had one, she only had to pay one shilling for the search. "Do we exist?" she wondered, hurrying back to the Town Hall.

Judging by the amount of correspondence waiting for her there she certainly did exist. Among the reports, Complaints and requests for inspections and meetings and talks to be given was a note from Miss Lankester saying that Mr Tennant had told her privately that Lucy had been appointed.

By lunchtime Lucy was in a whirl. Miss Squire had been quite calm throughout. "I was sure all along you would get the post. So I have been organising myself along those lines for a month or more. And Dr Dudfield knows that I hope Miss Dunbar will follow on from you. The Vestry will advertise very quickly now, so I shan't be alone long. Between us we have got the registers in quite a workable state, so we can at least find the names of the firms at the addresses on the list."

"You have been an absolute brick," marvelled Lucy. "I am so glad you didn't apply for Factory Inspector, you would certainly have beaten me to it."

Miss Squire laughed. She did not demur. "This post suits me very well – as long as the next person is as competent as you. Please ask Miss Dunbar to visit you and give her all the help you can with the application. Promise."

Lucy promised and spent the afternoon entering all the outstanding inspection reports. The afternoon was golden as she walked back to 100 Fulham Road, and Mrs Casey, delirious with good wishes, had polished the little house and prepared the vegetables for the evening meal. "Miss Hyacinth told me the wonderful news. I took the liberty of buyin' you a little cake for a celebration," she told Lucy. "I hope I din't act out of turn?" Lucy gave her a kiss and thanked her. Mrs Casey certainly didn't smell of alcohol any more, but Lucy noted how thin she had become, and how yellow her skin, and how the lines round her mouth had deepened. "I must talk to Matron about her," she thought, waving her off in the early evening sunlight.

Her evening was spent writing letters to the Boyce and to Bossie and the Aunts, and in washing her hair. Hye was trying to decide which of two Domestic College posts to apply for and they discussed these before the dying fire in their nightclothes. "Goodnight," they said to each other fondly. "Sleep well."

"Just as if it were an ordinary night," said Hye.

"Well, tomorrow must be an ordinary day for me," said Lucy. "For the Town Hall must get some work out of me for once."

Therefore, she inspected as usual, and saw good and bad as usual. She was heartened by the much improved state of the two dressmaking establishments that she revisited. They were less overcrowded; the owner of one had opened up her own sitting room for four of the women who were 'finishing' garments, and the other had lime washed the larger room and promised to do the other in a week or so. The top windows were all open, and the conveniences in the yard were almost salubrious. "We're beginning to make a difference here," she thought. "Oh, if there were hundreds of us, instead of two, how pleasant women's work could be."

In the late afternoon she took the bus to Holborn to call on her friend Miss Canny. Miss Canny was a small plump woman with thinning grey hair pulled back severely from her determined round face with its twinkling green eyes. She dressed always in serviceable greys and for twenty years had run a girls' club on Saffron Hill funded by several society ladies, one of whom was Lady Howard. You could not pull the wool over Miss Canny's eyes.

"Ah, Lucy, so good of you to come so soon. I need your advice. Some of my girls have been telling me of the fearful overcrowding in a factory near here." On hearing Lucy's news she remarked, "Oh good, let us hope you are the first of many. There are armies of us here waiting for generals. And plenty of skirmishes here to keep us busy." She spoke of various problems Her Girls were encountering. Lucy thought of Rose Squire, struggling alone, and other London Boroughs with no one at all. "I am getting more and more concerned that Women Sanitary Inspectors are more and more needed in London, especially here in the East, MUCH more than Factory Inspectors, if you don't mind my saying so," said Miss Canny. "But you say you and Miss Abraham will be the only ones in the country?"

"One other in Scotland, a Miss Paterson," said Lucy. "An almost impossible task."

"No, not an impossible task," cried Miss Canny, "because you will be doing it. Everything must start somewhere. People like YOU will start it. People like ME will keep it going."

Lucy set off the next morning for her medical examination. "There, you see, what a good idea to buy those good dull plain stays and drawers, just what was needed."

"Are you going to tell them about all the pain you get with your monthlies?"

"No, certainly not. I shan't mention it unless they ask specifically."

"Oh, Lucy, perhaps you should. You'll be travelling such a lot, I'll bet, and you don't want to be ill away from home. And maybe they could prescribe you something to make them hurt less."

"Absolutely not. They might fail me and I WON'T be failed because of THAT. There's nothing the matter with me. I'm strong and fit. Leave it!"

Dr Gavin passed her strong and fit and wished her well and sent her away rejoicing.

Then she went to the Town Hall to go through her Report books with Dr Dudfield, and took with her a letter from a Mr Lockhart, the Secretary of the Civil Service Commission.

"What does this mean, Dr Dudfield? 'We beg to inform you of your Certificate of Qualification to the Home Office and that you should at once communicate with that Department.'"

"It means they have finally sorted themselves out and you have been accepted by the Civil Service. You've got the post, Miss Deane, fair and square. If I were you I would write a note – I would be happy to help you draft it – and take it round, by hand, straightaway to the Home Office." He took her hand in both of his and beamed with pleasure.

Armed with her letter, Lucy went to the Home Office reception desk, and asked that the letter be delivered to Mr Sprague Oram, the Chief Inspector of Factories. The clerk looked at it. "May I ask the nature of the letter, Ma'm?"

"It is to say that the Civil Service Commission has accepted my appointment as Factory Inspector," said Lucy, suddenly feeling at a loss.

The clerk considered. "I will send it up immediately to Mr Peacock, Madam. If you would sit down for a moment. There may be a reply."

Lucy sat while a boy ran up the staircases and disappeared through a door two flights up. In a few minutes Mr Peacock came speedily down the stairs, a dark-haired, extremely thin middle-aged man, followed more calmly by the boy.

"Miss Deane, I hope you have a few minutes to meet Mr Oram. We have been waiting for this note with some impatience."

Mr Sprague Oram was a short fat bewhiskered kindly man, tending to drop his 'h's. "What a muddle they got into at the exam – not unknown in the Civil Service." He asked how soon she could begin work. She said the 26th.

He threw up his hands and laughed. "26th April!" Why it's the 19th today! Capital! If you are sure Dr Dudfield will let you go so soon. Miss Abraham is in Belfast at this moment. I will write to her to come back and initiate you in all the tasks directly I receive the official intimation from the Home Secretary."

She hurried back to the Town Hall exultant. But Mr Beedman, with a long face, indicated her into Dr Dudfield's office. Dr Dudfield stood up from his desk. "Oh, Miss Deane, I'm so sorry to break into your happy moments, but we have had such annoying and distressing news from the Vestry. The Vestry Sanitary Committee have withdrawn all their recommendations to the Vestry and decided not to increase the salary or to reappoint our Sanitary Inspectors. Miss Squire is very much vexed, and of course very disappointed."

"Outrageous!" said Lucy. "Miss Squire, where is she?"

"She is still in her office. I thought it wisest to leave her alone for a while."

"But why have they made such a decision? What can have possessed them? No more salary, I could understand that. But no more Sanitary Inspectors in Kensington. They will be a laughing stock, especially as several other boroughs are just about to follow our lead. After all YOU have done!" Lucy stamped with fury.

"I suspect we have shaken them out of their complacency. You have uncovered, and are discovering, their deficiencies. And there are so many friendships and allies between the JPs and the Vestry and the business owners."

"But does that mean Miss Squire will have to leave? And that no one will come to replace me? You can't permit that, Dr Dudfield?"

"No, no, we shall have to find a way through. We will find a compromise."

"A compromise!"

"Meanwhile, Miss Squire is alone in her room, and I am concerned for her. I'm glad you returned so soon. This news is still raw and I must think carefully how to mend the situation."

"I'll go to her right away." And she flew down the stairs. Rose Squire was sitting at her desk filling in report forms. She smiled as Lucy burst in. "You're back sooner than I thought. I was just thinking I would go and have something to eat across the road. Will you join me?"

"Heavens, Rose, of course." It was the first time she had used Rose's Christian name. "But why are you so calm? I'm livid!"

"I know, I've been trying to think WHY myself. I think it's probably Mr Braye behind all this. If we are appointed Sanitary Inspectors it would put us partially under the London Government Board, which he hates, because it makes all the tiresome Vestrymen do their duty. So I think in the end Dr Dudfield will find a way out. He's not going to let Mr Braye ruin his great schemes. We'll just have to keep quiet for the time being, just go on as usual."

"You are a wonder."

"Let's go and have a nice lunch."

After lunch she wrote out her letter of resignation to Dr Dudfield who read it to the Works and Sanitary Committee which met that evening. "It is a great pity we are losing a person of such calibre," he added, "especially as the work she is doing is having such excellent results. Many councils all over the country are considering to follow our lead. It does not do us credit to step down when we were in the forefront – when we WERE the forefront – of this necessary progress." The members of the Committee looked grave, some stony faced, some anxious. They'll sort themselves out, thought Dr Dudfield grimly, settling himself into a hansom cab.

Lucy went to 76 Sloane Street the next evening in reply to notes, from Gertrude Tuckwell and Lady Dilke.

"Laundries," said Gertrude Tuckwell, "Explain the laundry Regulations. I gather you don't like the Factory Act bit about laundries. Why not?"

Lucy told about the way they slipped through regulations. Most laundries were not factories but workshops; some were no more than private houses, not even 'workshops' but 'workplaces' and as such not at present bound by the rules of overcrowding, safety, hours of working. "The women like it to be that way, if it's piecework they can work all hours or no hours. I would emphasise extending the idea of public baths and wash houses to include laundry work for the smaller laundries." Miss Tuckwell asked to be taken over an insanitary laundry with a News Chronicle journalist. Lucy explained that the terms of the Inspectorship were on the distinct condition that no one could accompany them. "Miss Squire is the person you need for Sanitary Law. She is a mine of experience."

Then she sat with Lady Dilke in her small private sitting room.

They sat at the small table in the window basking in the late afternoon sunlight.

"Sprague Oram is loyal and nice. He is fair and to be trusted. Sir Charles and I consider YOU are to be trusted. And May is delighted you will be working with her. But it will be very hard."

"I am sure it will be. But I will work hard."

"Of course, my dear, that goes without saying. But you will have all eyes upon you and many looking for mistakes and chances to criticise. You also have many wishing you well. Sir Charles and I will tell you if there is anything done or said against you in the Department, when we hear it. We will warn you."

"Have you any special advice for me, Lady Dilke?"

"Yes. The best thing to do is to learn from May Abraham. She is quite exceptional at managing recalcitrant people; always manages to keep her temper and soothe theirs. And gets the job done. Extraordinary! And watch out for Asquith, many folk think him a bally fraud; he's clever and very shrewd; but I don't think he's wise. And watch out for the Press. Avoid Press interviews if you possibly can, but keep on friendly terms, they can be useful at times for publishing your own views if you want. But be in no doubt; if they can make a mistake, they will make a mistake."

Friday morning. Her last day. She took all her books, Registers, Reports, and a private letter of thanks to Dr Dudfield at the Town Hall. He said he would do his best for new sanitary appointments and asked a great deal about Miss Dunbar. She went round the offices saying goodbye, shaking hands and was heartened by the expressions of good will. Mr Beedman accompanied her and Miss Squire to the door – they were going to lunch at the Army and Navy Stores – and bowed them down the steps.

She arrived home to find Evelyn had arrived with a large basket of eggs, and pies, and cakes, and a bunch of spring flowers picked in bud from the Boyce, and that Hye had booked dinner for the three of them at the Northumberland Hotel.

As they left the house, Lucy popped a letter into the post box. It was to Mr Turner, the landlord, reminding him that the rain still came in to the back passage, and he had promised to remedy it.

So ended her six months as a Female Sanitary Inspector for Kensington.

5

First steps in a new world

Evelyn's longings; Lucy's first diary entry as a Factory Inspector; May Abraham is a very good teacher; Marlborough Street Magistrates' Court. Mr Sprague Oram sends her to Worcester; to the Opera with the Hedinghams. Mrs Hedingham takes over the sisters' wardrobe.

Evelyn woke early at the Boyce on Monday 27th of April, thinking of Lucy and Hyacinth. "My best friends, my only friends, I wish I were nearer, I wish I could have a proper job with a proper wage, just a small wage, I could manage on it. I wish I could help more than I do, especially Lucy, she'll work too hard and she's not strong, what will she do if she's ill while she's in a factory – how frightful!" She got out of bed and went to the window. Another day seemingly set fair.

"What are you doing, Evelyn? It's only just light," came Ethel's voice from the bed in the other corner.

"I'm going for a walk round the lake before breakfast. Do you want to come?"

"Don't be silly. I'm worn out from that house party. Such fun. You should have been there. Pity you missed it. Those chaps are such fools."

"Tell me all about it at breakfast."

The walk round the lake always comforted Evelyn. It was really a large pond in the trees with a small stream running through from the upper field beyond, and another leaving it to trickle through the farmyard, and off through other farms to Dymock. She walked as quietly as she could and was rewarded by the squirrels along the route, their red coats glistening as they leapt through the sun dappled trees, racing on branches laced with the early vivid leaves of spring.

She came back, having leant over the farm yard gate for some time, watching the cows swinging back to the fields after milking, and churns being rolled on to the milk cart to go down to the village. The family were all assembled at breakfast. Kidneys. Evelyn loved kidneys. She helped herself.

"I hear the house party was a great success."

"It was, it was, one of the best weekends we've had for a long time. Those Bisset girls are cracking tennis players. And the lawn had dried out splendidly so we were able to have the first croquet match. I won," said Horace.

"Only because you cheated terribly."

"Nonsense. What time did you get back? I was driving folk home," he explained. "You were in bed when I turned in."

Mrs Deane held out her hand to Evelyn. "How were Lucy and Hye?"

"Oh, Ma, they were both so excited. On Saturday we went shopping at Derry and Toms, and Lucy bought a lovely dark green coat and skirt, and Hye bought some beautiful flowers and veiling to do up the summer hats. She is so clever with her fingers; and we all three went to the Northumberland Hotel for a celebration supper; and I paid for the bottle of wine and the cab home. And on Sunday we went to church and then lots of friends visited in the afternoon to congratulate Lucy. And Hye is excited. She has an interview today as a Cooking Lecturer with the London School Board. Oh, and Kathleen came with Miss Austen Leigh."

"Kathleen?" said Mary. "Lord Falmouth's new wife?"

"Yes, she certainly thinks a lot of herself. But I thought she was very friendly, though Lucy was sharp when she had gone. Lucy said Kathleen was a PIG, that she was SO interested in their work now that they were out of their difficulties, and rising in the world! She asked us all to lunch one day."

"Evelyn, leave some kidneys for us," said her father. "Well, I'm pleased for them if they are pleased. It's a rum life for an educated woman though. Sir James Roll was asking me about them the other day. I told him Lucy was going to be a Factory Inspector and he seemed most impressed. No accounting for tastes."

The account from Lucy's diary read as follows:

'April 27th BEGAN MY WORK AS FACTORY INSPECTOR.
Early church. Lunched with Lady Dilke – and then found I ought
to have been at the Home Office at 11a.m. instead of, as I thought,
3 p.m. GOOD START!
Miss Abraham had been waiting there for me. She crossed from
Ireland last night. Conferred with Mr Oram. He said I was to begin
for a few days with Miss Abraham in London. Went to 8, Finsbury
Circus, (our Office), and Miss A. showed and explained to me
about the forms, notices, clerical work, etc. Prodigious.
Oram said Miss Anderson not yet appointed.
Hye had interview with London School Board. For lecturing work.'

For the next couple of days she trotted round with May Abraham from
small workshop to small workshop in Bow Street, Bond Street, Sloane
Street and Buckingham Palace Road re-inspecting on Complaints received
by District Inspectors specifically on women's workplaces and conditions.
Lucy made copious notes and learnt that Miss Abraham was more abrupt
and brusque than she was, that she never rang the bell and went straight to
the workrooms, that unlike Lucy, she always asked the supervisors questions
and spoke to the workers, that overtime was her bugbear, whereas Lucy's
was overcrowding.

At the end of each sortie they went back to the apartment in Tite Street
for tea and to discuss the day. "I must invest in two more pairs of walking
shoes," said Lucy to Hyacinth one evening.

"Perhaps I need some as well," said Hye. "I've been accepted by the
London School Board on probation and it seems they'll be sending me all
over the place as well."

"Oh, Hye, wonderful."

"No stopping us except blisters," agreed Hye.

Miss Abraham was an extremely good teacher, Lucy had to acknowledge,
although it took all her effort to keep up with her. There was an aura
of excitement and enthusiasm about her, she did not so much walk as
sprinted, as if she could not bear to miss a second of whatever it could
be that was waiting round the corner. She had tabulated the experience

gained by her work for the Royal Commission for Labour and was busy applying it to the day-to-day task of setting up the Women Factory Inspectorships. She had developed a confidence and enjoyed meeting with the multitude of various personalities of every class and attitude, and appeared to enjoy dealing with them all. She had prepared her material and carefully shepherded Lucy, introducing her to her various tasks and going through them – at breakneck speed. Basic principles; use indelible pencil for day-to-day notes, they don't break so often as ordinary lead pencils and are cheap to replace. Buy small umbrellas and cheap gloves. You will always be leaving them and losing them. Lucy's fingers had to work as fast writing notes as her feet had to move on the pavements. She was frequently out of breath. May Abraham said nothing but her eyes twinkled.

At the end of the first week they went to Marlborough Street Magistrates' Court. "Now, luckily, a nice little case has fallen into your lap," May said. "Nothing very serious, but it means taking a couple of declarations. We've had a second Complaint about a firm that's been working their people overtime, and they still haven't made a record of it. They are allowed to work a certain number of hours overtime, but they must inform the District Inspector. The complainant has kept the hours competently and now we need declarations from two of the workers to back it up. In this case the Inspector couldn't give personal evidence to the facts, but two women are willing to speak as witnesses and if they sign the declaration they can't go back on it in the witness box. We don't even have to do the interviews; the District Inspector has already done it but passed it on to us as it was an all-female establishment.

"So now we can lay the information." Lucy looked blank. "And you can do it, Miss Deane, it will be your court baptism, but I'll do the prosecuting. You watch. We have to lay the information at 10a.m. or 2p.m. sharp. That's the rule in any court, not just Marlborough Street. We must have the information forms – so you must always have some ready in your briefcase – and the summons forms. The clerk is obliged to make out the summons if you instruct him. The witness will be needed in court for everything, and of course he or she may be the person who was illegally employed. If so, they'll be scared of losing their job, so you have to give them courage to speak up!

"You must take out a different summons against the defendant for each person illegally employed. So for this case I shall need three summonses, two for the girls' overtime without reports, and one for not having prescribed the particulars fixed for overtime in that establishment.

"Each witness gets 1s as conduct money. We pay that to the warrant officer on the day and get it back in expenses."

Lucy painstakingly and obediently followed these instructions under May Abraham's watchful eye.

Back at the Home Office, Mr Sprague Oram informed her he was sending her to Worcester. "You're going into Chief District Inspector Arnold's District. He'll be nice to you. He's got several dodgy women's workshops, he'll be glad of your help. Then you can go to Gloucester and Stroud. Stay at the Bell in Gloucester over the Saturday and Sunday. Very pleasant place. Stroud sounds as if it's having overtime troubles. Be back on Wednesday."

Miss Abraham heard the news. "Yes, Mr Arnold will be very pleasant and hospitable but he hasn't made his mind up whether he likes us or not. While you're there find out about girls' clubs, they're a fount of wisdom if they're any good."

"If I'm going to Gloucester I could spend my Sunday with the folk at Boyce Court. Would that be permitted?"

"Why not, as long as you could be back on Monday morning bright and early."

Lucy wrote off immediately to the Bell Hotel in Gloucester, and bought herself a silver watch and the thick Bradshaw's railway timetable, so that she would never miss trains.

Hye heard the news and clasped her hands to her chest. "Oh, you're not going until Wednesday, thank goodness. The Hedinghams and I have booked to take you to see Faust at the Opera House, for a treat. It was to be a surprise. But thank goodness it's on Tuesday."

It was a wonderful evening. They all basked in the occasion, putting on their evening clothes and jewellery. Hyacinth's deep blue satin set off her fair hair and blue eyes and her mother's emerald and pearl drop earrings sparkled. She looked quite unlike her everyday mousey self. Leah Hedingham blew into the little house, followed by her mother, and swept the sisters back up to Lucy's bedroom. She rearranged their hair and exclaimed over Hyacinth's naturally wavy hair. "Why ever do you pull it back so violently? Poor hair, let some of its tendrils soften your brow."

"Tendrils round the brow don't look so good in a hot kitchen."

"I should have thought they would have improved the atmosphere immensely," said Leah.

She put a group of hairpins in her mouth and sat Lucy down in front of the small Regency mirror, and skilfully swept back the long dark straight hair into a soft and soignée knot. "There," she said with satisfaction, "but why do you choose black silk, Lucy? It takes the colour from your face. You should have a colour. Pink would be good. A darkish pink."

"Oh! Not PINK. I don't feel like a PINK person!"

Leah laughed. "Maybe not in the daytime. Night time is different." Leah herself would definitely have worn pink in the daytime. Tonight she wore a simple sheath of chestnut brown heavy silk full at the back and a very low décolletage – too low, thought Lucy and Hyacinth privately – and brown and black and gold fine ribbons twisted into her hair.

The three of them descended the stairs with Mrs Hedingham, dressed in a neat black grosgrain dress with a Paisley shawl, making admiring noises. "You ought ALL to go on the stage, not just Leah," said Mrs Hedingham nobly. "Aren't we just the Bees' Knees?"

At the Opera House they stood in the intervals in a curve of the staircase, watching the shining assembly passing them up and down, revelling in the smooth colourful throng, the black of the gentlemen's clothing setting off the women's fashions; the bare shoulders, the glittering necklaces, the long gloves, the fans. Leah and her mother appraised them coolly, Lucy and Hye treated it like an art gallery.

The opera enthralled them all. Lucy was flushed with excitement and was anxious to scurry back up the stairs after each interval to get ready for the next act.

"It's glorious!" She beamed on everyone as they leant over the stairs during the last interval. "It would be," said practical Hyacinth. "But my evening shoes are worn out and they let the wet in and my stocking has stuck to my foot."

Mrs Hedingham looked amused. "Are they your only pair?"

"They are. And I've only got two dresses really suitable for evening, this one and another one that needs cleaning. They don't get a chance to be worn very much."

"It's hard enough to keep the day clothes spruce enough," said Lucy. "And they get so muddy round the bottom, brush, brush, brush!"

"Oh, yes," Mrs Hedingham agreed. "And you both get home so late. And you're walking through all weathers. You need someone to take care of your clothes."

Lucy sighed. "Wouldn't that be blissful? But some hopes of a lady's maid for us."

"Well, I could do it," said Mrs Hedingham unexpectedly. "I live so close by and I could come, say, weekly, and collect anything that needed inspection or attention, sew on buttons, and hooks, and things, and sponge skirts and press them. I do it for Leah, she has always to look smart if she is to get auditions and engagements. I like doing it."

"I don't think we could afford you," said Lucy. "It seems too good to be true."

"Oh, I shouldn't want paying at all. Some weeks there wouldn't be anything to do."

"But some weeks there would be plenty, especially in the winter months."

"I think it would be marvellous," said Hyacinth. "I think it is vital that we are well turned out."

"Well, say two and six a week then."

"But that's only £6 a year or so. Say £10 a year. Would that do?"

"Done! Ten pounds a year. For both of you. It will be a pleasure."

They settled back in their seats. The conductor returned for the final act. "Now it really is a perfect evening," said Lucy, squeezing Mrs Hedingham's hand. "Thank you."

6

Whatever it is, it's new

The first foray into inspections; Worcester and Gloucester; a spring Sunday; beware of Captain Bevan; Mrs Munday's establishment; Leicester boots and shoes.

The next morning she arrived at the station with ample time to spare and made herself comfortable in a Ladies Only carriage. "You should travel First Class," said Hye. "Factory Inspectors don't go Third Class."

"I haven't checked that yet, so I shall go Third. Better be told to go up higher, than be told to take a lower place." She enjoyed the journey despite a frisson of nerves; had she packed everything in her small suitcase, had she got enough money, was her hat, with four small emerald feathers and bottle-green veiling, too frivolous?

Promptly at 11.50 the train drew in at Worcester Station and Mr Arnold greeted her, gave her his arm and bore her off speedily to the Station Hotel for lunch. "It's not a bad place to stay. But it can get noisy in the evenings and the Bell at Gloucester is calmer, if a bit old-fashioned, and the bedrooms are bigger and easier if you need to write or work after supper."

Over lunch they observed each other. She saw a fit, ruddy-faced country gentleman a little taller than herself, about middle fifties she thought, balding and with a well-cut military moustache, a well-cut suit and some really beautiful agate cuff links which she coveted. He seemed pleasant and easy, and determined to make her feel welcome, but his smiling eyes were shrewd. She was on the watch for a catch question or remark, but none came.

He saw a slim young woman with good posture, dark straight hair smoothly drawn into a bun, an attractive little hat with veiling and some saucy green feathers, a plain dark-brown well-fitting coat and skirt. She showed no trace of shyness, and was amusing and chatty as she told him of her early training with the Chelsea Infirmary and her stint as a District Nurse in Peckham. She told him of her panic over the mathematics paper in the Civil Service Examination and of her abject ignorance in the Mechanic Galleries. But he was not fooled by her self-deprecating comments. And she was not taken in by his helpful explanations of his District. He's out to hoodwink me and keep me harmless, she thought, and, those eyes are very sharp and those ears very alert for little details, thought he.

After lunch they walked the short distance to his office where she took out her Home Office notes and asked about the factories and workshops she had been asked to inspect. She made it clear that her role was to concentrate on the conditions and problems of women workers, their hours of work, their working conditions, the rates of pay and so on. He called his secretary, Miss Lance, with instructions to look out various registers of factory addresses for her to take with her on her first inspections. Miss Lance was courteous, but seemed uncertain as to what was actually required; however, she took the list and went off with an impassive expression into her office. Lucy asked about girls' clubs in the District. Mr Arnold looked blank and rang the bell again for Miss Lance. Miss Lance appeared promptly and Lucy explained why she was keen to get in touch. "The organisers of the clubs hear so many little details about the workplaces of the girls, and the attitudes of the girls vary so greatly." Miss Lance's attitude changed. She beamed, she was knowledgeable. She said she herself was a volunteer in the girls' club near her, teaching two classes, one plain sewing, and one for smocking. She offered to take Lucy there at the weekend. Regretfully Lucy had to refuse as she would be at the Boyce, but Miss Lance promised a list of other clubs and their organisers, and the Secretary of the General Workers Institute, a Miss Burne. Then she trotted off briskly to her files and registers.

Mr Arnold had been listening to this with great interest. "I can see for myself now, we are going to benefit greatly by our Lady Inspectors already. We had a source of information, a river of knowledge flowing at our feet and we have never even dipped a toe into it." He laughed with great good humour and nodded at Lucy with pleasure. "New ways of seeing things. Good new ways."

He took her to meet the Medical Officer of Health, Dr Garrard; he shook his head when Lucy asked about Workshop Inspections. "My staff is much too limited for us to visit them on a regular basis. But if the Factory Inspectors would give us a register of them with their cubic space we would try to require them to display the number of employees each is allowed and visit any grossly overcrowded." He looked at Mr Arnold. Mr Arnold looked glum and said HIS staff were hard put to deal adequately and regularly with workshops too. But he would see what he could do. Lucy explained that it was the small workshops with no machinery to speak of, and the outworkers' homes, both of which were staffed largely by women, where she would find the worst problems and working conditions. "I found this in my previous post as Sanitary Inspector in Kensington visiting dressmakers and laundries mostly. They sprang up and closed down at an alarming rate."

That evening she went to stay with Mr Arnold and his family in a comfortable small house on the edge of Worcester with a view in the distance of the cathedral from her bedroom window. Mrs Arnold was plump and welcoming, the two children, a boy of fourteen and a girl of eleven, smiling and chatty, and the conversation flowed easily enough with enough mutual acquaintances in the military, relating back to Mr Arnold's time in the Army, until Lucy excused herself and went to her room.

It was so good to take off her shoes and stockings and stays. She wrote her diary and tried to organise her thoughts for the next day, but the calm and quiet of the house overcame her. She sat for a while by the window in the dark brushing her hair, watching the lights of Worcester through the trees, and then climbed into the comfortable bed and slept soundly until the maid knocked at her door at seven the next morning with the jug of hot water.

It drizzled most of the morning. Mr Arnold and Lucy and the two children left the house together, the little girl turning off first to her school, Alexander waiting for the omnibus that would take him out of town to his school, Mr Arnold and Lucy to visit Miss Burne, the Secretary of the General Workers Institute. Miss Burne was a very small, very thin woman with a loud and clear Midlands accent. She had no great opinion of any of the girls' clubs in the area and, without actually saying anything derogatory, made it clear that she thought Mr Arnold did as little as he could, and that she was not expecting anything useful from Lady Inspectors either.

Lucy made her way back to Miss Lance in the office, who presented her with a thin list of workshops registers. "That's all we've got! There are certainly plenty more in the District!" She confessed that it was a good while ago since they had 'run out' of the Abstract forms, which set out the terms and requirements for both employers and employed, and had by law to be displayed in each establishment. It was raining hard, so Lucy spent the afternoon, as Mr Arnold was off on factory business, going through the registers and noting the vestigial information they provided. She applied the format that Rose Squire and she had drawn up for the dressmakers and laundry workers in Kensington; in no business on the Worcester list were half of the criteria even mentioned. However, there was no scope to deal with this problem now; she would confer with May Abraham.

She went through the rain to the station under her new small umbrella, and caught the train to Gloucester. The Bell Hotel was as quiet and as old-fashioned as Mr Arnold had promised. After supper she went straight to her room, warm and with heavy curtains and solid furniture. This is the first time I have stayed in a hotel without any of my family with me. I hope it doesn't look obvious. How many other hotels shall I stay in over the years? She slept well, and the breakfast was good, and the waiter attentive. But what has the hotel done with the bacon, she wondered? Like leather. It was a question she asked herself time and again over the years. Only on rare occasions was hotel bacon edible.

After breakfast she set off for the short journey to Cheltenham where she inspected unannounced the two places for which Chief Inspector Arnold had received specific Complaints. She could find no fault with either of them, no overcrowding, hours of work seemingly correct, sanitary arrangements adequate. By early afternoon her tasks were completed, so after a late light lunch she found a table in the Public Library to write up her notes and a few letters and then went to catch the early evening train from Cheltenham to Dymock.

Who should be on the platform but Ethel. "Ethel, what are you doing here?"

"Well, I've been shopping. It's been pouring with rain all morning. So boring. So I thought I'd have a little outing and go to some BIG shops. And as we knew you were going to catch this train I thought Cheltenham was as good a place as any. Horace is going to meet us in the dog cart. We are all longing to hear how you got on with your first inspections."

The rain had stopped as they drove through the village and the air smelt fresh and cool. The weekend was as usual, a true rest. "Just us," cried Aunt Georgie, enfolding her in an embrace smelling of lavender water. "We want to hear everything you've been doing – starting tomorrow – Tonight is just for relaxing, and what about a bath? We've been heating the water in the copper for you, and we'll wash your clothes ready for next week. Plenty for both! And Stephen Hobday's son caught trout this afternoon, so we're going to have it tonight instead of the beef and bacon pie. We'll have that tomorrow."

"Oh, Aunt Georgie, it's all ambrosia. You spoil me."

"Everyone needs spoiling occasionally," said Aunt Georgie serenely, leading the way through the stone flagged hall into the long high drawing room. The chairs, chintz covered and very comfortable, were just on the edge of being shabby, the silver candlesticks winked in the firelight, and although it was still light outside the lamps had been lit on the side tables, so that the velvet and chenille tablecloth glowed. The room was in a true Boyce family muddle; piles of sporting papers, knitting, embroidery, Ethel's ukelele, piano music, spare shawls, Mary's paints and drawing boards. If there was a houseparty or guests the room was tidied up and elegant; the maids came in early in the morning, after lunch, before and after tea, and during supper as well. (Ginny hated house parties, and the unending rounds of bedrooms with cans of hot water. And baths were her bête noire, and bedroom fires an abomination.) But if there were no special guests the room was only tidied once a day.

Lucy luxuriated in her bath in front of her bedroom fire, and slept the sleep of the just.

"Are you riding with us?" said Mary and Uncle George at breakfast. Lucy shook her head. Her monthlies had begun in the night, providentially, so if she was quiet today she would be free from discomfort this month. "Too lazy." She murmured.

"Quite right," said Aunt Georgie. "And Evelyn comes back this morning – She'd be furious to miss a minute of you."

At lunch they gave her two five-pound notes, one for her and one for Hye. "To buy something frivolous for you both. No sensible shoes or galoshes," said Mary.

"Much too much!"

"Nonsense."

On Monday morning Evelyn and Ethel saw her off on the train to Gloucester where Mr Arnold met her and took her first to an area in the centre of the city full of dressmakers and milliners who not only made the dresses and hats but sold them too in the tiny front shops. Of the six she visited three were very good, but the others paid low wages and were definitely not thriving.

In the afternoon they travelled to Stroud to see two model clothing factories. They were certainly marvellously clean and airy, but though Mr Holway told Lucy he closed at 7p.m., a girl told Lucy she worked till 7.30p.m. There were no Abstracts posted in either entrance, but Mr Holway said uneasily that he would rectify this when Lucy asked him about it.

Mr Apperley's mill was excellent and he seemed a good and kind man, explained the workings of his looms, was proud of his firm's sanitary convenience areas, and mentioned casually in Lucy's hearing that he had heard grievous complaints of sanitary matters in other Stroud factories. This annoyed Mr Arnold who did not wish Lucy to hear. His annoyance amused Mr Apperley and he told Lucy later that Arnold had 'spoken sharply to him about it.' He showed her a piece of weaver's work on one of his new looms, and took her round his model steam laundry. Both were exquisite. Out of Mr Arnold's hearing he promised her a list of the men's tailors around Slad employing women and told her that the sanitary matters were very bad there.

Lucy and Mr Arnold took their leave of each other on Gloucester Station, very cordially, each thinking they had managed to fence with each other competently, each holding their own counsel and reserving their own judgement.

Lucy arrived at Marlborough Street Police Courts on the morning of May 19th to hear May Abraham's prosecution and to see her gain convictions, penalties and costs in a remarkably short time. She marvelled at her colleague's composure and confidence, and wondered if she would ever be able to speak as clearly and concisely. "But of course," said May Abraham. "You can do the next ones."

"Mercy!"

"We'll go together to these next overtime Complaints. I wouldn't be surprised if at least one of them didn't rate a prosecution. They both seem pretty blatant to me."

She was correct on both counts; situated in Portland Street, Soho and 2 Hanover Square both were tailors' premises and both very dirty, overcrowded, and, in Hanover Square, working until 11p.m. four nights in succession. "There you are," said May Abraham. "Plenty of information for you to lay. I'll be back from Ireland next week in good time to come and hear you before you go to Nottingham."

"I'm not looking forward to Nottingham and Newark. The Chief told me confidentially that Chief Inspector Cramp and his inspectors dislike the idea of Women Inspectors, so I'll have to be careful."

"Oh, Cramp will be fair. But watch out for Captain Bevan. He is HORRID. You're being sent to re-inspect some places I went to a few months back. Chief was really annoyed when I took him a list of workshops from Nottingham – I found scores that had never heard of an inspection. And a couple that I visited I had to prosecute. Do you know who you will be sent to?"

"Yes. One or two lace and hosiery factories, and also a whole list of tailors and milliners and dressmakers."

"The George Hotel in Nottingham is decent. It's pricey, but they're kind, and there are plenty of places to write."

"Right."

"Oh, and you know what? It would be good to have another colleague such as you. I wish they would make their mind up on whether they are going to select Miss Anderson. I thought she would be really good when I met her. I can't think what they are doing. And she must be so frustrated."

They parted in Soho Square and headed for home and an evening of writing up reports.

Sunday was a warm, breezy day. Hye and Lucy spent it wandering around Kensington Gardens and then attending evening service at Holy Trinity Church in the Brompton Road. They wandered home in the dusk, arm in arm. Lucy could not think when they had had such relaxed and happy conversation. It feels as if we are true equals at last, she thought. All these years of having to be mother and sister to Hyacinth, trying to build up her confidence, trying to encourage her to find a profession that would suit her, coping with her sulks and depressions, trying to make allowances, trying not to get irritated with her refusal to join in society – and now – could it be that all the hard won patience was paying off? Was Hyacinth finally coming out into the sunlight? It seemed so, and Lucy looked at her sister fondly, her cheeks tinged pink with the exercise and the sun, and no trace of the dull uninterested tone of voice that Lucy had found so hard to bear.

There was a note on the doorstep when they reached home. "It's from Edith Boscawen. She's staying with Kathleen, says she'll be there in the morning if we want to go round. I could. Shall we?"

"Why not?" said Lucy. "But I can't stay more than a little while. I've got to organise all my clothes and diary for Nottingham early Tuesday."

As soon as she had deposited her cases at the George Hotel, which was certainly very expensive, she made her way to Captain Bevan's office, wondering what his welcome would be. It was quite clear. He was out. She put her card in his letterbox and went straight off to visit three workshops. All three seemed to be reasonably in order. The Medical Officer of Health, Mr Boobyer had had notices about the necessary cubic space prominently displayed at the staff entrances. She dropped in at his office on her way back to the hotel. Mr Boobyer was courteous and helpful, and asked kindly after Miss Abraham. "Tell her the suggestion about the cubic space requirements was most helpful. We can check up now within minutes if we need to. And the workers are much less argumentative. I am very new here myself," he remarked as he came to the door to see her out. "Please feel free to visit me whenever you wish."

So Lucy swung into Captain Bevan's rooms the next morning in an upbeat mood. Captain Bevan was long and thin with dark hair and bushy eyebrows, and a very long head, high forehead, long nose, thin lips, long chin. He apologised profusely for having missed her the previous day. "It was no matter," said Lucy smoothly, "I had with me the list from Mr Sprague Oram, so I was able to visit several places, and the hotel was helpful in directing me to them."

"But I must make amends," cried Captain Bevan. "I do hope you will dine with my wife and me on Thursday."

"I should be delighted," said Lucy. "And then on Friday morning I am off, first to Mansfield, and then to Newark."

"Do you need to go to Mansfield?" Captain Bevan seemed uneasy. "I hear that Chief Inspector Cramp is going to Mansfield on Thursday."

"Ah, I'm sorry we shan't meet. But my journey is concerned with a Prosecution Complaint from some weeks back, when Miss Abraham was here last – I don't think that will be concerning Inspector Cramp."

"That prosecution! I remember it. There were others, I remember. I was surprised that Miss Abraham had taken them to prosecution without consulting me."

"Oh dear, I'm sorry. I think the one I am to attend to is the only one outstanding."

They fenced, outwardly smilingly, for some minutes, and then Lucy went off to inspect more workshops. In most of them Miss Abraham's inspections had reaped good fruit. In one, she was told, Captain Bevan had said, "no need to send notices to those inspected if a Record is kept of one's time." Accordingly, when she returned to file her reports in his office, she discovered none had been sent. A very small, pimply office boy was in charge of Bevan's overtime book, very muddly indeed, and she found several cases of inspections done without Certificates of Proficiency attached in the registers.

May Abraham had alerted her to Miss Hawkesly, a Nottingham Council Woman Sanitary Inspector, so Lucy dropped in on her in the late afternoon and had a long conference with her. She was a small-boned working-class woman who had a good rapport with the working women and obviously did a huge amount of positive work in the face of much difficulty and discouragement, a situation exacerbated by a young and open, but inexperienced, Medical Officer of Health, and a jealous Captain Bevan. And all for £78 per annum.

At the supper on Thursday Mrs Bevan had provided a very simple tasty meal, and steadfastly refused to join in any conversation beyond the smallest of small talk, in case she let drop anything her husband might not wish to have disclosed. He talked enough for the three of them; Lucy hated the cruel spiteful way he spoke of Miss Hawkesly because she had dared to tell a magistrate, a lace maker, that his workroom was dirty and overcrowded.

It was hard to get to sleep in the George Hotel. Her room was comfortable but the hotel was noisy and people passed back and forth outside her door until very late at night. Her feet ached from Nottingham's uneven stone pavements and she had a blister on her right heel and a hole in her stocking. She gave up trying to go to sleep and wrote a letter to Hye. 'Nottingham is a horrid town at the top of a steep hill'.

In the morning she inspected, chiefly in the lace district, and also came upon the beautiful parish church, so Nottingham was not such a horrid town after all, and then travelled on to her third hotel that week, in Mansfield, the Swan. She found it charming, small and quiet, a peaceful oasis in the busy little town. She was out till late that night, knocking on the doors of small workshops, checking on overtime inspections, but found only one infringement, and the woman foreman there was completely shocked that a young gentlewoman was inspecting at 9.30 at night, alone. She fussed around Lucy like a mother hen, and wanted to send two of her girls to walk back with her to the hotel; the fact that her workshop was at fault did not seem to bother her in the least. Lucy had to gently remind her of the infringement and assure her she could get back safely.

On Saturday morning she was tired, and made only a few inspections. In the afternoon she went around the markets and the shops in Mansfield, and went into St John's Church where she met the rector. He was most interested in her and in her work and gave her several useful pointers and was keen to be of use. On Sunday it began to rain hard as she was coming out of the morning service at St John's. She felt quite relieved as it set in firmly for the afternoon and evening. The hotel was quiet with few guests, and she wrote letters, official and personal, to Gertrude Tuckwell, Miss Lankester, Hye, Evelyn, the Chief and Rose Squire. She collated all her reports, and very soon after the evening meal she went to her room and mended her stocking and slept soundly.

It was fortunate she had made good use of her restful day, as on the Monday she visited Mrs Ellen Munday, dressmaker, to investigate a Complaint of Saturday illegal overtime. Mrs Munday was aggressive and rude, and refused to allow her to question any of her work people. Lucy produced her authorisation and asked the women assembled in the workroom, "Were any of you working late on Saturday afternoons recently?" No one spoke, but several people nodded. Several people also shook their heads, though. Mrs Munday had already been prosecuted by Miss Abraham three months previously and it was clear that the dressmakers were unhappy with the situation. "The Law requires me to ask these questions to make certain of the position," said Lucy. "I shall ask these ladies" – and she indicated both the nodders and the shakers of heads – "to come with me into the front room as we sort this out." She opened the door into the front of the shop, half expecting that the women would resist or be frightened to stand up to Mrs Munday; but they filed through obediently. She noticed with surprise that although they seemed decisive, they looked on their employer with a certain amount of sympathy.

Mrs Munday was white with fury and dispatched an apprentice to fetch Mr Munday. The women agreed that there had been Saturday workings until 5p.m. most weeks since the prosecution; but that there had been great pressure of work, with several large orders to be completed in a short amount of time and that some of them had been threatened with the possibility of dismissal if they did not comply.

Mr Munday arrived, as red-faced as his wife was white, and demanded that Lucy should leave the premises. Lucy calmly threatened an additional summons for obstruction. "I have witnesses here who have seen the illegal Saturday afternoon working. The Factory Inspectorate here in Mansfield have never received any requests for special overtime working for you – which would have meant extra remuneration for the workers."

The women looked shocked and some began to look angry. "I suggest that you all resume working as normal, ladies. Thank you for your help. I appreciate that Mrs Munday saw that there needed to be some extra hours if the extra work was to be completed in time. I hope we can come to a satisfactory conclusion for all sides within the Law."

The women moved back silently to their places in the work room, and soon after the door to the workroom was shut the noise of the machines started up. Mrs Munday invited Lucy to sit down. Lucy did. Mr Munday asked if she would like some tea. Lucy said that would be very refreshing. Mr Munday went off to find a woman to provide it. Mrs Munday fanned herself with a dress pattern and told how pushed they had all been, with three separate wedding orders, three wedding dresses, fourteen bridesmaids' dresses, trousseaux, other outfits for the brides' mothers, wedding guests, all for the same two consecutive weeks. "We have been too successful, Miss Deane, but what can you do? You can't turn work like that away! Several of the women hate the Saturday overtime I know, they have small children to care for, but some of those women are my most skilled finishers – and I've used up all my permitted time or overtime – it's hard to be punished for being successful! I can't afford to have my name in the courts! And lose the clients I am building up." She wiped away a tear with the corner of the dress pattern.

Lucy made suitably sympathetic noises and wrote down the statements, and thanked her for the tea. She went across town to the Rectory to tell the Reverend Maples and to give him at least the bare outline of the morning's proceedings. He agreed that the Mundays were both obstinate, 'but good to their employees' and promised to find a way to visit and support them in the near future.

Back at the hotel she eyed with distaste a plethora of official letters. The one from the Chief vexed her considerably, sending her on to Leicester. She had only expected to be travelling for a week and her underlinen all needed washing, and in the case of stockings, mending, and her serviceable brown coat and skirt needed sponging and pressing. And she was tired of her hat. Also, importantly, she had hoped to be in London for her monthlies, relatively close to home.

However, she sent a letter to the Bell Hotel in Leicester and to Captain Armstrong, District Inspector there, with his assistant Mr Wright. And one to Hye to say she would not be home as planned.

As soon as she arrived in Leicester the next day she was met by Mr Wright, a short, fat, young gentleman, with apologies and a note from Captain Armstrong who was away from his district for a few days. Mr Wright would give her every assistance and he had arranged for Mr Wright to take her to look over the new Wholesale Co-operative Boot factory. He whisked her off at once and she thought it a splendid place. Any overtime was only worked early in the mornings from 6 to 8a.m. The regular hours were 8a.m. to 8p.m. It was light, airy, spotlessly limewashed, and the floors were washed daily. The fans and ventilation seemed new and most of the machinery had been imported from America. It had electric light throughout and the sanitary conveniences were ample and clean with good washing facilities. Lucy was charmed and could find no fault. Leicester was the known place for making light walking shoes and most pumps and slippers. Heavy nailed boots were the preserve of Northampton.

After a lunch at the Bell Hotel, an unpleasant meal and very dear,

Mr Wright whisked her off to a hosiery factory and here she thought the machinery was not well fenced; and their registers were non-existent, as during a quarrel between the two partners all the books had been torn up!

Mr Wright considered it had been a very fortunate and well planned argument, as many faults had been brought to the attention of the Factory Inspectors in the past, and it appeared that many others could have surfaced if the argument had not taken place!

And in the evening they went together to two workshops which the Chief had asked to be inspected for overtime working, one "for the third time of asking," said Mr Wright, smirking at his own joke. Lucy found him uppish, flippant, and arrogant. He had glanced at both premises superficially, and said firmly that no one was in them. Lucy thought she had seen lights gleaming from windows at the back of the building, quickly extinguished, and wished she had stuck to her guns and visited by herself. But Mr Wright evidently felt she was in need of protection.

She was grateful to be back in her hotel room and asked for a hot drink and biscuits to be brought to her room with her can of hot water. She bathed her tired feet and arms and body and felt refreshed and relaxed. On the Saturday morning, before she set off back to London, she went straight after breakfast to a large shop in Leicester and bought a new set of vest and chemise and summer drawers and put them on in the hotel before she caught the train.

7

Settling into the routine

Back to Leicester; Captain Armstrong is neither kind nor genial; her first prosecution; Mrs Casey is very sick; Miss Hawkesly turns up trumps; staying at Miss Simpsons; Mr Udale the tailor; pea picking problems; Mrs Collier, knows what's what; Miss Simpson's Office Days; Mrs Fisher erupts; the happy pickle factory; the young schoolmaster's family.

The sisters embraced. "I'm so glad you're back. Mrs Casey is ill, really ill, hasn't been to us for the whole week. Her sister came to tell me and said the doctor had been and says it may be an internal tumour."

"Oh Lord! So you've had everything to do!"

"Yes, but I haven't done it. I've been very tidy. I didn't bother with the living room fire in this weather. And I've been out and busy, so it's only dusty, not dirty."

"And you've been by yourself all week, too."

"Do you know, I really wasn't bothered," said Hye proudly. "But Mrs Casey! What will she do? What will we do?"

"I'll try to see Matron and find out what's best. But we shall have to give Mrs C. warning. We absolutely must have someone coming in daily."

At the Home Office the Chief greeted her cheerily and was pleased with her accounts. He asked particularly how she had found each inspection and nodded at her replies but made no comment. May Abraham was present, as pretty and lively and practical as ever. The Chief approved six of her eight recommended prosecutions and she spent the rest of the day with May Abraham, attending a prosecution and discussing the details for her own prosecutions. They exchanged opinions and discussions on the various hotels, and Lucy made May laugh. "I was writing my reports about midnight – in my nightie – and dropped my candle – and burnt a piece of woollen rug. I put the fire – only a tiny corner of the rug – out with some water, but it smelt horrible. I called for help and everyone rushed out of their rooms thinking the hotel was on fire. We were a funny looking crowd. Grins from all when I appeared at breakfast the next morning!"

She was able to spend the next two days in the Finsbury Circus office, writing up her reports, filing them and drawing up information forms, collating her travel expenses, and consulting May Abraham. She was glad of the home-based days as her monthlies were as troublesome as ever, and thankful that she was close to home. Rose Squire visited and chatted and drew her attention to the section of Mr Asquith's Bill that dealt with Factory Cubic Space. "He never mentions workshops," said Rose. Lucy mentioned this to the Chief. He nodded. He told her she was to go back to Nottingham and Leicester again the next week, so she wrote to Captain Armstrong and Captain Bevan with lists of places to be visited and prosecutions pending.

She also wrote to Evelyn. "I'll ask her to stay while I'm away. You can't be alone so much."

"I really don't mind, Lucy. And Mrs Casey's sister says she may be back again next week."

"Well, I mind. And I don't believe Mrs Casey. We must find someone else as soon as I get back from this next trip."

Saturday was a red letter day. Lucy's first month's salary arrived. £18.

Mrs Hedingham and Leah arrived to oversee the clothes, and Lucy and Hye went shopping and bought a neat dark red shantung summer frock for Lucy with a soft cowl neck line and a wide, shaped belt of dark red grosgrain. They bought two sets of pretty collars and cuffs for her day time blouses and some fresh summer curtain materials for the two first-floor bedrooms. Evelyn arrived in the evening, and they had a happy evening together.

Back in Leicester on the Monday she laid the information for the prosecutions on the Friday, and was greeted with bonhomie by the receptionist in the hotel.

She inspected numerous workshops in the small streets away from the centre and spent a great deal of time in Captain Armstrong's office hunting up addresses of firms that she discovered no longer existed. She wrote to Hye, "Very provoking and wasteful of time. Captain Armstrong is neither kind, nor genial, and his books have no system about them at all. He resents my having to ask for lists he has been too lazy to compile, but he also resents me compiling my own and has silly ideas of women spies. I should think he should be above that. Twice I asked him for directions to a factory out of town. Twice he promised to come back after lunch to put me on the right track. Twice he 'was called away' before he could tell me. Then he was jealous when I asked the hotel people and they gave me clear directions, and he was cross because I had found my way on my own."

Her money ran out one day as she had mislaid her train ticket and had to pay again, so she went to the Leicestershire Bank who telegraphed to Mr Child at her own bank for £7 for her. She was not going to be under any obligations to Captain Armstrong. She considered him much more unpleasant than Captain Bevan.

She found the prosecutions on Friday very stressful. They were the first she had to conduct by herself, with no May Abraham to give support from the sidelines. Her first one was simple and successful, although the magistrate said it was a 'trifling offence,' but the second, for Midland Drapers, had a very competent solicitor, who argued intensely and certainly overcame her. Lucy was mortified. 'Horrible. I could hardly speak. MUST practise,' she wrote in her diary as she travelled to Nottingham in the train in the evening.

After the inspections she travelled back to London to find Ethel at home with Hye. Evelyn had been deputed to be with Aunt Augusta who was feeling low, 'very low', as Aunt Gussie was apt to be every couple of months, and in need of 'young conversation' and sympathy. Mrs Casey's doctor had sent a note to say that Mrs Casey was truly too ill to go on working, so on the Sunday morning the three of them took her wages, and a bunch of flowers and a box of embroidered handkerchiefs. Mrs Casey, smelling strongly of beer, was sitting in a chair, and though talking volubly and gratefully, seemed to be turning her head away from their sympathetic faces. They left her watching her sister arrange the flowers and as they walked down her street Lucy felt an inexplicable ripple of relief smoothing her shoulders.

After lunch she called on Matron at the Chelsea Infirmary.

Matron was as clear-headed and decisive and drily witty as ever. "She is unfit to work for you or anyone, I fear. The drink has ruined her kidneys. You have done more for her than anyone could ever expect, now you must engage a SENSIBLE woman." Matron had been dealing all week with discord among her hospital laundry women. They had been to one of Lady Dilke's militant meetings and come back intending to strike. "I feel YOU have had more than a little influence without knowing it," she remarked.

"Horrors!" said Lucy. "What will you do?"

"Oh, I have already squashed it. They cannot exist without reasonable wages, and the hospital cannot exist without clean sheets. We have a mutual understanding," said Miss de Pledge imperturbably.

Lucy spent her week mostly on trains, shuttling between Nottingham and Captain Armstrong and Captain Bevan, with excursions to Derby, several factories in Basford, courts in Mansfield, a stocking factory in Hucknall, and back each night to the hotel, tired out. One piece of good luck came her way from Miss Hawkesly; when she dropped in at her office she was shewn a complete list of all the workshops in the area, extant and extinct, in perfect order, street by street. Miss Hawkesly promised to get them copied out for her. "You are a wonder," marvelled Lucy. Miss Hawkesly looked grimly pleased and made several remarks on the efficiency of the district Factory Inspectors, all without tact, and all completely true.

A letter came from the Chief during the week sending her on to Lincoln after the weekend, so she had a conference session with Captain Bevan and took copies of the workshops there from his Register. It was, as she expected, a very poor list, and Lucy thanked God for the Miss Hawkeslys of this world, and travelled home with relief to 100 Fulham Road on Saturday afternoon.

Ethel and Evelyn had been taking it in turn to keep Hye company, and while Evelyn had been paying court to Aunt Augusta, Ethel had engaged an excellent temporary cleaner. She had certainly polished and dusted the little house into a shining state. She came every morning and would do simple shopping as well as cleaning, but no washing or ironing; however,

Mrs Hedingham would take their laundry to the shop and collect it when she came to press and mend their clothes.

Lucy was amazed at Ethel's competence. She had always been a sweet-tempered friendly, docile young woman who seemed perfectly content with her comfortable life at the Boyce. She enjoyed the parties and amateur dramatics that went on in the houses around, to which she was always invited with her sisters, she was happy to accompany her mother on shopping expeditions, calling on neighbours, and tea parties. She had few friends of her own and very few hobbies; she had never been seen reading a book or a newspaper like Evelyn, or riding to hounds and dancing and painting like Mary, or expressing an opinion on any subject. So it was astonishing to find that she had taken the initiative of engaging Mrs Shaw. It just shows, thought Lucy, what women can do when they are required to do it.

Hye seemed happy as well, with her London School Board probationary time, continuing to rush from school to school lecturing and demonstrating. She had written to enquire for a residential post at the Oxford School of Cooking, and was waiting to hear if she had an interview. Lucy did not like the idea, but said nothing.

When Lucy arrived in Lincoln she lodged with a Miss Simpson recommended by Mrs Prevost, a friend of Aunt Georgie. "Much more suitable than staying in those awful commercial hotels, dear Lucy. Miss Simpson is a very sensible, ladylike person." Miss Simpson was tall and angular, with very surprised wide eyes, and a wide mouth which smiled too widely and too often. Her house was a tall, thin house halfway up the hill to the Cathedral. She led Lucy up a tall, thin flight of stairs to two rooms on the first floor. "These were poor dear Mother's rooms." They were very pretty; a sitting room with a writing table and two comfortable armchairs, and a shining bedroom with a posy of flowers on the dressing table, looking out onto a garden full of hollyhocks and roses. "Feel free to come and go as you choose," said Miss Simpson, "and we can arrange evening meals each day as you find your work dictates."

Several letters awaited her on the hall table, one from the Home Office which had obviously impressed Miss Simpson, and another letter from Mrs Prevost, giving her an introduction to the Sub Dean of Lincoln Cathedral and his wife. There were also two Complaints from Miss

Squire requiring inspection. So Lucy sallied forth, after a polite cup of tea, with her map of Lincoln and her stout walking shoes.

Rose Squire's Complaints, sent by a Lincoln friend, seemed perfectly reasonable tailoring establishments to Lucy, with only very minor infringements, and the third tailor's she went into was a model of its kind: roomy and clean, calm and busy.

The proprietor was a Mr Udale, a well-known Radical Unionist in the area and also a Poor Law Guardian. He invited her into his house, only a few doors away, to give her the address of the Secretary of the Lincoln Women's Liberal Association, and to meet his quiet, intelligent wife. They talked of the shockingly low wages in Lincoln generally. The large foundries were in a healthy state, but the Trades Unions, though moderate and steady, were weak in numbers. Lucy gave him her Home Office address and Miss Simpson's address and came away impressed; he was definitely a coming man, she thought.

Then she called on Sub Dean Clements in the Cathedral Close, and his wife gave her tea and cake and invited her to lunch after morning service the next day. Finally, she walked down the hill to Miss Simpson who provided her with two hard lamb chops, potatoes and cabbage, a sour rhubarb pie and cream, a small piece of hard cheese and some biscuits, and a pot of weak tea.

In all, she felt as she got into Mrs Simpson's pretty but lumpy bed, she had had a suitably polite day.

The Sub Dean and his wife Mrs Clements were a hospitable couple in a beautiful old house. After lunch they showed her over the Cathedral, glorious outside in the warm June sunlight and radiant inside with the rainbow colours from the stained glass streaming down the aisles. Norman and Early English, noted Lucy, a devotee of church architecture.

That afternoon the polite social interlude ended with a bump, and Lucy felt oddly relieved. She called on Mrs Collier, a young and energetic doctor's wife, Secretary of the Women's Liberal Association. She alerted Lucy to 'pea picking' and its racketeering, a business owned by the Mayor of Lincoln, a local grocer, and of the poor conditions and wages provided for his pickers, for peas and strawberries. These casual labourers, provided only with leaking hovels, and no bedding or sanitary conveniences, were in the fields before dawn to after dusk for a pittance. They and their grievances fell through all the holes in the Factory Acts, and their employer sent a couple of carts of provisions from his shops at the end of each day for them to buy with their paltry wages.

"So this is not a new situation?"

"No, no, annual," said Mrs Collier. "But the constant problem in pea picking time is that the pea pickers come into the edges of the town at night and steal from people and from their gardens."

"So not much sympathy for their plight, then?"

"Hit the nail on the head. They don't earn enough to live on, so they pilfer when they can, and they can't get other work because they are so dirty."

"There must be some who would act as witnesses."

"There might be. But as soon as the peas and strawberries are picked most of them go on to the surrounding counties to pick the plums which are ripe by then, or to the Fens for the new potatoes."

"So they aren't there any more?"

"That's it."

"Making them buy from the grocer's carts is disobeying the Truck Act. Can Captain Bevan or Captain Armstrong do nothing?"

Mrs Collier looked at her impassively. Her eyebrows rose very slightly and the corners of her mouth tightened imperceptibly. She sniffed. "I never see them unless I ask to see them especially. Will YOU see them while you are here? They never seem to be in their local office."

Lucy laughed. "Well, I wrote to say I was coming. Captain Bevan regretted he would be on holiday with his young family this week. Captain Armstrong hasn't replied. It is annoying. I have four dressmakers to inspect concerning night-time working in Lincoln, so I shall have to go by myself."

Mrs Collier was concerned. "Is one of them Mrs Fisher's firm?"

"Yes, it is."

Mrs Collier pulled a face, but said nothing.

On Monday Lucy had to go back to Mansfield for more prosecutions; there were two helpful magistrates for a change, and a conviction made with costs efficiently dispatched by the competent clerk. She enjoyed her train journey to and from Mansfield, and managed to do a good deal of office work. An empty carriage and a trusty firm-based writing case made a very adequate office, she thought, and she was glad to have got up to date, as her monthlies returned early and with a vengeance that evening. She was glad to get into her lumpy bed and lie flat.

In the morning Miss Simpson, without fuss, took in the situation and advised her to stay in bed for the morning, and she permitted herself to do this. She sat and wrote letters and reports in the afternoon. Miss Simpson provided beef tea and toast in the evening, and Lucy felt the pain ease and die away. She was very grateful to Miss Simpson and said so. Miss Simpson smiled. "I was always hampered with the same things myself. I learnt to plan my work around them – of course, it was only housework, not the travelling you have to do. I used to save up my correspondence for those times, and called them my Office Days. It was Mother's and my little joke, just between us."

"It's an excellent solution," said Lucy. "With your permission I shall adopt it."

"I should be delighted," said Miss Simpson, and her smile almost split her face.

On Wednesday evening, with a full moon rising, she set off for her evening overtime inspections. The first two firms were quite dark and closed, and the shirt factory appeared to have closed down completely. It was close to ten o'clock when she turned back towards the centre of town and knocked on the door of Mrs Fisher's dressmaking workshop. There were lights on behind the shop and sounds of chatter, but that ceased abruptly with her knock. She knocked again. Finally a servant opened the door a crack.

"Will you tell Mrs Fisher that the Government Factory Inspector wishes to see the workrooms about a Complaint from the District Inspector, Captain Bevan?"

The servant closed the door and went away. Lucy waited a good few minutes. She was aware of hustling sounds, as of people going as silently as possible down a gravel path at the back of the shop. She knocked a third time. Mrs Fisher appeared at the door, very angry, and refused her admittance.

Lucy proffered her authorisation. Mrs Fisher became abusive. Finally, Lucy sent the servant for the police and the girl set off, red-faced and flustered. Lucy waited for a few minutes, hoping the police station was not too far away, but as Mrs Fisher became increasingly noisy and abusive, she left the shop. Mrs Fisher slammed the door. At the corner of the street, with a few shadowy figures scuttling by at the other end of it, she met the servant accompanied by a solid looking constable. She showed the policeman her authorisation and they returned to the premises when the girl immediately ran in and slammed the door. The policeman rang the bell and knocked and called, "Police here! Open up!"

Curtains twitched in buildings along the street and faces peered out. The servant opened the door a crack again. "We wish to see Mrs Fisher," said the policeman. The servant took a deep breath. "Gone to bed!"

The policeman said, "I shall return in the morning. Be sure to tell Mrs Fisher that Inspector Deane is acting within her rights." The poor girl nodded and closed the door quickly and shot the bolts across. The policeman spread his hands out, and shook his head sorrowfully, and insisted on walking Lucy back to Miss Simpson's house companionably in silence. "Goodnight, Miss Deane," he said at the gate, "I shall have my report ready for you at the station tomorrow morning when you call."

"I'm afraid tomorrow morning isn't possible. I have to take the train to Market Rasen tomorrow morning, to inspect a pickle factory," said Lucy.

He appraised her solemnly by the light of the moon. "Quite so, Miss Deane. To Market Rasen. A pickle factory. Of course. 'T isn't an urgent matter. The day after tomorrow will do. Good night." He went on his deliberate way. Lucy let herself in to Miss Simpson's house, giggling. He thinks I am quite mad, she thought.

Surprisingly, Lucy slept soundly, and thought over the night's upsets as she travelled on the little branch line from Lincoln the twenty or so miles to the pretty market town of Market Rasen. She asked directions to the pickle factory and a woman pointed out the way. "Only about half a mile," she said. "You won't miss it. You'll smell it." This was very true. Not unpleasant, but unmistakeably pickle. A solid red brick building full of noise and chatter, and cheerful men and women preparing vegetables and great rows of cauldrons steaming and bubbling and rows of jars moving down a conveyor belt, and young boys whistling as they pushed boxes of jars around on great trolleys, and girls sticking different types of labels on. I wouldn't mind working here, thought Lucy. The owner was away, but the foreman showed her all over it, and she spoke to several workers who were pleasant and said they enjoyed the work. He called to a woman peeling onions. "Gracie, take the lady to your bogs. I can't go. 'T wouldn't be fitting." To her delight they were in a very clean condition.

"Who cleans them and how often?" she asked. "Elsie and Harriet comes in special, and does them lunchtime and going-home time. And we has clean towels twice a day too. And we has to wash our hands TWICE, everytime we goes. Same for the men in theirs. With soap."

Lucy said she was very pleased to hear it.

She expressed her pleasure at the conditions and the morale of the workers and the foreman was pleased and said he would certainly tell the gaffer when he got back. He insisted on Lucy taking a jar of pickle, and wrapped it himself for her.

By the time she had got back to the town school was out. She found her way to the home of the schoolmaster who had complained to the District Inspectors that his pupils were being employed, underage and out of hours, by a large local fruit and vegetable packing firm. Luckily, his house was close to the station. His wife opened the door and was friendly and hospitable and asked her in to wait for him. "He won't be long. He likes to close the school sharpish and get back to his babies, he calls them. He says they don't cause him so much grief as the big ones. The kettle's on for his tea. You'll have some with us. The table's laid." As she spoke the garden gate clanged and he came up the path. Three very small children galloped, staggered, and hotched round the corner of the house and hung on to his legs. A fourth was wedged into a high chair in a corner of the livingroom.

While his wife fed the children he talked with Lucy and gave her names and addresses. He had only been the headmaster for two years and had discovered the employing of his older pupils had been going on for many years. "There are four or five pupils each year who should certainly be going on to the Grammar School in Lincoln, and I discover no one from here – no one! – has been sent for 12 years. It is monstrous. And he – he named the employer – pays them less than a pittance."

Lucy gave the jar of pickle to the schoolmaster's wife, and the schoolmaster walked down to the station with her, and the eldest little boy, as a treat for him to see the train because his mother said he had been a helpful boy. They waved her off, and the train, with gusto. It was a sunny evening and the train seat was warm, and the steady chugging of the train and the fresh countryside going by was a relaxing influence. Tomorrow she would beard Mrs Fisher. She went over the details of the incident again, and actually smiled as she remembered Mrs Fisher's flushed face and bolting eyes and imagined Hye's indignant and sympathetic "Oh! Lucy!" when she told her. She realised that she had not only kept her temper but that she had positively enjoyed the confrontation. But that's because I knew I was in the right, she told herself, and that in the long run I have right on my side. I'll go back tomorrow and get it sorted out.

In the morning she went straight to Mrs Fisher's shop before it closed for the Saturday half-holiday. Mrs Fisher refused to let her enter the workroom, though the door was half open and Lucy could see the women inside listening and pulling faces at one another. Mrs Fisher stood squarely in the doorway, and refused to say what time she had closed, but insisted it was a permitted time. She would not allow Lucy to speak to any of the girls; she became abusive again and was, as Lucy wrote down, very, very rude. Lucy asked to speak to her servant, as she wanted her as a witness for the summons for obstruction, but Mrs Fisher would not countenance this.

Lucy remained calm and came back to Lincoln, secure in the knowledge that she could summon for obstruction, and spent the early golden evening in the cathedral and then doing her reports in her sitting room.

Miss Simpson was most anxious to please and did her very best to make her comfortable; but she was a poor unimaginative cook and the evening meals were always slices of cold cooked meat with hot but watery vegetables, hot or cold stewed fruit with a little cream, and hard cheese and biscuits. And she was just as expensive as a hotel. And then, there was the lumpy bed; and the obligatory little conversations at breakfast, boiled egg, toast, jam and tea – Lucy longed for the anonymity of a railway hotel.

She wrote curt notes to Captain Bevan in Nottingham and to Captain Armstrong. She had been in their districts for more than a week and received no word from either of them. She wrote that she would be inspecting in Nottingham on Monday and Tuesday and would call at their office for their message unless she heard to the contrary via the George Hotel. She wrote to the George for a room on the Monday night. She wrote to May Abraham bewailing the meeting she had had with the Medical Officer of Health who openly disapproved of Lady Factory Inspectors. And with a resigned sigh she replied to the Chief's letter sending her to Hereford with a list of Requirements and Complaints. Then she went to bed.

She spent nearly all Sunday with the Clement family in the close and around the cathedral. The Dean's daughters were lively and interested in all her doings, very amused by her battles with Mrs Fisher. "She is a horrid woman. It will serve her right to be prosecuted." The elder Miss Clements became serious. "I'm pretty certain one of the girls in my Wednesday Bible Class knows people who work for Mrs Fisher. I'll go very softly and see if I can find someone through her who would be brave enough to say what has been going on. It might take a few weeks though. She doesn't come every week." Lucy thanked her and said anything she heard could be useful.

On Monday she packed her suitcase and took her leave of Miss Simpson. She deposited her cases at the large George Hotel with lightness of heart – feeling anonymous even though the chambermaid greeted her going along the corridor to her room. Then she caught the branch line to Southwell to inspect several extremely small workshops in ancient buildings like almshouses, all innocently friendly and all with some quite serious infringements of which they were quite unaware. The rooms were so tiny and the walls so thick, three people in one room would have been overcrowding, and several of them had at least six. She showed them the rules about cubic feet, and left them cogitating. Perhaps some of the upstairs rooms could be used to relieve the stuffiness downstairs?

Southwell was an old-fashioned, stately, comfortable town, surrounded by well tended fields, the minster magnificent and the air heavy with the scent of syringa blossom. She could not resist buying some, nor visiting the minster, and sitting for a while in its cool aisles.

Then she returned to Nottingham. Still no word from Captain Bevan. Lucy went to his office to be told by the office boy that he had gone to London that morning. Lucy laughed out loud to the boy's surprise, and went back to the hotel where the chambermaid plunged her sheaf of syringa into cold water, and after supper she sat in her bedroom in her nightie, eating most of a box of chocolates and writing her reports with the perfume of the beautiful white flowers all around her.

As the inspections in the morning took less time than she had allowed for, because of Captain Bevan's desertion, she caught an earlier train and went straight to the Home Office to see Sprague Oram. Luckily he had not gone home, "I remember that you like to leave precisely on time at the weekend," she said placatingly, but he was not pleased to be kept a minute longer than necessary. He greeted her politely enough, but only gave a cursory look at her list of prosecutions, and was obviously not interested in them, not even Mrs Fisher.

"Miss Deane, I am sure you will have been quite correct. When we meet on Monday, we can deal with details."

Lucy was cross. Captain Bevan and Mrs Fisher and Miss Simpson's lumpy bed chased themselves around her head. Hye would not be back home for two hours or more. On an impulse she took a cab to Regent Street, put her case in the cloakroom at Dickens and Jones and went and had a good wander, first round that store and then into Liberty's to look at the most expensive fabrics she could find.

8

Hereford

A pleasant interlude

Mrs Shaw makes the house sparkle; Mrs Casey fades; Lady Howard writes another cheque; Lucy's travelling office; trudging round Hereford workshops; Lady Howard's palatial house; five hotels in one week; blistered feet from Cricklade to Cirencester; Hye employs the new maid, Emily Butt.

The next morning she was in a better mood, and so apparently was the Chief when she arrived at the Home Office before breakfast to present her report. He sighed when she mentioned the continued absence of Captain Bevan, but made no comment, and said he was sending her to Hereford and Worcester in a week's time. He gave her the Hereford and Worcester Directories and maps and the address of Her Majesty's Inspector Arnold. Lucy was pleased. Hereford and Worcester meant that she could spend the weekends at the Boyce, and she left the Home Office composing the letters she would write that evening to Evelyn and Aunt Georgie.

"Will you be able to come with me, Hye?"

"Yes, I think so. If they can have us. I could certainly do Friday night to Sunday night."

The temporary daily, Mrs Shaw, arrived the next morning and was considerably more competent than Mrs Casey had ever been. Lucy's bed was made up with hospital precision. After breakfast the sun streamed in through the front windows as Lucy spread her office work across the table, Mrs Shaw hummed as she worked in the bedrooms, Mrs Hedingham arrived middle morning and was busy with her weekly mending and sponging and pressing in the kitchen; they all felt contented and comfortable.

Late that afternoon she and Hye went to visit Matron about Mrs Casey. "She is not in a good way, very muddled in her speech and her thinking. She will have to go into the workhouse hospital. Such a waste of a good woman." And they pursed their lips and clasped hands and felt sad for poor Mrs Casey, who had drunk herself into liver failure while they had failed to notice.

Saturday evening brought a telegram from May Abraham. 'Back from Dublin tonight. Please visit me Sunday midday.' Lucy wired back 'Yes'. She climbed the Tite Street stairs as Chelsea Church clock chimed twelve. May was still in bed. "Wonderful to see you, I'm exhausted, back late last night from Dublin, awful crossing, I was so sick, and I'm NEVER sick." Lucy told of the missing Captains Bevan and Armstrong. May was not surprised.

"Our position as travelling inspectors is really difficult."

"And precarious."

"I seem to be treated as if I were a spy – certainly a nuisance."

"And all the travelling. Everyday a different train."

"Or a different hotel."

"Maybe we should have a District of our own," said May as she began to dress.

"What, in a geographical location?"

"Well, no, but away from the Home Office itself. Then we wouldn't be seen as peripatetic spies for the Chief Inspector."

"He wouldn't agree to it, would he?"

"Maybe he wouldn't, but he's retiring very soon. And I have the ear of Asquith and I think he will listen to me. It's important we act soon, because when Oram goes – or if the government changes – our position will be less tenable. However, I have to inspect several really unpleasant Complaints tomorrow. I just know they are going to be difficult and obstructive. It would be good if you would come with me, Lucy."

Lucy accompanied her willingly and learnt a great deal. "May Abraham is splendid," she told Hye that evening "Three Complaints, everyone so aggressive and bad tempered, and she was so sympathetic, but so persistent. She had the Piccadilly man eating out of her hand by the time we came away, AND we'd given him the Court declaration."

Hye was in a good mood. She had received her salary that day and passed her probationary period. She had decided against the Oxford Residential post, to Lucy's private relief.

"A good solid, respectable amount. Send it straight on to Mr Child at the bank. My word, he'll be pleased, our bank balance will be really healthy."

"Yes, and there's another envelope from Lady Howard. That'll be another £60 Lucy, we're rolling in it!"

"Actually, I've been worrying about that, Hye. Now that we're both earning good salaries we don't really NEED that money. I think we ought to write and tell her not to send it any more."

"Well, I don't earn that much – not nearly so much as you."

"Not yet, perhaps."

"Exactly. Not yet, and she is rich, rich, rich. She won't miss it."

"No, she won't. But she does it from the goodness of her heart. She's not a relation, just a good friend of mother's and Granny. We mustn't presume. We have more than enough to keep us going nicely now."

Hye pulled a face.

"I think we should, Hye. I really do."

Hye threw up her hands in surrender.

Early on Monday Lucy travelled to Hereford with all her necessary belongings. Her trusty writing box was filled to the brim with Abstracts, Complaints forms, Declaration forms, writing paper, official and personal, large envelopes, small envelopes, ink, several fountain pens, indelible pencils, business diary, blotting paper, the wonderful Bradshaw train timetable, Ordnance Survey maps of Herefordshire and Worcestershire, and street maps of the larger towns. Her two stout suitcases were filled with neatly pressed blouses and skirts; slippers; wash bag; face creams; spare walking shoes; gaiters for wet weather; a tussore jacket for hot weather; a soft wool navy jacket for cold weather; summer and winter vests and drawers; three white petticoats; two white nightgowns smelling of lavender; and a luxurious alpaca shawl in place of a dressing gown, all lovingly and expertly wrapped in tissue paper by Leah and Mrs Hedingham. In her hat box she had a spare small navy hat with veiling, and a straw boater with a blue and green silk patterned scarf folded around it. She carried her capacious black leather handbag and her new cheap black umbrella, and in one of the cases was a dainty white umbrella with an ivory handle for Sundays and in case of really hot weather.

"Buy yourself a new suitcase," advised Hye. "That big one is looking battered. I'll use it for my cookery uniforms when I go travelling. I don't have to look smart in a hotel."

The Green Dragon, Hereford was quiet and rather expensive, and the staff deferential and helpful. She had lunch in the hotel and then, as Mr Arnold had left a note to say that he would meet her at the hotel the next morning, sallied forth to inspect by herself. She discovered, as she was coming to expect, that most of the dressmakers the Chief had indicated in the Directories had never been visited, and those that had, had been visited within the week of her arrival – one of them at two o'clock the afternoon before. So he must have visited immediately after the receipt of my letter, and then rushed away from Hereford! Oh! Mr Arnold! she thought, amused, and slightly irritated by such flagrant carelessness.

Early after breakfast the next day Mr Arnold arrived to find out her plans. He said he had not known she was to arrive the day before and seemed concerned and apologetic. Lucy did not believe him. She spent the day, luckily not too hot and with a pleasant breeze, trudging around the outskirts of Hereford to endless workshops listed in the directory, most of which no longer existed. At teatime she gave up and returned to the hotel to find a bundle of letters awaiting her. The hotel manager arranged for a slightly larger writing table to be moved to her room and she spent the evening on reports and correspondence.

The letter from Hye contained a charming letter from Lady Howard.

'My dear Lucy and Hyacinth,

I was much touched by your letter and truly happy that you are both making your way in the world with such success. However, our original object was to ensure an assured £400 per annum between the two of you, and I have made a provision with my bank for the £60 to be paid as usual, quarterly, DURING MY LIFETIME.

I am most happy with this arrangement. You are both a credit to your family and your mother would have been so proud.

Let me know when next you will be at the Boyce and I will be delighted to show you my new home, St James, in Malvern now that I am settling in there.

Your admiring and affectionate friend,
Lucy Constance
Lady Howard de Walden.'

This set up Lucy to such an extent that she ordered a pot of tea and cakes to be sent up to her room, and wrote her letters surrounded by crumbs.

She wrote to Hye, and to Evelyn, saying she would go to the Boyce from Cheltenham late on Friday afternoon; to the Chief telling him she would go to Cheltenham on Friday and Malvern on Monday; to Lady Howard saying she would visit on Monday; she acknowledged a set of reports, a week late, from Captain Bevan; she acknowledged a letter from May Abraham with the lists of visits they intended to prosecute; she acknowledged a letter from the Chief with lists of places to visit in Leominster and she looked them all up in the directory.

Then she went down to dinner and ordered a glass of wine with her meal; finally she went to bed and slept soundly until the clatter of milk churns woke her up at 6a.m.

Lucy enjoyed her week, as she moved from train to train through the summer Herefordshire countryside. Her inspections took her to tiny clothes factories, dressmakers' establishments, nearly all calm, industrious places, with only minor infringements, such as insufficient vent pipes or sanitary conveniences. She could not resist the Priory Church in Leominster and was given tea by the ancient vicar who had restored it during his 50 years in the parish. She found the waiting room at Leominster station made a very good office as she waited for the evening train back to Hereford. The scenery on her journey to Ross was stunning, and the day in Cheltenham was useful. She left her luggage with the stationmaster there while the Cheltenham Women's Union Secretary drove her to several places on the edge of town in a horse and trap, and from here the train took her to Ledbury where Horace and Evelyn and Hye met her with the family trap and drove her to the Boyce.

"I have almost had a holiday week already," marvelled Lucy.

"Quite right," said Evelyn, "and now you can have a holiday weekend." If it had not been for the fact that the Annual Report had arrived to be checked, it would have been pure holiday. But Lucy felt rested and relaxed, and walked in the woods and was rowed on the lake, and Evelyn worked out that Lucy could inspect as she had planned in Ledbury, Malvern and Tewkesbury and return each evening to the Boyce, until the middle of the week.

"This is the life. No suitcases." Lucy was exultant.

She and Hye visited Lady Howard's wonderful new house in Malvern. "Lucy, it's a palace!" It was certainly palatial. From a quiet, country house to the West of Malvern, built fifty years before, it had been transformed into a vast mansion, with water gardens, and park land. Lady Howard was delighted with it and insisted on accompanying the two young women and the housekeeper over the whole of the first two floors, ballroom, drawing rooms, library, smoking and billiard room, dining room, breakfast room, parlour and countless corridors, bedrooms, dressingrooms, bathrooms, morning room. They sat on the terraces watching the gardener's boy mowing the lawn with an old donkey pulling the mower. Both the donkey and the boy were wearing large hats to protect them from the sun, and felt boots to protect their hooves and hob nailed boots from tearing the turf. They walked to the bridge and admired the fish swimming round exploring their new pools.

"But, Lucy," wondered Hye, when the groom had helped them down from the smart dark red carriage, and they were waiting for the train to take them back to Dymock and the Boyce, "What does she want it all for? She has never entertained much, she certainly doesn't play billiards. What is the point of it for her? She is an old lady now."

Lucy didn't know; and when they recounted their adventures to the family round the supper table at the Boyce, Uncle George was quite tetchy about it. "I know that house. Knew the family that had it built – pleasant pair – pleasant house – went there a couple of times – she should have left it alone."

"That's what I think," said Hye.

"I suppose she's got to spend her money on something," observed Horace. "Anything will do, as long as she can stop her son getting any of it, the bounder."

"She's very generous to many charities," said Evelyn.

Lucy and Hye looked at one another. They were one of the charities.

"She's a very nice woman," Aunt Georgie stated firmly, "and she loved your mother very much. She was your mother's godmother and she was so delighted when your mother called you Lucy. And I'm sure she will see that her grandson, young Tommy, is more than well provided for."

"Maybe the billiards room is for him," said Hye, "when he comes down from Eton."

The weather broke the next day, but Lucy was able to stay at the Boyce for two more nights, inspecting in Malvern and Colwall, before the suitcases came into their own again, in the Swan Hotel, Tewkesbury, on Wednesday, the King's Head, Cirencester, on Thursday, and the Crown and Rose, Evesham, on Friday.

Mr Arnold was almost as elusive as Captain Bevan, but they did meet at his office in Worcester. He was painfully civil. Lucy didn't trust him any more than Captain Bevan, and discovered via a clergy friend of Aunt Georgie's in Droitwich that he had warned a letterpress printer in Cheltenham NOT to let her in without authorisation.

At the Raven Hotel in Droitwich she got into conversation with an American woman at the next table who had come to Droitwich to investigate the home of her ancestors. She gave Lucy her card, 'Mrs Louisa Watson, Clark Club, 28 East 22nd St, New York City.' And they went off together after dinner to see the play *Private Secretary*, and enjoyed it and each other's company.

In Cirencester she found her first overcrowded and dirty workshops, over-crowded, dirty and the women working irregular hours; and in Cricklade she found three places, which were rough and squalid; in one of these a child was employed underage without a certificate.

Unluckily, she had to walk back from Cricklade to Cirencester as there was no train until the milk train. She completed it in one hour and fifty minutes, but arrived very stiff and with a pain as if her monthlies were due. The hotel staff were shocked she had had such a long walk and insisted on sending a warm footbath to her room after dinner and a glass of brandy and one of hot milk.

Though her feet were blistered and footsore she couldn't resist Cirencester's beautiful church with its Norman arch, after breakfast, before she caught the train back to London; but she did not stay long as she found the parson violently haranguing the verger about the frontals on the high altar and the side altars. Lucy decided he was mad, and crept out, leaving them to it.

Home again, and the front door was opened by the new maid, Emily Butt, who had been interviewed and employed by Hyacinth, all by herself. Lucy was extremely impressed.

9

Lucy attacks lead poisoning

Sprague Oram approves her tactics; a French-speaking lunch; Alice Ravenhill at the British Nurses Association; Mr Walmsley walks her through the Potteries; Miss Bennett's pottery girls; how to avoid earthquakes; tiny Mrs Plowden, the chemist; Lucy's thirtieth birthday; the sad collapse of the Leek Women's Trade Union.

Sprague Oram seemed pleased that Lucy had been able to combine her work with visiting her friends and laughed as she told him how various acquaintances had been roped in to provide helpful knowledge. "You are a regular social sleuth, Miss Deane, enlisting daughters of Cathedral Deans and titled ladies to do your work for you! However," he said, picking up a small folder from his desk, "this is your next assignment and it won't be nearly so comfortable. I want you to go to Stafford first and then up to the Potteries. Hard working conditions up there – you'll find it difficult."

Lucy looked suitably interested and eager.

"And there's a Complaint I want you to check out which will need real tact. Maybe you don't need to go as a Factory Inspector. Maybe you need to go on some other pretext."

He showed her the Complaint, from a Miss Bennett, and several other names, sent to May Abraham about a large pottery works, Jones and Brough, in Stoke on Trent. He seemed in terror lest the names of the complainants should emerge; he retained the signatures and the addressed letter, and only gave her the accompanying statements. "You're to see to it with Mr Walmsley, he's a new young Inspector. But you are NOT to shew

106

any papers to Walmsley or mention ANY names to him. Merely say such and such facts had been sent to the Home Office."

Lucy spent the rest of the morning copying out the Workshop Registers for Stafford and sent a note to May Abraham asking if she might go and see Miss Bennett privately about her Complaint. She posted it on her way to lunch with Sir Charles and Lady Dilke, only to find May Abraham there as well. It was a French-speaking lunch because the other guests, Monsieur Mongot, the great French engineer who had just launched the "Carnot", and his wife, spoke no English. Lucy blessed her French governess and the holidays spent in Dinard with the Boscawen cousins in the summers before her mother died. Hyacinth had hated them, and spent them with her head down, terrified that she would be required to make conversation, in any language, French or English. So Lucy had had to chatter for both.

Lady Dilke had other tasks for Lucy. Would she go with her to the Trades Union Congress in Norwich? And, if she was in the area, would she find out certain particulars about Mr Stubbs, the Trades Union Secretary at Leek – privately? Lucy said yes to both, if the Chief would permit her to go to Norwich.

May Abraham said the Chief didn't want them to deal with the Stoke Complaint together. "He seems to think Stoke is in your division, and he wants us to stick to our own divisions." Lucy thought this seemed odd, but kept her own counsel.

Hyacinth and Lucy met on their doorstep, Hye jubilant as her extra money from the School Board had come through. At that moment, Miss Dunbar, who had replaced Lucy at Kensington Town Hall, called to report that she was settling in well there with Rose Squire. The new maid, Emily, had left them a batch of newly made scones, still slightly warm, so Miss Dunbar stayed to tea. When she left Lucy told Hye the new plans. Hye did not approve. "Skullduggeries, Lucy, watch it!"

"Oh, I will, Hye, I will."

When she took back borrowed books to the National Health Society the next day Miss Lankester told her Alice Ravenhill, now the Secretary of the Royal British Nurses Association, had been asking about her, so Lucy dropped in at Old Cavendish Street to see her. "Alice looked very smart and she was already the life and soul of the office."

"Miaow!" said Hye.

"No, no, she is a WONDERFUL woman. She says she has dropped

instantly into the office work – very complicated – she says she has two clerks under her. She says the accounts were in an awful muddle as she suspects Miss Robins and Mrs Bedford Fenwick cooked the books."

"Oh yes?" mused Hye.

"She says that they can't get rid of Mrs Bedford Fenwick as she is a permanency in the British Nursing Association. But now that Alice has come and is sorting it out, Princess Alexandra – she's the patron – is devoted to her."

"Of course. She would be."

"She gave me some manuscripts to read about the Grimsby Women's Letters, which she had written in imitation of Miss Abraham's reports on the Labour Commission."

"In imitation, eh?"

"Yes, during her Saturdays and Sundays doing County Council lectures last winter. I have to say the ones I have read are EXCELLENT."

"I can quite understand why you dislike her," said Hye.

"I didn't say I disliked her. I said I think she is a wonderful woman. And she will certainly be something big one of these days."

"I don't know which of you is the bigger hypocrite," said Hye.

Mr Walmsley, the Assistant Factory Inspector for the Stafford District, met her off the train in Stoke on Trent and was patently amazed at the sight of her. She was clearly not what he expected to see as a Factory Inspector. He was a surprise to her as well, a young man, about her own age, tall and slim, clean shaven, dark-haired, brown eyed, with a dark-brown suit, a soft hat and a ready smile. He took her suitcase to the North Stafford Hotel, with large and prosperous reception rooms, all with electric light, and while she was shown up to her spacious bedroom, ordered tea for them both. She showed him some of the lists of places she was planning to visit. He was incredulous. "Workshops in Market Drayton? It's out in the wilds! There ARE no workshops in Market Drayton." Lucy laughed. He seemed open and ingenuous, but she was careful what she said, and did not mention the Brough factory in her itinerary at all. Mr Walmsley took her for a walk through the town, she thought it was hideous, composed of rough streets, pottery 'banks', breweries, and rows of small soot-encrusted workmen's houses. The strange squat kilns loomed over the streets and a grey powdery mist hung in the air. Where were the shops? He pointed out a few. Nothing was displayed outside their windows, and there were no market stalls. "Everyone keeps their windows shut," he said, "when the kilns are opened after a firing, the soot and ash gets over everything. A hooter is sounded fifteen minutes before the kiln is opened, so that the women can run into the yard and get their washing off the lines."

That evening she wired Hye NOT to put HMI on her envelopes and asked the same of the Chief when she wrote to announce her arrival, because she didn't want it generally known who she was. She made out a discreet copy, minus names, of the Complaint against Jones and Brough, ready to show Mr Walmsley when necessary.

The first post brought a letter from May Abraham advising her to call on Miss Bennett, the originator of the Complaint, so she wrote for an appointment. Then she bought an official directory of the pottery district and began her inspections in Newcastle under Lyme. When she returned to the hotel in the early evening a note from Miss Bennett asked her to visit her office after dinner.

Miss Bennett was a hard-featured, reserved, middle-aged woman, a lady from Lyme Regis, a clergyman's daughter. She told Lucy she had felt drawn to come North and work among the pottery girls after her father's death. Lucy expressed admiration.

"As a child my father had a parish for some years in the Cornish tin mining area. It was a terrible place, the hardship and poverty were unbelievable, my parents did what they could, but the town ruined my mother's health and they lost three other children, so my father moved to Dorset. They both became ardent trades unionists and I did too. My mother died when I was a young woman and now my father has died so I am free to come up here. I have recently started a Co-op Union."

"And is there much support for it?"

"Oh yes." Miss Bennett was decisive. "Three hundred already in just under a year. The Pottery women are rough and uncivilised, but they are STRAIGHT, you always know where you are with them. My President, Mrs Goodwin, and my Secretary, Miss Bedwell, are both working women."

"Do you have much dealing with the Factory Inspectors?"

"I hardly have any contact with them. The women know nothing of any inspectors and they certainly wouldn't look on one as a friend."

Lucy asked about Brough's factory, and told about the Home Office wish for discretion.

"The conditions there are very poor and unwholesome, certainly. There is very little overtime worked there, so no chance for extra pay, so the women don't like it. The lead fumes and the dust are the same as in other factories. Average age of death is forty in this neighbourhood, but then the general health of the neighbourhood is not so bad, except for asthma."

"What could the factories do against the lead fumes?"

"Oh, a great deal. They could forbid the lead being moved so many times for a start – in one firm they fired and painted, fired and painted, and fired and painted three times in one glaze. And there are many ways of getting equal results by healthier processes, but feeling is so conservative and so slow that the owners will not take the trouble to change or find out safer ways."

They arranged to go to Stafford Infirmary together, where Miss Bennett knew the Matron, and for Lucy to dine at Miss Bennett's home at the weekend. "Don't go to Brough's now, somehow I feel they may have got wind of something. If I was you I'd wait until well after Wakes Week – late August. They won't be so much on their guard, then," advised Miss Bennett.

After inspecting in Burslem and in Newcastle under Lyme for two days in a thin summer drizzle, which smelt unpleasant and left Lucy's white cotton blouse spotted with annoying smuts, Lucy met Miss Bennett on Saturday afternoon for a visit to the Matron of Stafford Infirmary, a friend of Miss Bennett. Miss Bennett introduced her as a friend, Miss Deane.

Lucy elicited:

that the Infirmary had numerous cases of lead poisoning and fibroid phthisis as local peculiar diseases;
that the Matron said it was more common among men than women but 'didn't know why';
that their cases were never fatal, maybe because the chronic cases went to the Union Infirmary;
that when they were relieved and discharged they either returned to work in the pottery industry, and then got ill again, or else became a domestic servant.
The Matron believed that their condition was due to carelessness among the workforce, as she had heard that there were preventative

measures taken and notices put up in the factories;
that Miss Bennett bridled at this and the Matron hurriedly said she
knew nothing of it personally.

Lucy remarked that the women might do a great deal to help themselves
by actually READING the Rules and taking an intelligent interest in them,
and then telling an Inspector when they were infringed.

The Matron nodded politely but looked as if she did not think there
was much chance of this.

Miss Bennett told of one woman who had lived healthily through to
old age working in lead rooms, but always used overalls and a respirator.
Lucy felt vindicated by this but the Matron, though silent, clearly did not
believe it.

Miss Bennett turned the screw by saying that HER working women
would do anything to hoodwink an Inspector, suspecting them always to
be on the side of their social friends, the employers, who would simply
turn the women off if it were known they were Trades Unionists or had
informed inspectors.

A nurse on the male ward said she frequently had three or four cases
in her ward, and that the fibroid cases and the tuberculous phthisis cases
symptoms were indistinguishable and fatal in the same way and equally
infectious.

"And hereditary, also," said the Matron.

They left the wards, and found walking in the grounds, convalescing,
a grey-faced, grey-haired woman about forty. Lucy got into conversation
with her. The Matron seemed slightly annoyed.

The woman said her name was Mrs Stanway and she had worked for
Ridgeways as a Ware Cleaner – "that's washing the pots when they come
out of the kiln, ready for packing – for four years – but I've been ill of lead
several times before in other works."

"I've used to stay at home," she said, "This is the first time I've been
sent to the Infirmary. I was much the worst this time. No, I've never seen
any Special Rules up in the workplaces – What do they say?"

"Did you eat your meals at your work?"

"Yes, we could take our bread to the China Warehouse, nice there, quite
free of dust or lead. And at Ridgeways we wear overalls and we had hand
protectors and they had respirators too, and we liked them, I think they

were good, but they are all worn out now, and no new ones have been got us. And Ridgeways used to have soap and towels so we could wash our hands before dinner breaks, but no soap or brushes now, all been used up. Our hours are good, only seven till seven. Never later than seven."

"Do you know of anyone else who has had to come to the Infirmary?"

"Yes, one, but she's gone home now. Ridgeways were very good. They gave her and me a Subscribers Ticket for coming here and Letters of Admission."

Lucy looked at the Matron.

"She means her costs were paid by the employers."

"And have you seen anyone inspecting in the factory, who you could ask about soap, and face towels?"

"Inspecting? No. Not one. Never, not in any of my jobs," said Mrs Stanway, laughing.

In the Matron's office Lucy was shown a Report for 1892 and 1893. The numbers stated as suffering from lead poisoning seemed small considering the way it was talked of as a common ailment.

"The women insist that the Infirmary, which is supported entirely by endowment and voluntary contributions, doesn't give a correct list of lead poisoning cases," said Miss Bennett.

The Matron appeared surprised. "We list all we receive. Idle talk."

Lucy made a list of the illnesses. Plumbism, fibroid phthisis, Necrosis of the jaw and bone. 58 males, 33 females all told in two years. One male died and two females died.

Miss Bennett and Lucy walked back to Miss Bennett's home for supper.

"Still, they seem to have a good record of cures, don't they?" said Lucy.

"I think the Infirmary sends them home before they die," said Miss Bennett.

Sunday was a hot heavy day of thunderous skies and short sharp showers, a particularly heavy one arriving just as she was wondering if she should go out to church. Very lucky timing, she decided, and left the blue hat in the hatbox, settling to a mountain of correspondence.

Before lunch she wrote to the Chief enclosing her reports, asking for Brough's Complaint to be postponed until September and asking Peacock to send more visiting forms; to May Abraham about Jones and Brough and a long account of lead poisoning in the Potteries; to a Mrs Adams of

Newcastle under Lyme, returning the Certificate for young employees; to Miss Bennett with thanks and asking the address of Miss Bedwell, Secretary to the Potterywomen's Union; to Alice Ravenhill.

The hotel was almost empty at the weekend and so were the streets in the centre of town. Mr Walmsley arrived for lunch and they dined early, sitting in solitary state at a table in the window. She told him of the Infirmary visit and of her findings. He undertook to inspect at Ridgeways and in other Potteries firms to check on respirators, soap, Abstracts and Special Notices, and regarded her with unwilling respect. The lunch was excellent, cold beef, new potatoes, and the freshest of salads, and a dish of pickled walnuts, her favourites.

When he had gone she needed a walk, but the skies were lowering again so she wrote more letters, to a Dr Rainger thanking for a book and asking for procedure in conducting a case; to Mrs Steward at Limpsfield accepting a holiday invitation for August 30th when she would be staying with the Streatfeilds; to a Mr Green of Woodfield Hall, Cheadle, thanking him for his civil note when they had met at an inspection; to Mr Child, to ask for a £5 note as she was getting short, and asking for it to be sent to the main Post Office at Stafford; and finally she wrote to Hye and to Evelyn. She ordered some tea and cakes and sat in the lounge listening to a young couple playing the piano and cello very well. But there were so few people that they packed up their music and instruments early.

By now the rain had stopped and it was a golden evening. Lucy walked around Stoke, marvelling at how pleasant it was with no smoke and no stress. She took herself to Evensong at the parish church, very passably sung. Then she went up to her room and fell asleep almost instantly.

Bright and early the next day she set off to Kidgrove, Tunstall and Fenton. The three small Fenton potteries seemed reasonable enough and the train to Kidgrove clattered amiably along. There seemed to be no town as such at Kidgrove at all, nothing but collieries and iron foundries; the narrow streets of low houses huddled together and the pottery workshops were little more than a series of sheds each clustered around their kiln, producing little more than small brown jugs and bowls with a poor glaze on the inside and roughened sides. The women packing the jugs onto pallets looked ill and careworn and several were barefoot. They stared at Lucy, and their forewoman treated them as children, scolding them if they stared too long.

On her way back to the station she missed her way; there were no street names that she could see, and when she asked for directions a man gave them civilly enough, but with a dialect so thick she could not understand him. So, when she reached the station, the only train for Tunstall for nearly three hours had long gone.

The stationmaster was helpful and sent a porter to accompany her to a stables some three hundred yards away, where a man with a surprisingly neat dog cart and well groomed horse agreed to drive her to Tunstall. If he was surprised at a lone gentlewoman wanting to go to Tunstall factories he showed no sign of it and was happy to chat as they trotted along. All the colliers were in the Great Strike last winter, he told her, and had not yet got over it.

Lucy mentioned the depressed workshops she had just seen. "Ah!" he said, "An' the Stroike 'as 'alf rooined the Pottery Tride, now wonder they'm under the weather."

A muffled blast rumbled around them, it seemed to come from under the earth. The horse shied and stopped nervously. The man was down by its head in a moment, comforting it and stroking its muzzle. "It's a gas explosion down mine, not much of one." Lucy looked alarmed. The great heaps of slate from the pits gave the countryside a strange menacing look, gleaming purple in the morning sunshine, and steaming gently as yesterday's rain dried in the warm air.

"Never fear," said he. "Ower mines don't 'ave many explosions, not in this country. It's this hot weather causes explosions. The heat seeps into the pit and then the gases roosh together and blow up. All this land round yere is undertunnelled by the mines. That's what prevents 'arthquaikes – oh! Yes. The 'arth is full of gases in America and all they foreign parts where the gases can't get out, sow they bursts out, and breaks through the 'arth because there's now room for them, but 'ere there's great owpen spaces for them, and free passages, and draughts to blow 'em away through the pit mouth, sow way down't get now 'arthquaikes. They'd stop the 'arthquaikes in America if they'd start working collieries like way do, and groob out the ground underneath like 'ere."

"Well, you HAVE given me a lot to think about," said Lucy.

"Ah! Think on!" said the man and they drove into Tunstall in a friendly silence.

From Tunstall to Fenton, from Fenton to Stoke in the dusty heat. It was a very tiring day and after a short rest she took her baggage and caught the train to Stafford and the Swan Hotel and fell into bed there.

She was woken in the night by another cracking thunderstorm, and severe stomach pains. At first she thought it was gas explosions and earthquakes outside, but then pulled the heavy curtains apart to watch the lightning flashes slit the dark sky. The pains in her stomach? What were they? Period pains? Definitely, the familiar cramping, gripping, pincer feeling – but not due for another fortnight, surely? And so fierce! She felt sick and dizzy, took a sip of water and lurched back onto her bed. The pains were as strong as anything she had to cope with each month. She lay facing the window, counting the seconds after each thunderclap, to see how far away the storm might be, several were immediately overhead, counting the brilliant flashes that lit her room, counting the seconds between each pain contraction. Soon the rain came, a deluge settling to a steady patter, and with it Lucy's pain decreased. At dawn she drowsed off, waking late, to a perfect summer morning, damp and cool, and tree branches, glistening green, outside in the hotel gardens. She realised there had been no trees in the Pottery towns.

No sign of a period, thank goodness, but Lucy was nervous. She went to the Post Office in Stafford where a fat wodge of letters had been collecting for her, nearly all from the Home Office, but no letter enclosing a £5 bank note from Child. She wired to Child at once asking what had happened to it. Her own money was becoming dangerously low. Then she spent twenty minutes with a tiny person in a chemist's shop, hardly visible on the other side of the counter; the person was wearing a white coat, with very thin hair scraped back from the forehead with a miniscule bun at the back, a beaky nose and bright boot-black button eyes; for a moment Lucy could not tell if it was male or female; but the voice was unmistakeably female, formal yet friendly. Lucy explained her night pains, and the tiny woman drew her around the counter into a consulting booth, provided her with some pads and a pain-relieving draught, and asked her several questions as to her job, her travelling, her diet, her lifestyle, her previous life and childhood health. Then she said decisively that Lucy should rest for the next 24 hrs, NOT to be shaken about on ANY vehicle, and to go to her doctor as soon as she got back to London. No trains, no cabs today, she said firmly.

The young handsome male chemist was dealing with the other

customers when Lucy came out of the booth, and an extremely beautiful young woman came hurriedly in through the shop door. "I'm so sorry, Mother, Mrs Redshaw kept me talking." "It won't do, Mary, Robert will be late for his lecture. Put on your overall, I needed these lists of pills made up half an hour ago." She swept her daughter with her tiny arms into the back room and gave Lucy her purchases and her change. Robert came out of the back room in a black suit and with a smart black brief case, bowler hat and rolled umbrella, opened the door for Lucy, and swung off down the road in the other direction.

Lucy was overawed by this miniature Amazon and went back obediently back to the Swan Hotel, practically penniless, but extraordinarily relieved, and delighted to find a letter forwarded from the North Stafford Hotel with the £5 from Child. She spent the day quietly dealing with the Home Office queries and writing her reports of the lead poisoning hospital visits. A friendly chambermaid discovered her snoozing on her bed in the afternoon and Lucy told her about the tiny woman in the chemist's shop.

"Oh, that's Mrs Plowden, she'd keep the Queen in order. We all pay attention when she walks by. She'm a marvel. They say when she were about twelve and were about to leave school, the schoolmistress said she'd not get a job in domestic service, she were too small. She said she were not about to try for one, she said she 'ad decided SHE were going to be a doctor, and she went to the hospital and asked for a job, all four foot six of 'er, and they laffed, but they give 'er a job in the dispensary delivering the pills, an' after a bit one of the doctors paid out 'isself for 'er to 'ave chemist's training proper, and she come out top of all of them, and then 'e married 'er after 'is wife died, and she ran 'is dispensary and looked after his children, and when 'e died she set up the shop."

"Marvellous!" said Lucy.

"Oh yes, she'll see you right," said the maid. "You rest there and I'll bring you something nice and light to eat. Or she'd carry on at ME and I can't 'ave that!"

The day's rest did the trick and so Lucy risked an inspection in the attractive little town of Stone only a few miles north of Stafford. Several small dressmakers' units had banded together to produce overalls, aprons, and uniforms for shopping and cooking establishments and were in process of turning a collection of farm buildings into a miniature factory. The orders were coming in thick and fast. Meanwhile, the dressmaking shops were overcrowded and the farm buildings' sanitary conveniences were non-existent. Lucy promised to arrange an inspection in early October for them with the District Inspectors 'before the cold weather gets us' and to send a report within the week. They were a cheerful lively group, asked her a lot of questions, seemed like a true co-operative force, and several workers at the farm buildings came down to the gate and waved her goodbye as she walked down to the station! She could hardly believe it.

August 2nd was Lucy's birthday. Thirty years old. She felt well and, looking critically at her face in the mirror, thought, I am still a young woman. To her surprise a letter from her childhood friend Tini, in London, sat on her breakfast table, with a birthday note, and a ten shilling postal order. How had she managed that? No letter from Hye, but she had not expected any, she would be home on Friday and Hye was out and about and giving her cookery lectures all day. She ate her toast and looked around the hotel dining room full of bustle and coming and going, and with the smell of bacon and the brilliantine of the young businessman at the next table. 'It has been a runaway coach ride since my last birthday. Last August the second I had just finished my National Health Society courses and was working as a nurse probationer with Matron in the wards of the Chelsea Infirmary.' How nervous she had been, and then how much she had enjoyed it. And how nervous of the lecturing – and how much she had enjoyed that. And how nervous of the exams for the Sanitary Inspector's post – and now here she was, a Female Factory Inspector. I am a Pioneer. I am a Professional Working Woman with Great Responsibilities, she told herself. Right, said Herself, so finish your toast and get on with it. She scooped out her final spoonful of egg and ate it, laid the spoon down, drank the last mouthful of coffee deliberately, put the cup down neatly and got up, laughing at herself. The young man at the next table looked at her oddly.

Off to Congleton to some silk mills. She should have visited there before coming down to Stafford but had not planned her Bradshaw times well enough. She wondered at the beauty of the countryside as the train rushed past the Potteries and the Staffordshire Moorlands. What have we done to our beautiful country? And in the silk mills she shook her head.

How did this clatter and noise and dust and bustle manage to produce this beautiful cloth, such texture, such colours, such art?

The next day she gloried in the train journey as it took her to Leek through the North Staffordshire fields and hills on her mission for Lady Dilke. She left her luggage at the station, but soon realised she had come on the wrong day, and on enquiry found it was a Festival Club Day, and all the shops were shut. She asked the way to Ardbourne Road where Nellie Shenton, the Assistant Secretary of the Women's Trades Union, lived. "Don't go to the Secretary himself," Lady Dilke had warned. "He is the cause of the considerable disarray."

Nellie Shenton's house was in the middle of a small grey terrace practically opposite Brough's great mill. But Nellie and her husband were away on a Club Day outing and the door was opened by her mother-in-law, who received her very politely, and invited her in to the tiny front parlour. She was very ready to talk, and voluble in championing her daughter-in-law's hard work, all come to naught. The union had collapsed; originally it had been 500 strong. Mr Stubbs had been the Secretary and Nellie, a corder at the Silk mill, earning 10s a week, was the Assistant Secretary. But it had been getting weaker and weaker, partly because of the 'bad times', with the women not wanting to pay their 2d a week subscription, and partly – mostly, said Nellie's mother-in-law – because some of the women quarrelled with Stubbs, accusing him of exploiting it for his own benefit. They paid him 10s a week at first, then 15s a week. Nellie collected all the money and worked hard for it – for no wages – and all he had to do was audit the accounts and keep the banking accounts.

Finally there was a regular quarrel, Stubbs having charged £5 for 5 days for making out accounts. Two weeks ago a meeting was called to consider closing the Union and last week another was called to draw up a distribution fund. Several of the early members got 30s. Several would not come themselves, they would not meet Mr Stubbs, they sent Proxies. "The Union is no more," said Mrs Shenton, shaking her head mournfully. "It only had eighty members left when it ceased. Trade is very bad, the highest pay in the silk mills is only 10s a week, and they are only putting in slack time. Nellie is very sorry the Union broke up. She was keen to keep it on and took great pains over it."

Lucy took careful notes and thanked Mrs Shenton for her clear explanation. She felt sad as she walked back to the station for the loss of a thriving Women's Union through one man's dishonesty. They could have done so much good, she grieved, so much good will was built up, and now nothing left. The sadness turned to anger as she walked and then waited for the train to Burton on Trent. When the porter had lifted her cases into an empty carriage and the train moved off she punched the padding on the seats.

10

A nasty setback

The doctor is called for Lucy; Matron makes an appointment for her examination; to Leicester again; shocking pay for hosiery outworkers; Lady Howard wishes to pay for Lucy's treatment; Ethel and her ukelele; false smiles for Captain Armstrong; Hye panics; schoolchildren employed illegally; Lucy visits the consultant; Matron is comforting.

Holiday time at the Home Office and only a skeleton staff. May Abraham at home in Dublin. Sprague Oram away for the whole month. Hye and Lucy planned to spend their time criss-crossing the South of England, to the Boscawen aunts and uncle in Kent and the Deane cousins in Gloucestershire and days together in London.

But after a few idyllic days in Dymock the period pains struck again, on time this time but with gigantic waves of pain, so that Lucy was doubled up, dizzy and vomiting, and had to be helped by Evelyn, and one of the gardeners, out of the rowing boat and across the lawn to the house, and laid on her bed by Aunt Georgie and Ginny. Aunt Georgie was frightened when the pain had not abated by teatime and Lucy was exhausted and crying out. Hye sat by the window, as white as Lucy, gripping her hands together. Evelyn cooled Lucy's brow with cold cloths.

"I have sent John off on Brownie to fetch Dr Rivers," Mrs Deane told her husband. "This is no ordinary monthly pain, and Hye says they have been getting worse since she has begun this inspecting lark."

"Not surprising," he huffed. "All this travelling, rattling around in trains, smelly, smoky places. Too much joggling about."

"Don't be silly, Father," snapped Mary. "I do masses of joggling about – riding to hounds, jumping fences, galloping around here for miles and miles; joggling never bothers ME – or YOU!"

"That's NATURAL joggling. Natural joggling never hurt anyone. It's this MECHANICAL joggling. Unnatural. And particularly for the female frame!"

"Nonsense—"

"You are neither of you helpful, please stop," said Aunt Georgie. "Ethel, go to the kitchen and see how far on they are with the evening meal. Tell them to simplify it as much as possible. We need to be able to concentrate on Lucy."

She went up to Lucy's room with the doctor when he came and gently put both the girls outside. Doctor Rivers examined Lucy and gave her a laudanum draught. He asked questions, when had her monthlies first started, had she always had pain? "Oh, always," said Lucy. "But only for a few hours on the first day. Very occasionally I feel sick, but I never have been sick until today, and often my back aches for a couple of days after they begin, and often I get bad headaches. But if I can lie down for a few hours with a hot bottle I'm usually fine the next day."

"And what happens when you are travelling around? Do you still take your train journeys?"

"Oh yes, sometimes I have to. But often I treat that first day as an Office Day. I call it my Office Day and I spend it in the hotel if I can, catching up on my correspondence and writing up my reports."

"Would you say the pains have got worse in the past few months?"

Lucy considered lying, but finally said, "Yes, I think so. I think this last year they have been much sharper every time."

"I advise you to go to a good consultant and get a full gynaecological examination. You may have some fibroid growth which should be removed, or there may be some misalignment which could be rectified."

"Meanwhile," he told Aunt Georgie, "let her rest tonight and take this prescription. And let her get up and take gentle exercise, walking in the garden if the pain goes, and small, soft, tasty meals."

He patted Lucy's hand. "No more putting up with this, my dear, it has needed attention for a long while, it seems, and it must have attention now. Luckily you are on holiday, the perfect time to make an appointment."

On the landing he found Hye and Evelyn, looking woebegone. "This won't do," he beamed, "Your job is to cheer up the patient. She needs some fun. See she gets it."

Evelyn brightened up immediately. But Hye's eyes were frightened and her mouth set. Her sister was ill – all she had in the world.

John and Brownie trotted back to the village to the pharmacy with the doctor, and Lucy lay in the darkened room as the waves of pain rolled in, and ebbed away as the laudanum took effect, and she was able to drift into sleep.

Below in the dining room, the family talked about her in quiet voices. Hye was distressed. "I knew! I knew she had these pains, each time she would go to bed early with a hot water bottle – and the next day she said she was well again. I should have thought! I should have paid more attention." The tears dripped down onto her plate.

"I knew something of it as well," said Evelyn, putting her arm round her. "But she never made anything of it, and she never let it stop her doing what she had planned."

"That's Lucy all over though," sighed Aunt Georgie, "And we shan't change her. However, now that we know we must pay attention, we will. Don't fret, Hye. Tonight I will write to Miss de Pledge at the Chelsea Infirmary and she will advise us who to consult."

Uncle George and Horace took themselves off for a walk in the dusk. The Squire neatly decapitated a thistle. "Best out of it. Women's troubles, not for us." Horace stopped to light his pipe. "Home Office should know better. Office work perhaps. Industrial arguments and trains, never."

During the next few days envelopes with various feminine handwritings flew backwards and forwards and friends and relations informed and advised and expressed opinions of various and occasionally dubious worth; Lucy recovered and rested and rowed on the little lake, and played croquet on the lawn, and walked the pleasant bridle paths and byways round Dymock, and ate fresh food lovingly prepared by Cook, and sat in the sun and became quite rosy cheeked, and enjoyed the gentle cosseting.

By the end of the week, Matron had swung into action and organised a visit to Mr Holmes of Hertford Street, the eminent gynaecologist, and a

Mrs Douglas, one of her former nurses to accompany Lucy. He examined her thoroughly – "Dreadful!" said Lucy to Hye that evening – and said the womb was misplaced and malformed from birth, and was getting worse and worse and that she must undergo an operation, or else in 12 months' time she might be reduced to spending the best part of her days on a sofa. He would do it, he assured her, on his return from his holiday in October.

Lucy and Mrs Douglas came home in a cab and broke the news to Hye who cried fearfully. "Oh, Lucy, must you have an operation? Is there no other way?"

"It seems not. But I shall write to Lady Howard and ask for Althea Harding's doctor, as I want a second opinion. An operation would mean my not being able to work for at least six months. I can't be away all that time."

"Oh, Lucy, please give up the job now, it's too hard, it's killing you. Get a job like Alice Ravenhill. She doesn't have to rush about like you do."

"Not at all, Hye! I LOVE the work. I'm just getting into it. We're both of us really beginning to make our mark. Do stop crying, Hye, your bodice is getting all soggy – get a fresh handkerchief; and make us some tea. I'll write to Evelyn straightaway."

The next morning she went and bought a new writing case at the Co-op Department store for one guinea, had her hair done and wrote two reports, one on Infant Mortality, and one for Time Off for Women after Confinement, and sent them to Miss Bennett, before she packed and went off with Hye for their final week's holiday with the Streatfeilds in Limpsfield, riding the Streatfeilds' horses every day with Granville.

Monday September 3rd and Lucy reported to Mr Sprague Oram at the Home Office and fumed inwardly as he informed her that May Abraham, and not Lucy, was to go to Norwich Trades Union Congress on Infant Mortality. "All that work sent to Miss Bennett for nothing!" He was sending her to Leicester and to Captain Armstrong armed only with an extremely ancient report: 'Mrs White's Children's Commission on the Hosiery Trades Outworkers and Domestic Clothiers, 1863.'

"This says children of six years old work all night!" The Chief waved the book about. "You are to make enquiries concerning conditions of children's employment now!"

Lucy saw the title page, "1863! – has NOTHING been done in the meantime?"

"Nothing that's ever filtered down to me," said the Chief cheerily. "But now I've got YOU. They tell me the Bell at Leicester is the best. We've told Armstrong you're coming."

Captain Armstrong met her at the station next day, and shook her hand as if it was broken glass. They conferred in his office and he assured her he kept no lists of hosiery outworkers; that all those lists were in the large factory offices. However, in the several factories she visited she could not find any regular form for outworkers' lists, although they were all willing to give her the names and addresses that they had, haphazardly written down over the years, certainly not alphabetical, and many totally out of date. Lucy spent the evening with the Leicester street map, making her own lists of names.

Armed with a short plan of campaign she began to call on the outworkers' homes, finding the women mostly at home, but very few working on stockings or gloves.

"The trade's that slack – no children employed at home any more, no, only in the factories, and only then if they're over 12, and then part-time. Us outworkers did the hand seaming, but the factories has the Grismer machines now so the hand work's gone. We gets the link machines – treadle machines now – it pays 2d for a dozen pair."

"I do glove stretching for woollen gloves," said another, "but often when I goes to collect them, there's none to be done."

In the afternoon she visited the Hosiery Trades Union, a very strong Union with 2000 women, and the Secretary there told her that labour was much cheaper in the outlying villages, so that, when slack hours were being worked in Leicester, perhaps overtime might be being done in the villages by those manufacturers who had factories in both town and country.

She trekked out to the villages of Countesthorpe and Great Wigston and there she found no lists of outworkers in any of the factories. The chief outwork was 'toe-ing', sewing the tops of toes together; and now that this was done by a machine in the factories there was very little work for the village home workers. Pay was between 2d to 3d a dozen for the same work. Hardly any men were employed in the factories now, only women and older children because of the simplicity of the machines. "Hand sewing has nearly died out," one woman mourned, "I get mine from a middleman. He keeps a store and if you buy from him he sees you get some handwork to do. Of course, you've got to buy from him. But he's a fair man, he pays a fair price and he asks a fair price. My two children help with the sewing after school and at night. I can remember being kept up all night when I were a child to do the seaming – took it to school the next day."

Another was resentful. "The Government's let us down. They took away our contract for Army socks, said they wanted them all made by factory machine – not so good – but much cheaper. And much quicker. So, many of the men have been turned off."

Lucy reported all this to Sprague Oram and received a telegram the next morning saying the manufacturers MUST keep lists of outworkers, asking her to make a full report on the outworkers and to confer with Captain Armstrong.

Captain Armstrong was not best pleased with any of the Chief's remarks concerning the hosiery outworkers lists. "There IS a prescribed form for outworkers lists, and they HAVE been sent to the factories. But it is impossible to keep them up to date as there were always so many names, and families coming and going. I suppose they could be kept in a book, but, again, difficult to tabulate. Geographically? Alphabetically? Date of joining the list?"

"For myself," said Lucy, "I only saw some lists in a wages book. In a couple of places I was given some names from memory, but there was never a single outworkers list for inspection, except at Taylors and Co."

Captain Armstrong closed his eyes and sighed.

That afternoon she visited two schools in Shilton and Hinckley and found the same story. The tiny schoolmistress in Shilton complained of bad school attendance, saying the children were left at home while the mothers went to the factories. The Hinckley schoolmaster complained that the children who were legally employed half-time went to the factories for half an hour BEFORE school on school mornings, and got in an extra half hour's work that way.

It was a long journey back to Leicester that evening, on a slow train that huffed and puffed and complained and stopped for several rests. Outside the train windows there was a glorious September sunset and so Lucy gave up any attempt to write up her notes or her business diary, and simply sat and gazed at it.

Two letters were awaiting her at the hotel desk; one instructed her to inspect in Worcester on Monday and the other was from Lady Howard, stating she intended to underwrite the entire costs of any operation or treatment, and asking when Sir John Williams, who had been chosen to give the second opinion, was arriving back in London after his summer holiday.

She wrote to Lady Howard that night, and to the Aunts Florrie and Gertrude, and to Hye, now well settled into her new term at the London Cookery School near Marylebone. Her period began that night and she lay as still as she could while the familiar cramps gripped and ebbed and flowed, and thanked God she would be at the Boyce the next night with kind Aunt Georgie and loving Evelyn.

She rose early about 5a.m., and pulled the curtains back to find the soft mist which presaged another fine September day. She still felt faint and weak, but the reports to be sent loomed ahead of her, so she wrapped herself in a blanket and an eiderdown, and sat at her desk writing with determination, while the light strengthened and the hotel morning sounds went on above and below her, and footsteps went back and forth outside her door.

At 8.30a.m. she realised the cramps had gone and she was ravenously hungry, and by nine she was downstairs, soignée and cheerful and ready for hot tea and toast and honey. Thus fortified she had finished the reports by midday and sent the telegram asking to be met at Ledbury mid-afternoon.

The weather broke at the Boyce that weekend, so the girls and Aunt Georgie fussed over Lucy and kept her in bed until late on Sunday morning. They arrived in her room with an enormous breakfast tray complete with fruit, toast racks crammed with toast, and flowers. Lucy disliked breakfast in bed intensely. "I never seem to want to eat when my legs are out at right angles to my stomach," she always complained to Hye. This morning, though, she made the best of it, as they all swished around her, beaming and chatting. Hye had sent on a letter from Sir John Williams' assistant, giving her an appointment on September 28th at 12.20.

The afternoon was for letterwriting; to Hye, who said she had a bad cold; to Sir John, confirming the appointment; to Lady Howard; to the Bell in Gloucester; and *The Star* in Worcester; the Bell in Leicester and the Royal in Derby. "What would I do without my Bradshaw? How would I exist?"

The evening was spent chatting, and sitting by the first evening fire of the autumn, and listening to Ethel playing some of her pieces on the ukelele. Ethel practised dutifully and had a great repertoire of songs and tunes. The family had evolved the activity of listening to Ethel playing and singing down to a fine art. Ethel would never suggest herself that she might sing or play. She needed to be asked. She would spend the evening obviously needing to be asked. She played and sang accurately, and more or less in tune. Luckily, none of her family was in the least musical. A song was a song was a song. And the jollier the better. But they had friends who were musical, and they had learned over the years that friends were hard pressed to be patient and appreciative for too long when Ethel performed. One or two songs were applauded, after three or more, the clapping was perfunctory. The Deane family was fiercely loyal. They had perfected a programme to suit all. After dinner and when the guests had met up again in the drawing room, one of the hosts would make a great show of drawing up tables for cards, or proposing some parlour game, and then, when the activity looked set to begin, another member of the family cried, "Oh, but we haven't heard Ethel play yet. Do let's hear Ethel play something! WOULD you, Ethel? Just one! Just for a few minutes! Then we can settle to—" whatever it was. So honour was satisfied, and guests could be magnanimous.

That weekend had been devoted to Lucy and so Ethel sang several more songs. But Lucy basked in the cloud of kindness and affection and tolerance and was comforted by Ethel's earnest missing of notes.

On the Monday and Tuesday she inspected in Gloucester, Leominster, Malvern and Worcester and lunched with District Inspector Arnold who held forth on the sins of Mr Sprague Oram. Lucy listened dutifully and thought what a humbug Mr Arnold was. In the middle of the week she went again to Leicester, visited several workshops and dined with Captain Armstrong, determined to be friendly. It was no good. He aired his notions of the indecency of having to inspect private workshops; Lucy said that public workshops were sufficiently inspected by their publicity, but private ones, sweatshops, and outworkers, for example, needed inspection far more, and therefore adequate lists and reports needed to be drawn up and kept up to date. Both parted with false smiles.

The weekend was tense as Hye, whose cold was running its violent course, got into a panic when she realised the second opinion appointment was to be the coming Friday.

"How will we manage if you have to have an operation?"

"Perfectly well," Lucy comforted. "Evelyn will come here to visit me, and be with you. Wonderful Lady Howard will pay for everything. We have good friends who will keep an eye on things for us. Emily is more than competent. You have your work which you MUST continue, whatever else. We are extremely fortunate women – not like some of the poor souls I see in the factories every day."

Hye burst into tears.

"Oh, stop it, Hye. You think I shall die if I have the operation. Well, I shan't. In fact, I am half looking forward to it. A month in bed – a good rest – and then, with luck, no more pain and undignified discomfort every month. Splendid."

"But – maybe you won't be able to have children," spluttered Hye.

"I hadn't been planning to have children," said Lucy. "I was planning to have a career – and now I've got this one I'm certainly not looking for a husband. I never dreamed I should have such an exciting chance to do anything as worthwhile as this. And now I've got the chance I shall take it. Do YOU want a husband?"

"Of course I do!" Hye blew her sore red nose, and wiped her swollen eyes, "If I ever meet anybody who wants me, and that seems unlikely. But I can't live without you, Lucy, can I?"

"Certainly, at this moment, you don't seem the most desirable catch. But if you ever did, you'd find you could live without me very well. Meanwhile, I'm going to make you some lemon and honey. Come, let's have a cuddle, and then I'm going to spend the weekend writing to all the Aunts and friends."

She wrote to Evelyn, enclosing a silk scarf someone had sent her as a present. 'Would you like this, darling, I think it is hideous. If not, donate it to some good cause.' She wrote to Miss Bushall and Miss Moffatt inviting them to tea, and to the Aunts Augusta, Florence and Gertrude about the operation. She sent the cheque for the rent, she wrote to Alice Ravenhill, and Lady Howard and Mrs Douglas, and Matron, and May Abraham, and to the Chief, asking for leave on September 28th.

Hye busied herself in the kitchen making a beef casserole and a wonderfully light Victoria sponge, and she also wrote a letter, to Sir John Williams, the consultant, and slipped out to post it separately.

The week before the appointment with Sir John, Lucy left the outworkers inspection, and visited Trades Unions, and girls' clubs, and schoolmistresses. The Bell at Derby was full so she went to the Royal, and was pleasantly surprised, the cooking better than the Bell, and she had one of her treats, pork chops and apple sauce, beautifully cooked. In Derby she talked to Mrs Alexander, the President of the Girls Friendly Society, and on the School Board, a kind, fussy little woman, who showed her the Girls Friendly Recreation Rooms in Hardwick. Lucy spent two evenings there, impressed by the happy and purposeful atmosphere, dropping in on some of the classes held there, which included Mathematics, English, Hygiene and Dressmaking.

Miss Baddeley, the schoolmistress of St Athelmund's School, was particularly welcoming and helpful and confirmed that school attendance was bad, but said it was because the local magistrates absolutely refused to convict their friends the factory owners. "I sympathise with you," said Miss Baddeley, with feeling.

Back in Leicester she visited a Roman Catholic School and found here the same complaint made by Hinckley Board School members – half-time children working odd hours after school when they had already been working all morning. She spoke to two children who had been working in a morning set, then gone off to afternoon school and were rushing back to work till six or seven, at a shoe factory, leaving no time to prepare their lessons for school. Inspecting hosiery outworkers in Silsby and Wigston Magna villages she found work brisk, and the same infringement for the child half-time workers.

When she arrived home at 100 Fulham Road on Thursday night she found a friendly and helpful letter from Alice Ravenhill. She recommended two other consultants and said that Sir John Williams was dead against operative treatments. Forewarned is forearmed, thought Lucy and wrote and thanked her. She was determined to try for an operation.

On Friday September 28th she went to 65 Brook Street, with Mrs Douglas, a sensible woman of few words, in the morning. Sir John Williams was a careful, cautious old gentleman, very interested in her work, and in her early life and illnesses. He examined her slowly and with extreme care with Mrs Douglas, on Matron's instructions, sitting in the room at the extreme edge, and watching and listening to all that went on. Sir John's nurse was calm and comforting and Lucy was not as tense and alarmed as she had been on her previous examination. When it had been completed he said firmly that he would try everything else before he would operate, and ordered iron tonics and pain-relieving draughts for the next few months.

Lucy and Mrs Douglas took a hansom cab to Matron at the Chelsea Hospital as they had done the time before. She told Matron, "He let slip that Hye had written him a letter, and I suppose she was begging him not to operate. So now I shall have to drag on as usual. I had SO hoped for a time of rest, followed by relief." Lucy's mouth was set. Matron seemed unperturbed. "Well, what he has prescribed to begin with is good and sensible and can do nothing but help. And a hysterectomy, or the removal of a growth, is a VERY different kettle of fish than a little discomfort and a month of rest, I can assure you. Go along with it for three months and then we'll see."

So Lucy and Hye wrote to everyone who wanted to know the result; and Lucy wrote to Mrs Hubbard and asked her to make her a winter dinner dress for five guineas.

11

Ribbons and shrouds

HMI Cooke Taylor welcomes her; 'Clobber' workshops; a model ribbon factory; frilly brown shrouds; a superior children's workhouse; Sunday lunch with Bossie; useful 'Office Days'; wooing Mr Cramp; school teachers become allies; the new dinner gown; fearful school uniforms; chasing up birth certificates for minors; rescued from the storm by the White Lion in Banbury.

Her Majesty's Chief District Inspector, Mr Whately Cooke Taylor, met her on Coventry Station and seemed genuinely pleased to see her, taking her to the Kings Head hotel in a cab for a light lunch, then to his offices to confer, and to give her lists, maps and addresses, and information of the places Sprague Oram wished her to inspect. Then he drove her back to the hotel at teatime with strict instructions to have a rest before he came again at six to take her to his home for dinner. "My wife is looking forward to giving you a nice homely meal. You'll be having long days while you're in this part of the country. Make the most of a quiet comfortable evening."

Lucy was taken aback by the hospitality, and half cross with herself for wanting to distrust his bonhomie; but the evening was delightful, Mrs Cooke Taylor smiling and friendly, and the house and the meal certainly comfortable and homely.

She visited textile and ribbon factories all next day in Coventry and then set off with Mr Cooke Taylor the following morning to visit workshops of boot and shoe 'clobbers' and dressmakers. He was concerned about the general dismal standards of small workshops in the area, and keen that Lucy should bring a case against the Shoemakers Association about a workshop he knew of in an outlying village. "I've complained to the Association about the general condition several times, but they don't act. If YOU go to this workshop, which was still DREADFUL when I visited two weeks ago, and prosecute, I can bring an action – with a Secretary of State order – against the Association for default."

"Will that be a good idea?"

"A VERY good idea, if it's feasible; it will do more than anything else to rouse the Shoemakers Association throughout the country about workshops conditions."

He took Lucy to several Coventry boot and 'clobber' workshops. The ones she saw were dark and dismal, mostly wooden sheds at the back of a row of terraced houses, with a row of windows on one side and a low roof, very stuffy and dirty. The usual working hours were 7.30a.m. to 7.00p.m. in summer with a dinner break 12.30 – 1.30, and no teabreak, and from 8.00a.m. to 7p.m. in the winter with a dinner break from 1p.m. to 2p.m and no tea break. The dressmakers' workshops were just as bleak. It was rare that there was any cross-ventilation. The bootmaker girls were a slightly rougher class of girl than the dressmakers, but both very pale and starved of sun.

Another excursion was to Pizzie and Cramps huge ribbon-making factory. "I'll introduce you to Cramp. Cramp runs a model factory, good employers, high standards, well set out. And his wife is very anxious to meet you. She's the Secretary of the National Liberal Association in the Coventry District. Very knowledgeable lady. Helpful for you to see a factory running as it ought to run."

Lucy thanked him, and indeed, Mr Cramp showed her the whole process from start to finish, from preparing the warp and weft on the harness of the frames to sending out the finished bolts to the stores. She saw some of the new looms where the warp drums were under instead of over the loom, so that it was no longer necessary to climb up to clean or repair the warp. Women were the chief workers even on the largest frames. The foremen preferred to have them from children, 12 – 14 years, and train them. An average full week's work was 13s to 14s. The trade paid women the same wage as the men per piece, but the weft was wound in the bobbins for shutters by workers paid by the day.

Trade was very slack throughout all the Midland counties, Mr Cramp told her, particularly with bicycles, watches and ribbon. The bicycle trade was going to Birmingham and Wolverhampton as the parts of the bicycle were made there, and so it was cheaper to complete them on the spot.

The watch trade was almost killed by cheap American watches.

The ribbon trade was sorely crippled by Swiss and German trade. Those countries had longer working hours, lower wages and were very scientific, but the Coventry factories, particularly Cramp's, were trying hard to regain the customers.

In his comfortable light and airy office at the front of the factory Lucy met Mrs Cramp, the Secretary of the Women's Section of the National Liberal Association. They had split from the Liberal Association, Mrs Cramp told her, because the latter had become so bold and narrowly eager over Women's Suffrage. There was also a large women's Co-operative Union in Coventry with over a thousand members. Mrs Cramp offered to take Lucy over the new Coventry Infirmary and Workhouse in a day or so.

Then she went on to two more large ribbon-finishing works in Coventry. She noticed from their books that a good deal of overtime was being done; it was a trade where the entire gain was derived from sudden 'rushes' of fashion. "Maybe," said the forewoman showing her around, "suddenly everyone must have 'watered silks' ribbon edging their skirts, or a certain coloured ribbon, so it would be CRUEL for Factory Acts to put a maximum limit on overtime hours, as no management could avoid it. We see-saw between levels of demand. Three quarters of the year we might only be on one quarter time, and then, such as now, coming up to Christmas, there's a sudden craze for green and gold silk ribbon. It's the uncertainty is the bad part," she said.

To finish off her day she was shown a specialist shroud workshop where they had just got an order from Ireland for such strange shrouds! They were to be brown and woollen, shaped like a nightgown and trimmed with bone ribbon in frills, forming I.H.S. on the breast and at the waist a large crimson stuffed satin heart – a Sacred Heart – and with hoods and stockings and gloves to match!

She told Cooke Taylor when she returned his Workshop Registers; he seemed mildly shocked that she should have had to endure such a sight. Lucy was amused and decided he was a kind man. He was a gentleman to all he met, like most of the older type of Factory Inspectors; he reminded her of Sir Alexander Redgrave, who had disapproved of her so courteously. But she felt that Mr Cooke Taylor worked with no pioneering spirit or genuine enthusiasm for reform. In fact, she thought, he is a moral coward and lazy, he doesn't want to stand up to the bad practice when he finds it – he'd prefer ME to do it! But he is pleasant and generous, and Mrs Cooke Taylor is a dear and practical; she is a Preston mill owner's daughter, she knows the ways of factory owners.

Mrs Cramp came on Saturday morning to take her round the Coventry Infirmary. It was a fine building, only three years old and run by the Master and Matron of the adjacent Workhouse, a visiting doctor and two trained nurses; the chief part of the work was done by pauper nurses, under the supervision of the two trained nurses. Mrs Cramp had been instrumental, with great difficulty, she assured Lucy, of appointing a Ladies Visiting Committee and they were still agitating for a Lady Guardian.

But what interested Lucy was that the children of the Workhouse were taught and taken care of by a foster father for the boys, and a foster mother for the girls. They seemed a superior class of person. She thought it a good and enlightened plan. The children, only twelve of each at the moment, were sent to various Parish Schools, and were not dressed in workhouse uniform, so they did not stand out as workhouse children and after a certain age they were boarded out, in properly inspected houses.

The Infirmary, though small, was well appointed, with an isolation ward. Nobody was in it at the time.

Lucy travelled home in the afternoon to sort out her Civil Service income tax papers and to do the household accounts. Hye's cold was gone, and she was looking very pretty and as slim as a wand. "What have you done to yourself? You look beautiful!"

"Mrs Hedingham and Leah came in the week," said Hye, "and made me try on all my clothes, and said they were all two inches too big, so they've taken most of them home to take in for me, and they made me buy two belts for my skirts, and some new stays, and get my hair done, and buy some different facecream!"

"It's a transformation!"

"Well, they're itching to get going on you!"

Lucy laughed.

"And Bossie came this morning and says he will meet us at twelve tomorrow for lunch at the Charing Cross Hotel and talk about stocks and shares."

"What stocks and shares?"

"The ones we've got."

"Well, that won't take long."

"Actually, he says it will. He says Mr Child thinks we ought to reinvest now that Lady Howard gives us the regular money. It seems he thinks we don't spend it on the right savings for us."

"In that case we'll get the household accounts out of the way tonight."

Promptly at midday on Sunday, the young women walked into the Charing Cross Hotel. Edward Boscawen, who had come up from Sevenoaks, rose carefully out of his chair to greet them. His arthritis was annoying him, as it always did in cold, rainy weather, and his back was stiff. But he carried himself well and tried hard to keep his shoulders back. He saw considerable change in his nieces. Lucy looked pale and drawn with the beginnings of lines round her fine eyes, and he thought her brown suit frankly dowdy, though he approved of the perky hat with the feather. Hyacinth, on the other hand, looked remarkable; her anxious lumpiness was gone, her eyes shone, her waist was trim, the sky-blue georgette scarf sang against her damson outfit. Edward, a confirmed bachelor, enjoyed a pretty woman. His home life had been filled with his two unmarried sisters Gertrude and Florence, and then with his widowed sister and her two girls who had been with him for many years, so he was used to feminine ways at home; he escaped daily to the City, and to his club for more manly company. Now in his semi-retirement, he dealt carefully with his female relations' financial affairs and it kept him busy.

"Well, well, how you do bloom," he cried, kissing them both on the cheek. "We'll go straight in and eat and then we'll go back to your house and spread our papers out. Then I shan't be late getting home. We'll talk shop over the meal if you don't mind."

And so he did, darting questions about expenses and coal bills over the roast beef, and salaries and savings through the apple charlotte; and finally went through the papers about rent and income tax on the Fulham Road with a box of chocolates on the side table, and finally put his silver pencil away as Hye brought in tea and crumpets.

"Crumpets eh! You certainly know how to reward a chap!" He spread out his large white handkerchief under his chin, and pushed his old knees towards the cheerful fire, and cradled the hot cup to comfort his aching fingers.

"Thank you, thank you, dear Bossie. That's cleared our heads of any worries. What would we do without you?" said Lucy, kissing his head.

"I think you'd survive," said he. "You'd got it in pretty good order without me. You've both got pretty good heads for business."

"Only because you taught us. We'd sink otherwise."

"You won't sink! You? My word, not. You'll float to the top, both of you."

They helped him on with his greatcoat and his top hat, kissed his thin red cheeks and waved him off. He walked briskly to the hackney cab rank, sank thankfully back on the cushions, and rode to his club with its newspapers and brandies and a soft warm bed.

Lucy spent the first two days of the next week in Leamington and Rugby re-inspecting factories where May Abraham had prosecuted previously, and finding to her satisfaction that they were in fairly good order. May's efforts had proved effective. The inspections in Rugby where May Abraham had not visited showed the difference immediately – overcrowded workrooms, and no Abstracts displayed. Lucy suspected a shoddy Medical Officer of Health. She wanted to do as much as she could before her periods began, so that she could spend her 'Office Days' safe in the George Hotel, which had a pleasant drawing room with two private writing rooms attached. To her relief the pain this month was certainly less gruelling, thanks to Sir John's control medicines which she had taken every day; but the pain killer was quite useless to her, neither covering the pain, nor curing it.

She spent two days in the hotel, writing reports to the Home Office, Mr Cooke Taylor, Captain Armstrong in Leicester, sending Abstracts to the recalcitrant factories, and chasing up birth certificates for children she suspected were being employed underage.

On Friday and Saturday she inspected in Nuneaton for underage employment, and found many of the apprentices very young indeed, and, as May Abraham had never been there, nine of the eleven places she went to were in bad condition, and, of course, NO Abstracts. She visited a schoolmistress, Miss Thudwell, in Caxton Road to check on certificates. Miss Thudwell was enthusiastically helpful and Lucy made several declarations to the courts. She stayed at the George in Rugby over the Sunday, but wrote a long letter to Hye. Rugby was a nice town, she decided. She took a good walk round the centre in the afternoon, went to Evensong, had a long sleep and was ready to set off for Northampton on the Monday morning.

Northampton was bootmakers again. Lucy noticed how generally clean they were considering the dirtiness of the trade, which spoke well of the efforts of the Sanitary Institute. But she knew that they were not overcrowded only because trade was slack; where the trade was brisk the overcrowding was rife and the ventilation dreadful. Five factories were so bad they warranted prosecution.

When she returned to the hotel she found Mr Cooke Taylor who had brought his Associate, HMI Superintendent Cramp to meet her, and they gave her dinner. Mr Cramp, no relation to the ribbon factory owner, she thought a rather narrow minded man, and evidently had a great prejudice against her which she exerted herself to overcome. 'And I flatter myself that I succeeded,' she wrote to Evelyn, "partly because Cooke Taylor, by gassing humbug about "Women and their noble work", gave me a good opening to incidentally inform Cramp – while speaking to Cooke Taylor – that I was NOT a NEW WOMAN, and didn't believe in revolt and marches, etc., etc.'

She told them of the numerous instances of underage employment and of the dreadful stuffiness at the Pitts factory. "You'd better deal with that yourself," said Cooke Taylor. "And notify the MOH." At the end of the evening Mr Cramp shook hands almost cordially, and Lucy went up to her room well pleased with herself.

However, the Medical Officer of Health for Northampton was not pleased with her the next morning when she handed him her list of five failing establishments. "You are too severe, you must be elastic about over-crowding!" You are both lax and stupid, thought Lucy and she returned to Pitts' factory and insisted that the windows should be prised open and kept open, or else some workers would have to be turned off. Alarmed, the manager assured her roomier quarters would be ready by Christmas. "If windows are kept open no hands need go until Christmas," she agreed.

She rode the branch line to Earls Barton to see a clutch of bootmakers' workshops, and found them all pleasant places; but a preponderance of half-timers worried her, very young apprentices, undersized boys, the girls still in plaits and fresh faces. She visited both schoolmasters in the village and heard the same old story as in Hinckley, half-timers doing TWO factory attendances as well as school attendances each day. Lucy pressed them for a definite case and they promised to look one up. The hours of work were definitely too long. Twelve hours a shift. But what was she to do? It was for the workers' own preference, and authorised by the District Inspector, yet illegal. She noted it as yet one more thing to write about to May Abraham, and to press for a meeting with her and for her advice.

There was nowhere to eat in Earls Barton, not even the public house, and she had a good two mile walk to the station in drizzle. She arrived back at Northampton ravenous. Soup AND meat pie AND jam sponge. And a hot water bottle in her bed meant she slept like a log.

Waking very early she answered the letter from the Chief asking why she had not prosecuted several factories. She took trouble in detailing her decisions and then, feeling she had deserved it, she played truant and took a mid-morning train to London for a fitting with Mrs Hubbard for the new dinner gown. They had decided together on a simple shape of blue-grey grosgrain with handfuls of very small cream flowers embroidered as a corsage, and scattering on down the left hand side of the skirt. It was a young and pretty dress, unlike the usual elegant and severe styles she chose. She was very pleased with it and arranged for a final fitting the next Thursday. To redeem herself she wrote a long letter of report to May Abraham and caught a late train back to Northampton.

She ran around Northampton and environs all Saturday morning to registrars, and magistrates' clerks, and recording magistrates, and back and forth to various parents of underage workers for signatures, all very time-consuming and stressful. She spent a useful hour in the Ladies' waiting room at Nuneaton doing office work while waiting for a connecting train.

Sunday was a day of Indian summer, and she went to Matins at Holy Trinity and enjoyed it. A Dame's school had the three pews in front of her, there were about twelve girls aged from eight to sixteen, all with purple woollen berets and black cloaks edged with purple braid. Lucy decided that the uniform did not suit any size of girl in shape or colour; but the girls seemed happy enough with it. She lunched with Mr and Mrs Cooke Taylor and spent the afternoon with them, and then, after tea at the hotel, wrote to Hye and Evelyn and her cousin Amy Murray, studying in Somerville

College, Oxford, who had invited her to tea in Oxford next week when she was due to inspect there.

Autumn rains set in that week and Lucy needed the galoshes and the cape and the umbrella. On her way to Oxford she was caught at lunchtime in a torrential downpour in Banbury, while visiting a Registrar's Court for a birth certificate. She had not buttoned her cape securely and the wind swirled it open. The rain streamed around her skirts and stockings; her small umbrella, recommended by May Abraham, was quite inadequate to shield her hat, or stop the rain going down her neck. She was forced to take shelter in the Banbury's White Lion while her coat and skirt and shoes and stockings were dried out. The management gave her a small room and the friendly chambermaid provided her with slippers, a large shawl, and pots of tea and sandwiches until, mid-afternoon, her wonderfully clean, warm, dry, pressed clothes were brought up to her.

So she was able to arrive at the prestigious Clarendon Hotel in Oxford without looking like a drowned rat. She treated herself to a hot bath before dining with Uncle Murray and her cousin Amy in the evening.

In the morning she inspected a few workshops on the edge of Cowley, before they took her to see *Christopher Columbus* at the theatre in the afternoon and she travelled home to Hye in the evening.

12

The Lady Inspectors fight their corner

May and Lucy plan their campaign; Harold Tennant casts his first shadow; the meeting with Mr Sprague Oram.

On Sunday 4th November Lucy received a short note from May Abraham. 'Thank you for your full letter. Come to tea this afternoon at 3 o'clock and we will have a good long conversation, share our ideas and experiences and plan for the future.'

May Abraham was leaning over the banisters waiting for her as Lucy toiled up the stairs to the Tite Street apartment.

"You are a stranger," she said, as she took Lucy's umbrella, "and so are Adelaide Anderson and Mary Paterson. We have got to devise methods to meet more often. I have hardly any idea of what you have been up to these last few months."

"No, and Hyacinth my sister says she feels the same. We pass like ships in the night."

"Gertrude says she sometimes forgets what I look like. And I haven't see, Miss Anderson since the summer. This can't go on," said May.

"And I hardly ever see Mr Sprague Oram," said Lucy, "but he sends me letters all the time with lists of places to inspect all over the Midlands, and wants the reports almost at once. But I must say if I need advice he is very quick to send it to me."

"That's all very well. But the Chief should be asking ME to contribute advice. The thing is, he's using us to spy on the District Inspectors and of course they don't like us, and they don't trust us. They call us peripatetic spies in petticoats. There have been vicious letters of complaint about Adelaide from the West of England."

"I knew nothing of that."

"There you are, you see. And there is Mary Paterson beavering away in the North and none of us – not even me – hardly know of her existence there. We must sketch out a workable scheme. Not just this taking the train from town to town on a day-to-day basis. My Bradshaw is in tatters. If I lost this job, I could get a good one working for Bradshaw."

They talked on into the evening. May Abraham had been able to spend much more time in and around the London area and the Home Office and the Houses of Parliament. She wanted the three of them to be responsible for women's working conditions across London, but also, whenever they were sent out over the country on specific Complaints, to be given the powers to issue prosecutions where they considered necessary.

May's plan would be that each Lady Inspector would be given responsibility for a third of the country, while the fourth, Mary Paterson, would remain in the Northern regions – Liverpool, Manchester, and all the way up to Edinburgh and Glasgow.

They decided they would telegraph to Miss Anderson and invite the Chief to dine with them all to discuss revising their present working arrangements, and May went to invite him, early on Monday morning.

He was more than ready to meet them and set a date for the very next evening. Adelaide had been inspecting in the Southampton and Portsmouth region and had travelled up especially. Mary Paterson was unwell and could not be there.

The Chief was strongly convinced of the necessity of making some permanent arrangements NOW, "as, when I have retired from office, your position could become much worse, unless it has been clearly DEFINED." But he remained strongly against their London District plan.

"I want you to be even more independent. I want you to be on a par with the Superintendent Inspectors and Special Commissioners. And to take on research into Special Enquiries, on women's pay, for example, physical conditions of work, women's and children's hours of work, dangerous trades, and so on."

"Special Enquiries are one thing," observed Adelaide Anderson, "but if all of us were given Superintendent status it would simply fan the flames of resentment. It will increase the present friction still more, and eventually it will prove unworkable."

Sprague Oram regarded them gravely. "We will discuss this more fully on Thursday afternoon, when I shall have thought over all you say. I shall call Miss Paterson down, and possibly ask Miss Collett to join us for her opinion."

The three young women met in the Finsbury Circus office the next morning. May was decisive.

"We must have a conference with Mr Asquith himself. I'll go and ask for it now, before the Chief does. I think he can be got onto our side and overrule the Chief's objections."

"Why should you think that?"

"Because I know that Asquith is trying to make an agreement with the Independent Labour Party and they are very keen that Lady Inspectors should be seen to be powerful, and they are pushing for Trades Union Sections for Women. And also—" she stopped.

"And also – what?"

"Well, Harold Tennant is his secretary, and Harold is rather keen on me, and Harold's sister is Margot Tennant, and they say Asquith is keen on HER. So Asquith listens to her."

Adelaide Anderson laughed. "Skullduggery."

Lucy did not laugh. "It sounds like the old boy network – or the old girl network – at its very worst! – I hope you are not going to leave us for Harold Tennant?"

"No, of course not." May Abraham was too vehement. "But it means he is on our side."

Adelaide Anderson set off back to her inspections in Southampton. May Abraham set off for the Home Office to try to make an appointment with the Prime Minister. Lucy tried to settle to some filing in the office but niggling thoughts of May Abraham and Harold Tennant stayed in her mind. On an impulse, she caught an omnibus and went to Derry and Toms and decided to order a severe dark-grey tailor-made suit.

On Thursday afternoon they all met at the Home Office and Mr Sprague Oram listened to their suggestions while his secretary took notes. Mary Paterson had arrived in London the night before and had spoken briefly with May Abraham before the meeting. She sat almost silently throughout the meeting, turning her head to gaze at the speaker of the moment, occasionally nodding imperceptibly, but not offering any opinions. There was a weight about her, though, as of a person who would not be pushed into or out of an opinion until she was good and ready. Sprague Oram agreed that they should organise regular monthly meetings in London amongst themselves – Mary Paterson sighed but made no comment – to plan and to keep one another abreast of issues that arose. He gave them particulars of a Special Enquiry that he required them to conduct into the sanitary conditions of factories and workshops with a view of interpolating extra clauses in the new Factory Bill.

He gave them their instructions for their next excursions across Britain. Lucy was to go to the Black Country, Wolverhampton and Dudley, Wednesbury and Walsall, to HMI Hoare's District.

They took themselves off to tea at the Army and Navy Stores, feeling more positive and promising to keep each other in touch with the outcomes of their individual Special Enquiries, before their next meeting at the end of November.

13

Wooing Mr Hoare

Rain, rain, rain; impressive Kidderminster carpet factories; primitive nail-and-chain makers in Stourbridge; giving thanks for good fortune; medieval conditions for nail makers in Dudley; Dudley has NO sewage system; Lucy makes friends with the Thursfields; HMI Sedgewick resents her; Lucy likes Black Country people; HMI Hoare plays hard to get; HMI Sedgewick is obstructive; HMI Cramp is awkward; Morland Match Factory is an unsalubrious place; Happy Christmas.

The next day their trusty Bradshaws were pressed into service again. Over three days, Lucy inspected and slept in Shrewsbury and prosecuted in Northampton against an Earls Barton bootmaker. To her surprise she found the clerk of the court helpful, and both the magistrates impartial and fair-minded even though one was a bootmaker himself. Then she went on from Northampton to Buckingham following up five workshops where she had found children working between five and seven p.m., and routing out birth certificates for children suspected of being underage. In two cases no birth certificates were ever issued, so no possibility of checking the age for a prosecution. Cooke Taylor shook his head. "Leave it. Prosecutions are always difficult to obtain for minors. It's not worth it unless they're flagrantly underage."

She finished the week in Towcester in pouring rain, went on to Oxford to a magistrates' court and two prosecutions with a tiresome Bench which gave only insignificant costs, and arrived home to London and Hye, tired out and gloomy.

Hye was weary too; she had been examining and supervising cookery exams in north London. They spent the weekend indoors, Hye writing school reports, and Lucy court reports.

November weather at its worst. Lucy packed her rain cape with hood, her thickest winter shoes, thick stockings and two pairs of galoshes for her trip to the Black Country. Sprague Oram had warned her, "Pavements aren't much of a priority up there." Arriving in Wolverhampton, she lunched with HMI Hoare, a tall, dark, very thin young man, with deep-set dark eyes; he looked ill. But he did not seem as prone to humbugging as all the others, and she suspected he was a better Inspector. He was certainly better organised than most, and provided her with clear lists and directions for the places she wished to visit. However, he looked askance at her request for chain and nail makers in the Stourbridge area, but said nothing. He glanced down at her footwear, that was all. Lucy wondered why the Chief had specifically chosen Stourbridge.

Wolverhampton streets seemed reasonably clean, and, more to the point, the dressmaking establishments well up to standard. She caught the train to Kidderminster in the late afternoon and checked in to the Lion Hotel, a small warm comfortable place where she was the only female guest, and made much of by the manager and the chambermaid when they learnt why she had come. She was very impressed by the carpet factories and the huge looms, and the intricate patterns being hooked up, but worried by the thick mist of wool particles floating in the air. "My sister works there," the chambermaid told her. "No, she's not in a Trades Union. She can't be. No women are allowed to be at her works. Go to the Girls Working Co-operative Association. They'll fill you in." After the day's visits she went there and met the Secretary, Miss Cordner, and found it flourishing. But no girls clubs' existed in the town, and no Women's Guilds either, which surprised her.

In Stourbridge the next morning she found that Mr Hoare had instructed Assistant Wright to accompany her, and in the event she was glad of his presence. He led her through a muddle of unpaved streets to numberless nail-and-chain makers' workshops at Lye and Old Hill near Stourbridge. They were similar to the boot clobbers and in each one she found one or two 'gleeds', waste coal furnaces, with a lever behind and one or two 'stales' or anvils, on which the nails or links were struck and shaped. The workshops had no windows and the whole area was extremely rough and wild, a sort of slum village flung on the side of beautiful hills and valleys, lit by a thin November sun, and enveloped in smoke from chimneys; and never a proper street name except for one narrow High Street.

The nail making here was very slack owing to the growth of machines to make nails, and the women could only get four shillings a week, as it was and always had been badly paid. But many women were engaged in it, hammering the glowing iron, shaping it and working the bellows. It was hard bodily labour, but Lucy was much struck by the extreme health of their looks. They were very rough and uncouth in speech and their clothes terribly poor and dirty. In Waggon Street, Old Hill, she found a place as poor and as squalid as anything in the Westminster slums.

The chain making trade was good by comparison. The women could get ten to thirteen shillings a week; it required more skill and larger furnaces, and also appeared even harder work. Whereas in the nail trade nearly all the workshops were domestic, in the chain trade there were many more with six or seven women employed besides the family. They were all bathed in perspiration, the men with bare throats and arms, the women with kilted up skirts, sacking aprons and loose cotton bodices, despite the November draughts. Sparks and waste iron flew all round, occasionally singeing their arms and hair.

They worked from seven to seven, an hour off for lunch and half an hour for tea. On Saturdays they were there from six until two.

The women wore shawls on their heads and stood in groups in the street, staring directly Lucy appeared. "It's because they have never, or rarely, seen an ordinarily clad woman," said Mr Wright. He complained that this habit of staring and assembling in crowds was what 'fetched his hair off' and made him mad.

As she travelled home on the train to London, Lucy considered the difference between her life and that of the Old Hill women, their clothes, their outlook, their homes, their wages – four shillings a week for them, four pounds a week for her. It seemed inconceivable that one small island could house such contrasts. What did they think about? What were their hopes? What use could she be to them? Well, that was easy to decide – to make their lives more comfortable, to better their working conditions, to allow them to have some leisure with their loved ones. Lucky Lucy, to be surrounded by such good friends, and family, to have such opportunities, and to have Hye, gaining in confidence every day.

As soon as she reached 100 Fulham Road she suggested, "Let's have a spree day on Saturday. We could go round the shops, and maybe visit the Streatfeilds, and go to a theatre."

"What's brought this on?" said Hye.

Lucy explained. "I feel we're so fortunate. We treat all this as normal. We should have a day when every second we feel truly thankful for the nice things we are able to enjoy."

"I partially agree with you. But how would you feel if I said I'd had a letter from the Boyce, about an acquaintance of theirs, Janet Holloway, who asks if she could board with us for a pound a week?"

Lucy looked horrified. "Janet Holloway! Oh, no, Hye! What did you say?"

"I told them, regretfully, 'no, thank you.' It's out of the question. I wouldn't have her here for fifty pounds a week. There are limits, you know, Lucy. Let's see if we can get in to see *Rebellious Susan* at the Criterion."

Fortunately Lucy did not set off for Dudley by the early train on Monday, because two letters arrived by the first post, one a vague letter from Mr Sprague Oram concerning the Special Enquiry into Sanitation, and possible extension into Dangerous Trades, and the other from May Abraham to say she was busy in the West Country until early December, but would hope to have letters from Mary Paterson and Adelaide Anderson on the subject of the Female Inspectors Department very soon.

Back once again in the wild medieval atmosphere of the chain and nail making, this time in the village of Gornal, near Dudley, she found herself puzzled as to how the working hours should be set. Several people called 'stallers' were working independently in some workshops. They hired an anvil or 'stale' for sixpence a week and then made and sold their own nails and chains. They could not be classed as employees and it seemed that they could work as many hours as they chose. But, as defined by the Section on Employment in Workshops, they could only be employed 12 hours a day. And what to do with the case of the three adult daughters working voluntarily for their mother? The area was very dirty and the sewage smell pervasive.

She called on the Medical Officer of Health in Dudley, a Dr Bigham, and called his attention to the filthy workshops and lack of drainage. He appeared unmoved. "They tell me they have only ash middens, four for ten houses, that they are cleared weekly and the waste sold to farms."

"Quite correct," he replied, "it has always been so; but the Local Authority will be superseded on Dec 17th by the District Council who are going to make new Byelaws. I advise you to write to them, and make sure you will be checking on their new decisions."

Lucy did so, forcefully, the same night.

The standard of sanitation was very little better in the centre of the town of Dudley itself, and she discovered several instances of sweated labour in two tailoring establishments in the High Street. The town, an ancient town, with substantial remains of a great castle in the centre, and although it had a deep drainage system, seemed only to have privy and ashpit sewage outlets.

She visited the Vicar of Dudley, round, unmarried and energetic, who complained bitterly of sweated labour he knew of in two tailoring establishments in the High Street. Lucy asked him to let her have particulars and he appeared relieved that something might at last be done about it.

Somehow Lucy did not feel like staying in sewage-ridden Dudley much longer and was glad to climb into the train for Wolverhampton at the end of the day. She had a long talk with Mr Hoare the next afternoon. She found she admired the man, though she knew he disliked the very idea of her role, and she suspected he had a bad temper; but he was certainly extremely well organised and his office and his District was the most orderly of any she had seen to date. He told her, politely, that, as regards her official role, he disliked her very much, but personally, he didn't object so much!

He agreed with her that Dudley's Sanitary Authorities were atrocious, but then told her he had written a strong report countering her complaint to the local Authorities in Shrewsbury over the case of twelve girls in a brush workshop with no sanitary conveniences on the premises.

"Well, you are open and honest in your dealings, at any rate!" said Lucy.

He bowed, with not a shadow of a smile.

She wrote to him in the evening, enclosing a list of places she had visited up to that moment, and enclosed a copy of the letter she had written to the new Local Authority in Dudley.

At breakfast the next morning she received a package from Adelaide Anderson with clear, detailed explanations as to how she was going to tabulate her findings for the Special Sanitary Enquiry. Lucy saw at once how her own material could be ordered and written up, and wrote in her diary 'I felt relieved and grateful to Adelaide Anderson. She is so helpful and lucid, just like Rose Squire, cautious, clear and conscientious. ADMIRABLE! SPLENDID!' With this new clarity she saw the way ahead and spent her morning in Wolverhampton factories feeling much better equipped for gathering information. In the afternoon she visited Wolverhampton Hospital to find information about a lead poisoning case, and met Dr Codd, House Physician. 'He was belligerently opaque. Not much information to be had from HIM!' her diary recorded.

She called on the Medical Officer of Health, but he had gone home for the day. Three steps forward, and two steps back, thought Lucy. She wrote after supper to Rose Squire, Adelaide Anderson, May Abraham, Hye, and Evelyn, secure in the knowledge that she was writing to trusted friends. She slept well.

December 2nd was Advent Sunday with hard pellets of snow driving past outside. The hotel was very quiet. She was given a table close to the cheerful fire in the dining room and drank excellent coffee and ate scrambled eggs and bacon. Then, when she realised it was Advent Sunday, she wrapped up and set off to Matins and enjoyed the service and the sermon. She sat in a pew with a handsome middle-aged couple and got into conversation with them at the end of the service. They walked back with her to the hotel. "Are you staying here?" asked the lady. Lucy explained who she was and why she was in Wolverhampton.

They were most interested. "What an undertaking! We often come into the hotel on our way home from church, particularly on cold days like this, for a brandy to set us up for the walk home. Join us, please." She accepted gladly and found her new friends to be a prominent local doctor, Andrew Thursfield, and his wife, Margaret. She was on the board of governors for Wolverhampton Schools and very active with the Girls Public Day School Trust. She promised to provide Lucy with the names of elementary head teachers in the area, particularly where Lucy felt children were being employed. She mentioned her impasse with the Medical Officer of Health. "Not much help there, I fear, ever," said Dr Thursfield. "But in reality there is little he can do. The Workshop Act, as far as the Sanitary Authority is concerned, has been dead for a long time in Wolverhampton. No employers take any notice of it, and no Magistrates will convict, so no prosecutions are brought. Inspector Hoare conscientiously prosecutes the most blatant offenders, but they all get off scot free."

A new week, and she braved the bitter cold and fog and set off to Bilston visiting various enamel works, and then transferred to the George Hotel in Walsall, to inspect several factories on a list that Sprague Oram had sent from the Home Office files all still full of unfinished business. She had written to Assistant HMI Sedgewick and presented herself at his office on Tuesday morning for a conference. Mr Sedgewick was a rough, angry man who clearly resented her presence, and told her he had written to HMI Cramp to ask why she had been sent to his District. Fortunately, when she had written the note announcing her coming she had said only that 'she had been instructed by HMI Chief Inspector to visit in his District and should be obliged if she could meet him on December 4th at 12.30p.m.' Grudgingly he sent his office boy to give her a list of workshops, a very old and dog-eared list, which Lucy suspected was wildly out of date, and said he would send the relevant Factory Registers to her at the hotel that evening.

She scurried around the Black Country towns, Bilston, Tipton, Wednesbury, Darlaston, inspecting and collecting material for the Special Sanitation Enquiry. Evelyn had sent her a pair of flexible leather gloves lined with the softest wool. Lucy sent a delighted thank you note. 'Perfectly splendid, just like another layer of heated skin, I can even write neatly when I am wearing them.' A Black Country it certainly was, but not forbidding, and she was very taken with the High Street in Wednesbury that led up the hill to the wonderful church at the top; and the people, though rough, were not unfriendly. Their dialect was unintelligible, but the timbre of the voice was full of rough humour, and she wished she could understand a little of their stories. Mrs Thursfield gave her letters of introduction which she found helpful. One led to a useful interview with Dr Adams, Medical Inspector to Balfe and Jordan's enamel works, about employees' health records, one of the very few firms that kept them; and she spent a cheerful, noisy happy evening with Mrs Thursfield's friend Mrs Smith, who ran the Factory Girls Friendly Institute in Darlaston. She watched a raucous but highly competent group playing the new game of Ping Pong, and another calmer group at another table cutting out intricate patterns of holly and ivy to make three-dimensional Christmas cards.

She noticed that the file of contacts gained in her various travels was already full to bursting. "I shall have to divide them somehow – maybe into those who actively want to help and those who actively want to hinder." In the end she divided them into Districts. 'Maybe ONE day the Chief will think about giving us some secretarial help!' she wrote in her diary.

However, there were some horrors. In Darlaston she went to a turning shop where the flames were so acrid that she could not breathe in it, and where she found two girls and four women eating their bread and cheese in the galvanising shop where the metal was dipped in the acid solution. She kept HMI Hoare scrupulously up to date with her visits and was irked when he wrote an annoyed letter over her having investigated an accident which happened as she was inspecting at an iron foundry, before he had been informed.

She wrote a long and full epistle to him to try to pacify him. "I do think he cares about standards. Others would simply have let it slide to save trouble," she told Hye at the weekend, "but he is an awful tease notwithstanding. Still, in my heart of hearts, I thoroughly sympathise with his point of view because he has worked conscientiously. Many of the others don't work conscientiously, and they deserve the trouble they get."

At the Home Office on the Monday she reported to the Chief and was shown reports he had received from the other Lady Inspectors. "A very good collection of fearful practice," said the Chief proudly, as he waved them about. "That should provide us with plenty of ammunition for a clause in the new Act!"

She met Miss Squire and Miss Dunbar at Kensington Town Hall and they all had tea together. They told her the National Health Society was stirring vigorously over the New Examination Board for Sanitary Inspectors, and hoped to gather the accreditation of Lady Sanitary Inspectors into the Society's hands.

Lucy travelled by the evening train to Walsall and prepared herself for an awkward meeting with HMI Sedgewick the next day. She found a private letter of Complaint for her, left at the hotel, about HMI Cramp, saying he was unsympathetic. "I should think so too," she wrote to May Abraham, "Bad, dirty, and humbugging."

Mindful of her letters to and from Mr Hoare, Lucy was punctilious in her interview with Mr Sedgewick, mentioning all the places where she had found faults and omissions, and showing him the lists. He explained away, or tried to explain away, most of them, and both were relieved when the conference ended, and Lucy caught the train to Worcester to beard HMI Arnold. He remained painfully civil, but had carefully provided up-to-date Factory Registers ready for her to copy names and addresses, and warned her that the situation in factory and in sanitary matters in Stroud was still extremely bad. She mentioned the Dudley Local Authority, and he said he was not surprised, that in his District he did not apply to the Local Authority for anything at all, in connection with Factory Sanitation. "I prosecute straight away," he said, "and leave it to the magistrates to sort it out with their factory cronies."

"What happens if they don't sort it out?"

"I prosecute again."

However, the Worcester factories' sanitation seemed to have improved; she was impressed with a leather tanning factory which had had six cases of anthrax reported, one fatal. They were due to a batch of Russian hair and fur. They had discarded its use, disinfected the entire factory and begun to wash each hide with a mixture of water and disinfectant. "There is no remedy for anthrax except to disinfect and cover the scratches, you don't inhale it."

She was shocked by the intense heat in the small salt extraction works she visited in Droitwich. The steam from the brine vats and the scrapings of the salt pans made for exhausting work, and the salt girls, only fifteen in all, looked pale and thin.

Morlands, the match factory in Gloucester, was a wretched place. They boasted that they made their matches with the far less toxic red phosphorous rather than the white phosphorous, but of course the red was twice the cost of the white, so they tried to lower their costs by using very young labour wherever possible. Certainly there seemed to be many young employees. Children were not allowed to be used in the 'Boxing' rooms or in the 'Dipping' rooms, but only in the box making and labelling. Lucy, wise to the ruse of using the 'half-timers' before and after school hours, caught an early train from Worcester and visited the match factory again at 7a.m. catching several children filling boxes; breaking the rules of the Dangerous Trades. She was back in Worcester by 11a.m. and found an unwelcome telegram from Sprague Oram saying, 'the Home Secretary would meet all the Lady Inspectors at the Home Office on the Monday – Christmas Eve.' She sighed. Her leave began on December 22 and she and Hye had planned to spend Christmas with Bossie and the Aunts Gertrude and Florence at Sulpham in Kent.

So she packed all her papers untidily into her small trunk and went home, arriving by teatime, determined to complete all her reports by Friday night. Then she could do all her Christmas shopping on the Saturday.

The Monday meeting with Mr Asquith and the Chief Inspector was little more than Good Wishes for Christmas and to reiterate what they already suspected. May Abraham had already gone on leave, presumably having been told the news that Mr Asquith and Mr Sprague Oram had made up their minds and were determined to keep the Women Inspectors directly under the Chief Inspector at the Home Office. They could be sent to any District to gather information on specific knowledge, health, working hours, conditions, safety. For this purpose Miss Paterson had been recalled from Scotland and placed under the Chief instead of the Scottish Inspectors. Both men were extremely affable but anxious to go to their own Christmas festivities, and the women went gratefully to a week of rest and peace.

14

May Abraham takes the reins

Memories of Hyacinth's 14th birthday; a peaceful Christmas and a noisy New Year; May Abraham plots; the Annual Report and the unflappable boy; more planning; friends at the George in Nottingham; HMI Bevan blows up; Miss Hawkesly welcomes her back; Lady Oldknows visits her own factory; impressive lace factories; some magistrates are actually friendly; Hyacinth takes over the running of 100 Fulham Road.

Hyacinth and Lucy arrived at Sevenoaks Station on a bright frosty Christmas Eve. The Sulpham dog cart was there to meet them with George Waters, the gardener, beaming on the platform. He and his wife Dorothy had been enormous friends and confidants to the girls when they had first arrived with their mother from India, uncertain and disorientated, and again when their dear mother had died. Their uncle and his two unmarried sisters had given them a home and much affection, but without their mother's sense of fun and without her social links they had led isolated lives in their adolescent years. Mr and Mrs Waters provided for their entertainment in different ways. George suggested to Edward Boscawen riding lessons for them both, helped to buy a quiet pony for Hyacinth, a spirited bay for Lucy, chaperoned them to the Hunt meetings – which led to social meetings and good friendships.

Hyacinth was happiest when she was allowed to help Dorothy in the kitchens, and surprised the Aunts by asking first to be allowed to choose the menus for her birthday and then to be allowed to go with Dorothy to select the ingredients from the local stores. Finally she asked if she could help Dorothy to cook them. Edward thought this a bold venture and asked if he could invite a friend or two to lunch. This nearly scuppered the whole idea, Hyacinth losing all confidence. But Lucy suggested that the Hortons from the Rectory should come to lunch on the birthday, without knowing that it was anything more special than a birthday meal for Hyacinth. "It can't go wrong, because Dorothy won't let it. Only us will know, and we won't ever tell!" So the Hortons never knew that the perfect roast pork and the crackling with apple sauce, and the roast potatoes and the exquisitely iced birthday cake were anything more extraordinary than Hyacinth's fourteenth birthday lunch.

"It'll be good weather for the next few days," George predicted, as he stowed their luggage in the trap and helped them in, "so you'll be able to go for some long walks. And country air and Mrs Waters' food will soon get rid of that peaky London look."

The Aunts were standing at the front door to greet them, waving as they turned into the driveway, with Mary and Margaret the housemaids behind them.

"I'm afraid it will be a very quiet Christmas. We are invited to the Hortons for lunch on Boxing Day; but otherwise just us old things."

"Oh, nothing could be nicer than to be with you and to sit and chat and read—"

"And sleep," said Lucy.

"And be with you here. And catch up with Lucy! We hardly see each other. It's just lovely just being able to bask here, at home," said Hyacinth.

The two aunts were touched and smiled mildly at each other.

"Edward will be home early today. He is closing the office until after New Year. We thought if we had dinner early we might play cards this evening – if you felt you would enjoy it—"

"Anything! Just to be here!"

Three days of cosseting and peace did wonders in banishing the stresses and strains. Christmas Day Service, Christmas Day lunch, Boxing Day brisk walk with Bossie in the sharp sunny morning air, and to a late lunch with the Hortons at the Rectory and early bedtimes and late breakfasts. And then off to the Boyce for New Year, and a noisy house party, and much shrieking, and bursts of laughter, and dancing and mistletoe, and Mary's fiancé looking out of place, a tall angular featured Scot, anxiously pleasant, a civil engineer, about to build bridges and dams in Southern India; and Mary looking as brilliant as a humming bird, charming and amusing all around her.

"What does she see in him?" wondered Lucy as they finally undressed in the small hours of the morning.

Hye sniffed. "What can he see in HER? He's much too earnest and serious. He'd be better off marrying Ethel!" And the mere thought of this sent them giggling to sleep.

January 4th 1895 brought them back to the grim reality of earning a living. Lucy met May Abraham back from her leave in Dublin. She was more than dissatisfied with the new regulations that Mr Asquith had set out before the holiday. She still hankered after a District of some sort for the women with herself as Senior Woman Inspector. Harold had clearly not been persuasive enough in his role as private secretary. She had been writing to contacts in France and in America and discovering how the system was developing there.

"And," she continued, "I am still going to try to get an informal conference for us with Asquith – for you and me – just us at the moment, because I'm not satisfied with the regulations for our pay and our promotion! As it is Female Inspectors can't rise any higher than £300 a year now; Miss Collett is at the Board of Trade and she could go up to £500 a year, and Miss Newson at the Local Government Board could get £350."

"Goodness, you have been busy."

"I certainly have. Our work is considerably more stressful than theirs. I'm finding out about other rates. Gertrude is sleuthing for me with Marion at the Trades Union Council. Mary Paterson gets less than us from the Scottish Department. And there is NOTHING definite in our arrangements about sick leave."

"No, and I'd want ten days sick leave a year instead of just seven. I'm with you every step of the way with all your suggestions. But don't you think we should sound the others out?"

"Of course. But I wanted to have collected a good batch of facts and figures first before involving everyone."

Lucy went on to the Home Office to hand in the lists of Abstracts that needed to be sent to Droitwich and Stroud. Sprague Oram called her into his office, looking flustered. "Annual Report time. I'm deluged with papers, here and at home. Can't get on to the dining room table at home for all the papers. You and Miss Abraham, come tomorrow morning to my house and help Peacock and me get some order in them. We'll supply some sort of lunch, but you'll have to eat it on your lap. 9.30 sharp please."

"You know," said Lucy, daring. "Adelaide Anderson is the woman you want. She can cut through piles of papers within minutes."

"I'll get Peacock to telegraph her."

As the three Lady Inspectors arrived next morning at Amherst Road, Mr Peacock and an office boy were unloading boxes of papers from a cab, and carrying them into the hall.

"Not MORE boxes, no MORE boxes!" cried Sprague Oram.

"I thought I would keep the boy here till after lunch, sir," said Peacock, "and by then we can have sorted out the essential reports and he can take the unessential ones back to the files."

"He can only stay if he's an unflappable boy," huffed the Chief. "Is he?"

"I only hire unflappable boys," soothed Peacock. "Ibbotson, line these boxes up in the dining room under the window in date order." Ibbotson nodded solemnly, and silently took off his cap and coat, and put on a smart navy blue apron, and began to move the boxes and files, peering at the dates and writing on the boxes. Adelaide was beside him at once with her notebook. "An apron, what a good idea! We should have thought of that. If we're here tomorrow, I shall bring one."

"My mother gave it me, madam," said Ibbotson, pleased. "She said as I only had the one office suit, I couldn't afford to get dust on it."

"How eminently sensible," said Adelaide, and they beamed at each other. He brought in the boxes, she checked the order, the type, and the dates.

While they were sorting out relevant paragraphs from the files and reports, May Abraham told Lucy that Harold Tennant had told her that the new regulations were already in the hands of the printers.

"What to do, then?"

"We'll ask the Chief now to hold them back until the reports from France and America that I've been trying to check on arrive. That can delay them until we can reach Mr Asquith." And in a few minutes' talk over some sandwiches they persuaded the Chief not to publish the new regulations concerning Women Factory Inspectors until the American report had arrived.

"Now I have to find a way to stop it arriving at the Chief's Office for a few days. Anything to gain time!"

The next day the women worked at Amherst Road as filing clerks and secretaries all day – "Wouldn't it be nice if we could have someone to keep all OUR reports in order?"

"All in good time, now, all in good time!"

In the evening they took themselves off to Frascati's to talk shop. Each of them told their anecdotes of rude and obstructive magistrates and District Inspectors.

"I think the Chief's plans for us, which can truly be summed up by his words, 'Peripatetic spies and stirrers up', are utterly incapable of any future development," said Adelaide, vigorously stirring her spaghetti. "Plans like his are calculated to increase friction to breaking point, and can't have any lasting good results."

"He is depending upon us gradually raising the Inspector standards."

"But that's HOPELESS!"

"But that's what needs to happen!"

"But not by sending in a team of snappy governesses. The men don't need to take any notice of us. They ARE 'the men in possession'. They hold all the cards. They have their rooted traditions. They are a solid body."

There was a long silence.

"There's a third alternative for us," said Adelaide Anderson. "They could make us Regular Special Commissioners, not call us Inspectors at all. Let us work as an entirely different Department. We wouldn't have the power to insist on pinning up a twopenny form with Rules, Abstracts and so on, but we could recommend and require improvements – on women's issues – to be carried out."

"No, no, Adelaide, there MUST be Female Inspectors. It must be understood that working women will need WOMEN to be Inspectors as well, and that Society needs to recognise the Women Inspectors as valid and as valued as Men Inspectors."

"Hmm," Adelaide considered. "But the remit must be that the men and women inspectors should work side by side and complement and uphold each other's judgements."

"And standards."

"Yes, and standards. But not by whistle-blowing or by prosecuting unless as a last resort." Adelaide tapped her fingers with a coffee spoon and became thoughtful.

The Chief had a long session with Lucy before sending her back to Nottingham. He went over all her reports to date concerning the Sanitation Enquiry and wrote several letters to District Inspectors concerning various cases needing attention.

The receptionist at the George Hotel, Nottingham greeted her like an old friend, and gave her a small bedroom on the second floor with a smaller room leading off equipped with a writing table, a chair and a minute fireplace. "You can get it cosy quite fast in here," said the chambermaid, "And I know you have a lot of writing to do in the evenings. But we shall have to put the fire out at midnight because of the Regulations." Lucy was grateful and thanked the manager when she went down for the evening meal.

She called at Captain Bevan's office the next morning and he accompanied her to Whitehalls Tennants factory. There was a bitter wind blowing outside, but inside, although warm, there was no ventilation, so the place smelt foul with the damp and dirty bodies and clothes of the workers, and the sanitary conveniences were unspeakably bad. Lucy was shown the plans for sanitation improvements, but did not speak of them to any of the workers as Captain Bevan was present. She did speak to the foreman about opening windows at mealtimes, in front of Captain Bevan, and saw immediately she had committed a grave offence; not that she had found any fault with him, or the foreman – or even the factory, merely suggested opening the window at mealtimes. Captain Bevan left her to continue the inspection, saying he had some urgent shopping to do and invited her to meet him for a midday meal at the Railway Hotel.

Lucy made her way through the cold squalls to the hotel to meet him and they had hardly been seated, fortunately at a corner table, when he burst into a furious tirade at her. 'He was an Inspector of twenty years standing, and she was undermining his authority in his District, going into places and finding fault where he had never done so.' It transpired that the Medical Officer of Health had visited and complained of that particular factory and had offered to go over it with him but Bevan had refused. 'All the inspecting must be done through him' and 'He wished to make plain…' And a great deal more to the same effect, including the assertion that 'Oram was a fool.' Lucy said very little and was determined not to quarrel. She suggested referring the matter to the Chief. She pointed out that she was not an Assistant Inspector, but a full Inspector and had not exceeded an Inspector's instructions. He said he would write to Oram, that he wished it to be a private letter and not an official protest; but he implied he would report it to Cramp, his Superintendent.

Lucy wrote that afternoon to Chief at his private address and asked, after explaining the situation, if he thought she had actually exceeded her instructions. A wire came for her at breakfast the next morning. 'You had better visit alone where you consider it necessary to speak to the owner or the occupier on sanitary matters. Letter follows.'

She paid a call on Miss Hawkesly who had been so helpful to her on her first visit to Nottingham; Miss Hawkesly was delighted to see her and still had an encyclopaedic collection of anecdotes from working women on the state of the various local factories. She gave Lucy a short list of the worst aspects of the worst-run factories from the viewpoint of women employees. Lucy gave her a shortened account of her visit to Whitehalls Tennants Factory with Captain Bevan. Miss Hawkesly did not seem at all surprised.

Armed with Miss Hawkesly's list Lucy went to Oldknows Factory and found it a dirty and depressing place. A forewoman, detailed to take her around the washrooms, said as they came out from the wet floors and the filthy walls and ceilings, "I don't expect Lady Oldknows 'as to wash 'er 'ands in a place like this."

"Have you ever seen her?" asked Lucy.

"I 'ave. She were going to church in 'er cab one Sunday," said the forewoman. "Never 'ere, though. A pretty woman, dainty. Owns this one outright and 'er son 'as two more."

Lucy wrote a note to Lady Oldknows, introducing herself, and suggesting Lady Oldknows should accompany her on her inspection one day that week. She sent it off that afternoon. To her surprise she received a reply the next morning, accepting the invitation to visit her own factory.

They met at the Hotel, and drove, with a friend of Lady Oldknows, to the factory where their arrival caused a great flurry in the manager's office. Lady Oldknows was indeed a very attractive, fine boned woman, in her late fifties, and greeted her manager warmly, asking to be accompanied by his most senior long-serving forewoman.

As they began their tour, Captain Bevan arrived in the manager's office! He had clearly prowled after Lucy from the hotel and seen her set off in the smart little fly.

Lucy took Lady Oldknows all over her own factory, including the filthy WC. She had never set foot in it before. Lucy explained that the conditions were such that she would be obliged to make Complaints, especially as another Inspector had found the same conditions a year before. "If nothing is repaired speedily, Lady Oldknows, there will be prosecutions, and that would be very bad for your factory and for its publicity and standing. I feel I am bound to warn you urgently."

Lady Oldknows listened carefully and her friend looked grave. "You have done me a service Miss Deane, and I am grateful to you." The forewoman, sensible and discreet, took them back to the manager's office, where they made their farewells to the works manager. "I will write tonight and we will meet tomorrow," she told him. Lucy refused the lift back to the hotel, and went on her way to Claters, another factory with deplorable sanitary arrangements, inwardly rejoicing.

She found, though, that many of the Nottingham and District factories, and many of those producing lace, were well run and pleasant to work in. The girls were rough but intelligent and friendly, and their employers practical and enlightened. She was fascinated by the lace-making processes, the detailed setting up, the intricate patterns, the rough fingers threading the filmiest threads with skill and patience, the hawk-like watching for missed threads as the great looms began to weave the shawls, or the great widths of curtaining or the narrow ribbons with their minute pictures.

The workers – 90% were women – took a pride in their work and Lucy was posed with several problems regarding working hours. Three smallish factories had asked to work on Saturdays from 8 till 4, and Captain Bevan had permitted it. This was clearly illegal; but the women were glad of the overtime. Lucy felt she must confer with May Abraham and the Chief before making any decision.

She lost another case in the magistrates' court brought for illegal

Saturday working. Miss Mayers, the chief witness, admitted working till 4.30 on a Saturday, but alleged she was interested in the business, having invested a small sum in it – would not say how much – but SMALL – and was, therefore, a manager. She was actually a cutter as well as a seamstress.

The magistrate said it was a difficult case and that there was a doubt about the genuineness of the evidence, but, as there WAS a doubt, they could not consider her as a bona fide employee.

Surprisingly, the magistrates were courteous after they had dismissed the case. One complained to her about another uncertified dressmaker's establishment in Houndsgate; she subsequently visited the workshop and cautioned the owner, just as her long stay in Nottingham was over.

She arrived home half an hour earlier than Hyacinth who had been thoroughly enjoying examining some first year cookery students in Chester for two weeks, living at the college and mixing with the staff in the evenings. Lucy marvelled at the change in her over the past year, from nervous, frequently tearful, and indecisive, to a competent, independent, handsome young woman. Emily had stayed until the sisters returned and kept a good fire burning, and sat and had a cup of tea with them both. "You must get home," Lucy told her. "The temperature has dropped like a stone. It's bitterly cold outside. We got through January with no bother, but now it's terrible."

"I will Miss, I told my mother I'd wait for one of you to come. It's lovely to see you both. It's lonely in the house when no one's here for so long." She wrapped her shawl over her head with her woollen beret and went out into the freezing street.

Hye had written to Emily asking her to buy chops and various vegetables and other groceries, and Lucy enjoyed chopping and slicing under Hye's supervision.

"I can see why you're such a success, Hye, you're a very good teacher! Isn't it surprising? What made you want to go into cooking?"

"I didn't. I didn't know what I wanted. I went to the Food and Hygiene courses with you because you were going, that's all, and you said I could give some Hygiene lectures like you, and I thought, NO WAY! And then one day some lecturer was giving a recipe for winter soup, and I thought, that sounds HORRIBLE; and I remembered dear

Dorothy showing me how to cook those wonderful soups at Bossie's and the Aunts, and I thought, I could do it MUCH better than that lecturer. So I thought I might as well take Domestic Science classes—"

"Well! Hurrah for Mrs Waters. Next time you see her you must tell her."

15

The Special Enquiry into Dangerous Trades

*Mr Asquith makes his final decision; May and Lucy begin hospital visits; Patients'
Registers are extremely variable; unexpected dangers appear; the Thames freezes;
Girls Friendly Clubs are friendly; bookbinding; artificial flower making; cigar
makers; waterproofing; brush making; Evelyn makes herself useful; repulsive fur
pulling; building up evidence; Lucy's health; a pink dinner dress; Miss Sharpley
and the fur pullers' petition; prosecuting Miss Moore, dressmaker; the House of
Commons dinner; 'Sprague Oram is a slave driver'; the Laundries Report; the
Dangerous Trades report.*

May Abraham, Adelaide Anderson and Lucy met with the Chief Inspector
at the Home Office and were given Mr Asquith's definitive decision
regarding the New Regulations for Female Inspectorships. An anxious
moment, but he pronounced it definitely settled; and substantially the
same as Sprague Oram had drawn up.

May Abraham's hope of a separate District was completely quashed,
but she had been placed in a definite seniority as Secretary of the Female
Inspectors Department. Adelaide Anderson and Lucy had never expected a
Female District, but May Abraham had hoped against hope, and then only
to be given the title of Secretary, albeit in the most senior position, was a
blow to her self-esteem. The women received the news politely, and made
little comment. Sprague Oram was left at the end of the meeting with no
notion of their true opinions, a sense of wariness, and a feeling that kid
gloves were called for.

Lucy and May had been told to make enquiries concerning diseases of women caused by their occupations. Leaving the meeting Lucy and May set off on their preliminary tasks to try to collect statistics. Over the next few days they made introductory visits to the London Hospital, to the Metropolitan Dispensary and the East London Dispensary.

The difference between the way Patients' Registers were kept in the various hospitals and clinics was striking. Those of St Thomas' Hospital were badly kept and of little use, whereas at the London Hospital, there were detailed Registers, well kept and mostly up to date. Miss Collett had visited there, three years before, for the first Commission on Women's Work, and had seen the Registers of 5000 female inpatients for one year, but the information had not covered the specific trades of the women.

At the London Hospital the House Governors would not let Lucy see the Registers but would give valuable information from them. "Only," added the Board Manager, "the collecting of it from various Departments with relevant dates would require a clerk's time, for which the Government must pay."

Lucy told the Chief. He was put off by the thought of payment. Lucy was dismayed. She indicated that she would pay herself, but Sprague Oram had some notion that it would appear 'too official' if the information was paid for, so he dropped it. "Funny notion," fumed Lucy.

The officials at the Metropolitan Dispensary in Fore Street were enthusiastic, and wanted to know how to help. Dr Perry, the Superintendent at Guys' Hospital was interested and said he would see if there was a way to collect the information. The City and East London Dispensary regretted they couldn't help at all. They had no records of cases or occupations, and said that 'no other Dispensary had.' Lucy was amused, having just come from one a stone's throw away which had both; but she said nothing.

At the end of the week May and Lucy dined together at the Grosvenor Hotel and pooled their findings, and pondered how best to proceed. May, a Dublin doctor's daughter, had many Irish hospital contacts, and they decided that they would make a joint report, she in Ireland, and Lucy in London.

The Patients' Registers had thrown up hints of various health hazards and practices in several trades and outworkers' establishments. Match making and phosphorus, lead uses in potteries, steam in laundry work were already well known, but health dangers appeared in unexpected workplaces. Bookbinding, artificial flower making, waterproofing factories, fur pulling – Lucy spent the next week searching out establishments and visiting in the East End of London.

The weather was bitterly cold. Ice packs and floes hindered the boats and ships on the Thames. The icy air, mixed with the smoke, and the heavy cloud, gave the city a strange dimness even at noon. The bitter cold and the frozen Thames had thrown armies of men out of work. Sea-borne coal was scarce as the ice prevented it being unloaded or brought into the centre of the city. Carts with vegetables and meat could not get in from the country. People and horses slipped and fell in the streets.

Lucy visited the Girls Friendly Club in Farringdon Street and talked to the girls for several evenings. Many of them worked in the book-binding workshops and most enjoyed the work. The 'Bible Shops' were much the best class, much sought after, and required skilled fingers. At times the work, both folding and sewing, had to be done by hand as it was too fine for machinery. The workers were apprenticed for a year at a shilling a week and then went on to piecework; for six months they got half of what they earned, and the other half went to the firm instead of their having to pay their own premium. The hours were not long except at pressure times, and then they were paid the overtime. Another group of girls at the Friendly Club were employed as artificial flower makers. They too were apprenticed; for their first month, they told her, they earned nothing, and then 2s a week for three months. But they enjoyed their work on the whole. "We only pay 2d a week," they said, "and we get two cups of tea a day for that to have with our break at lunchtime." Apprentice cigar makers were paid 4s a week for two months, but then were paid for piecework, "and at first we earn less than 4s a week even if we take it home to do in our own time."

"And even then," moaned another girl, "if we are a quarter of an hour late in the morning we are locked out for the whole hour, so we lose the hour's work, even if we are on our own time." Lucy took the names and addresses of those workshops and promised to visit very soon.

May Abraham and Lucy went together to Slazengers Waterproof Factory in Deptford because of a tip-off from a local doctor. A hundred girls were employed there in the Naptha Department. They complained that the fumes sometimes made them sick and often gave them headaches. The food they brought with them was kept in the same room and became impregnated with the garment fumes, and those same fumes followed them so that they were obliged to eat it inside the room because if they ate it outside, i.e. in the fresh air, they would observe the taste and be sick!

However, their greatest complaint was about the cold. The bitter winter freeze was not dealt with in any way, the roof was neither snow nor rain tight, and there was no proper way to warm their food.

Both inspectors were horrified to hear that they all served FIVE YEAR apprenticeships. First month, nothing. Second month 3s a week, rising by 1s a week every six months until at the end of the five years, when they were on piece work, they could earn 14s a week. But no one there was out of her apprenticeship, as they were then 'turned off', 'having no work for them,' and also because of disputes concerning their hours. There was a brutal manager who evidently had entire control.

When they met Mr Slazenger himself, a few days after, he promised to amend the conditions for sanitation, and provide rooms for meals, but would not attend to the need for warmth. "That problem was only temporary, and the spring would solve it."

The London Hospital had told Lucy that cases of anthrax had been reported in the brush making trade, because of the imports of foreign horse hair, and the London County Council had drawn up a report; but though she went to the County Medical Officer and was shown the report, she could gain nothing conclusive. The brush workshop on Tabard Road was a dirty place, had never been visited or inspected before, and had never heard of an Abstract needing to be pinned up, or any rules of ventilation or cubic space. The whole neighbourhood around the Borough was given over to brush making, mostly done by outworkers at home, very dusty and dirty work, and all using Chinese horsehair and bristles, but all denying any illnesses. She called on Lady Dilke, and was given tea, and related her findings, and Lady Dilke valiantly promised to find out the address of any Brushworkers' Union.

She visited several artificial flower workshops in the City and in Hoxton, and was amazed at the skill and charm of the posies, sprigs and sprays and various fruit and flowers that were produced for hats and corsages and button-holes and dress decorations. The workgirls took pride in their creations, and there seemed to be no specific danger from the processes; but all the workshops were bitterly cold, and could not be warmed adequately owing to the methylated spirits and inflammable materials that were used to stiffen the petals and leaves.

To her surprise and pleasure the Chief changed his mind and prepared her a letter for the London Hospital agreeing to pay for a clerk to collect information on Dangerous Trades from the Patients' Registers. She visited both the Miller and the Shadwell Hospital to enquire about any patients from the Slazenger Works. The Miller Hospital gave her the name of a GP to contact.

At the Provident Dispensary for Women in Blackfriars Road she discovered Dr Ethel Williams, an admirably down-to-earth woman. She was most interested in the Dangerous Trades Enquiry and promised help. "Women's sanitary information and knowledge is needed urgently in every street in Southwark and Blackfriars." Lucy recounted some of her findings with the apprentice girls.

Dr Williams said, "Yes, yes, but many of the ills of working girls are from their own ignorance as to food storage and preparation. And to lack of exercise in sunlight – they can never be out in sunlight. And, of course, carelessness in childbearing." She was strongly in favour of restrictions for married women's employment, and for time off before and after giving birth. A very useful woman to know, thought Lucy.

She paid a visit to Marion Tuckwell at the Women's Trades Union office. "I've got such a lot of information for you, Marion."

"Oh, excellent, and I've got a Complaint here for you, sent by a journalist from *The Star*. It's about sweatshops, and extortionate deductions from pay in a clothing factory in Aldgate." She introduced Lucy to the Secretary of the Printers Union who promised to help with the problems with bronzing at printers, "But would you investigate Cawston the Lithoprinters? I hear he always takes girls from a home for destitute women, because he can get them cheap."

Lucy took out her business notebook to make a note to visit. She sighed. "There's no end to it!"

Mercifully, there was an end to the cold weather, but not before Hyacinth had to return home from the Cookery College with a very bad sore throat. Evelyn came to stay to provide constant sips of hot drinks and company. Lucy was glad of her when she returned home each evening, and Emily too was thankful at not having to work in an empty house, despite the extra fires and housework they all involved.

"Evelyn, you are a brick," said Lucy. "What would I do without you? I depend on you. I know you are my best and most faithful friend."

Evelyn became very pink and looked surprised. "Do you? Of course I am – ever since we were very little, the first time you came back from India and stayed with us at the Boyce. You were so clever and tall, and I felt so small, and I could never keep up with you. You ran so FAST. And Hye too – you'd be at the top of the field, and I'd hardly started."

Lucy laughed. "Yes, we had a good turn of speed. Horace called us the Hares, and Mary said she'd put us in the kennels to train the hounds. And Uncle George said we made more noise than the hounds as well."

"I thought you were wonderful," sighed Evelyn. "And you were so kind to Hye when she was so miserable."

"Oh dear, yes. She was so homesick for India and for lovely Runi, our Ayah. She spoilt us, especially Hye. Hye was desperate when she found Runi couldn't come to England. She howled and howled – well, they both did – and then she was so sick on the boat, poor Hye. And of course, it rained all the time, and we didn't know anyone. And then Mother went away again back to India. Hye didn't have anyone."

"But it was awful for you too."

"It was. But I was eight and I had lessons. Hye was only five. Everyone was very kind always, and Bossie and the Aunts did all they could for us. But there were no other children – it was such a relief to come to you all in the holidays, and rush about, and be noisy. And to have some boys around – we never saw any of those – and the chance to shout and be untidy. Grand!"

"And now look at you both. I envy you in some ways Lucy, leading such useful lives. And me with no training for anything."

"Maybe no special training," said Lucy thoughtfully, "but plenty of interests and talents. Mary is exceptionally talented with her drawing and painting – and such a wonderful horsewoman – and Ethel has her music – and you are caught up in all sorts of local work and organising relief societies. Life couldn't go on without people like you. I couldn't, anyhow."

Evelyn gazed into the dying fire, her hands solidly upon her knees.

"I would like to do more for you, though. And see more of you, much more of you."

Lucy patted a hand. "Meanwhile," she said briskly, "let's get Hye a little hot milk and go to bed. Tomorrow I have to go and visit groups of fur pullers in Southwark. Almost the WORST possible trade and done in their homes. Horrors. The conditions are truly unhealthy for the whole family. They will figure almost top priority in our report. If you would like to, you could help me make a copy of it."

Evelyn's eyes grew bright. "Certainly, certainly. Thank you Lucy."

Sure enough, Lucy came home in a temper and spilt out her vexation onto the delighted Evelyn.

"I've spent all morning going round fur pullers' homes in Southwark. Terrible places. Filthy work, in poverty-stricken places, all among the damp washing and the babies. All of them with no exception would prefer working in a factory. They are groaning that the occupation is not one for a home. Of course it isn't. It makes so much mess and trouble that it makes more work for them to have to do it at home."

"What is the work?"

"It's repulsive. The firms – this one was Gay's in the Marshalsea Road – buy furs, pelts, from all over the world, Russia, Canada, Britain – rabbit – fox – beaver – and send out batches to the workers to smooth the skins and brush and cut out all the impurities and powder the back. The firms give it out because it's cheaper and cleaner not to have it on the firms' floors. I hear nasty tales of Gay's and Armstrong, their premises look so inviting, they keep all the expensive glossy stuff, mink and sable and so on to look impressive, so all the dirty stuff goes into the outworkers' homes."

"Oh dear!"

"Then in the afternoon I went to Guy's Hospital and saw a fool of a man who didn't even know how to read an inpatients list. I went to the Evelina Hospital, really rude people there. Then I trailed over to St Saviour's Workhouse and the Matron was out!"

"Poor Lucy. I'll get your slippers. Tea?"

"AND hot buttered toast!"

The next day was more productive. She visited the MOH at Marylebone and gave him packets of bronzing powder to analyse for the Special Enquiry, and she visited a retired doctor, Dr Whitwick, who had been the MOH at St. Olave's in Southwark. He was knowledgeable and helpful and was very keen to help with the fur pullers' grievances. He had no doubt whatever that it induced attacks of pleurisy and outbreaks of typhus due to overcrowding and bad air, as it was impossible to open house windows lest the hairs and fluff blew about.

He told her where to buy special 'raw' New Zealand rabbit skins, from Pearsons in Levoy Road and to send it to Dr Blythe to test for arsenic.

She discovered two families who preferred outworking 'so that they can look after children.' The children looked very pale and dirty and so did the mother, "had eight and lost five," she said simply. "We used to live across the river," she said, "but my baby Lily died, and that winter I lost my lovely little Minnie and I couldn't bear to stay in the room we had. My husband found us this place. It's better, two rooms, but two more have died 'ere. The fur gets in their lungs, I think. Gets in mine too."

One woman preferred outwork just because she had a Domestic Workshop – a room solely for work. But she kept her two daughters, aged 18 and 17, in there all day every day.

It was certainly very pleasant having Evelyn in the house. Hye recovered from her sore throat and went back to work, but Evelyn stayed on, and she and Emily had simple stews and casseroles ready for them in the evening. Emily loved having Evelyn around and between them they happily cleaned the staircase and all the skirting boards, chatting all the time and Evelyn was particularly proud of the results. After their meal Lucy dealt with her reports and correspondence while Evelyn listened to Hye's accounts of her students. Their cousins, Dennis and Georgiana Dighton, came home from India for a three months' leave and dined with them one evening. One morning Evelyn accompanied Lucy to Sir John Williams for a check-up on her health. He was pleased with her, gave her another prescription and impressed upon her the importance of rest on the days when her monthlies were due.

"I try, but sometimes I simply have to travel."

Evelyn looked anxious. "But you must at least try. You have so much office work to do." Lucy told her of Miss Simpson's Office Days. "Well, there you are. Perhaps some of the more repetitive stuff could be stored up to do quietly on those days. And if you can't be at home or at the Home Office, you could use the hotel writing rooms. Even an hour's rest on a bed would be better than nothing."

Lucy considered. "I probably could. I usually do a good chunk of it in the trains going to and from. I like the train journeys, actually. They give me a chance to catch my breath. But I know you are right."

"I like calling them Office Days. Then you don't have to make up excuses to all those horrid inspectors."

"Clever Evelyn. Clever Miss Simpson. Let's go to that ABC and have some soup, and then I want to go to Peter Robinsons and buy a dinner dress. Lady Dilke has asked me to a dinner at the House of Commons. Help me choose it."

To Lucy's surprise Evelyn was most adventurous in choosing gowns. She went up and down the racks with an eagle eye, fingering materials, frowning over prices. Lucy gravitated to darker colours, heavier fabrics with discreet flowers and decorations. Evelyn kept arriving in the fitting rooms with various blues, mauves, frills and roses. Finally she brought a dark pink watered silk with a deep V neck and decorated with brocaded patterned ribbons. Lucy put it on to please her. It looked wonderful.

"Well!" said Lucy.

Evelyn and the fitter beamed. "VERY nice, madam," said the fitter. "If we take it in at the waist and the back seam it will be perfect."

"You are a dark horse, Evelyn. I would never have thought you would go for anything so frivolous."

"That's not frivolous, Lucy. It's DISTINGUISHED. Not for me, of course, but with your dark hair and you so tall, it's really striking. You can't go to dinner at the House of Commons in a SERVICEABLE dress."

Lucy became increasingly concerned about the plight of the fur pullers and wrote to May Abraham about it. She replied suggesting a petition to be signed by fur pullers, pressing for better conditions and designated workplaces. 'This will mean much more work for us though, unless you can get some organisation to underwrite it.' Lucy went to Marion Tuckwell at the Women's Trades Union, who suggested the Women's University Settlement and when Lucy visited there the next day they accepted it with alacrity. So Lucy visited her Uncle Murray to advise her on the ways to get Petition forms and publicity posters printed.

Within a few days the Settlement wrote to say a Miss Sharpley would be overseeing it. Lucy went to meet her taking with her a list of all the furriers' firms in South and East London, copied out by Evelyn, and the draft of a letter asking for the names and addresses of all their outworkers. She discovered Miss Sharpley to be a tiny dormouse of a woman with glorious eyes and forehead, like a saint. She also discovered Miss Sharpley had a First in Moral Philosophy and Mathematical Tripos.

"When I think of some of my young male acquaintances who wasted their time at Oxford and Cambridge, and came away with pitiful degrees and then think about your achievements, I despair of the Professors who won't reward women with degrees! It's shameful!"

Miss Sharpley nodded sadly. "I'm afraid I agree with you!"

Evelyn went with Lucy for a final fitting for the pink dress, and then returned home sadly on the Thursday to help her mother with a weekend house party. "There's a hunt ball on Saturday night at the Alfords' and we are putting up three or four people and having a dozen more to lunch on Sunday. I shan't know them. They're Mary's cronies really. How I wish I could stay to see you wear the dress to the House of Commons. Make sure you have your hair dressed properly before you go."

Lucy had no intention of doing so, but said she would.

The next two days she had to go to Peterborough for the prosecution of Miss Mary Moore, dressmaker, for persistent un-notified overtime. When she reached the court the magistrates' clerk told her 'it was not very necessary she should see her witnesses if she didn't want them to give her away.' The girls had been intimidated both by Miss Moore and by the lawyer for the Defence. Lucy smelt a rat and visited Miss Moore who would not allow her to see the girl witnesses at the public house over the road, so Lucy said, "Very well, then, I shall exercise my right to see them here, in a separate room, alone." And in spite of Miss Moore's protests, she did.

The three young women who were to give evidence as to the overtime hours were terribly nervous, but determined. Lucy heartened them up and 'they stuck to me like bricks.' The lawyer was a 'self-important cad' who said "Will you keep quiet!" and "sit down and hold your tongue," whenever she spoke, until the magistrates' clerk had to rebuke him; but he bungled the case and was so inaccurate, so full of unsubstantiated assertions and so ignorant of the basic facts that Lucy's task was easy, and despite a very lax and lenient Bench of Justices she won her case with 7s 6d for each informant.

Captain Bevan was in the court and to her surprise congratulated her warmly, and said he had just failed in a prosecution for a similar offence regarding lace dressing. "The law is so vague," he said crossly. "The lawyer spent half an hour arguing over the term lace dressing – said, as it was not a manufacturing process, it need not stop until the end of the hours the women had spent on cleaning the machinery! There is NO definition of 'Main Factory Process!'

Lucy sympathised, and urged him to report it to the Chief and ask for a change to be inserted into the forthcoming Factory Bill, and he accompanied her to the station, and they shook hands quite cordially as she got on to the train.

Doctor Blythe's report on the bronzing powder awaited her at home – no arsenic, but copper and poisonous amides were present. May Abraham had written a long letter about her part of the Dangerous Trades Enquiry. And Hyacinth had received a letter from the Kensington Church Board offering her a Cookery appointment. Hyacinth said firmly she would not take it on any account. She said the salary was derisory.

On Saturday morning Hye accompanied Lucy to Peter Robinsons to collect and pay for the pink dress. Hye was in raptures. "It's lovely, Lucy! And now we are going to the hairdressers. I've made the appointment and Evelyn has given me the money!"

"Hye, I haven't the time. I'm going to meet May Abraham."

"I wired and told her you would come this afternoon," said Hye equably.

The House of Commons dinner was a splendid occasion. Lucy was conscious that Lady Dilke regarded her with approval and Sir Charles with admiration; May Abraham and Harold Tennant were there, and both were delighted by the dress. Lucy had a nasty feeling that Sir Charles and Lady Dilke already regarded them as a couple. The other guests, Mr and Mrs Kilmuir, Mr McMillan, the Liberal Whip, and a Miss Irvine, were easy conversationalists. The Dilkes were both experts at mixing a social occasion with social planning, and everyone went home well satisfied with the evening.

Hye had stayed up to hear all about it, and it was after midnight before they went up to bed. The usual small packet of letters sat on the table in the hall and Lucy would have left them till the morning if the familiar Home Office envelope had not been on the top of the pile.

Dear Miss Deane,

I have just heard that the Clauses in the new Factory Bill relating to Laundries are to be brought forward in the listings and will most likely be dealt with on Thursday afternoon next.

Will you provide me with the relevant reports by Tuesday at the latest?

Yours

R.E. Sprague Oram.

"Oh help! Hye, when did this come?"

"They all came by the late evening post."

"Look at this! How can I possibly do this in time?"

"You can only do what you can do. Get up early and set about it."

Lucy fumed. "By Tuesday! He's a slave driver!"

"Definitely! Set the clock for six. It's half past twelve now."

She spent the whole of Sunday and Monday, from dawn through to late night, with inky fingers and tired eyes and a stiff back. Lucy was thankful that her notes were in good order and marvelled that Rose Squire had sent such well crafted and tabulated lists. Hye kept her supplied with hot drinks and soups, and took the pen out of her hand, and screwed the top on the ink bottle in the early afternoon on Sunday and took them both to Battersea Park for a brisk walk by the river.

On Monday Emily continued with the hot drink regime, and May Abraham called in response to Lucy's note, and the Laundries report was tied with its ribbon and its brown folder ready for the Home Office.

She was able to give it to Mr Sprague Oram himself. He accepted it and congratulated her. "Wait until you have read it first," said Lucy. "I look forward to it," he replied. "Good Heavens," he said, seeing Lucy's inky fingers. "I feel quite guilty!"

May Abraham saw them too. "All in the line of duty. But I'm glad he noticed. Now I can pressure for some secretarial help. It's shameful that we have to manage all the office work as well as everything else. How could you have done it in the time?"

"I couldn't except that Rose Squire was so clear and organised."

May considered. "Once the laundry part of the bill is passed we had better bring her name formally before the Chief."

They discussed how to parcel out the writing of the reports for the Dangerous Trades; Lucy took the Bronzing and Bookbinding trades and the Fur Pulling Trade; May took the lead poisoning in the Pottery Trades.

The rest of the week passed in a blur. The two young women rushed from Hospital Registrars to Medical Officers of Health to Lithographic firms to fur pullers' families, checking on details, each evening collating their notes and absorbing them into each section. Hye was off around the Home Counties examining the Spring Domestic Science Examinations, so Lucy worked on late into each night.

She invited herself to Bossie and the Aunts for the weekend and wrote a large part of her final draft sitting in the sunny window looking out across the lawn at the carpets of yellow and purple crocuses under the great bare trees. She made the Aunts furious by suggesting nationalisation of land. Aunt Gertrude went quite red in the face with irritation. Bossie laughed but scolded her. "You do it on purpose, Lucy, just to annoy!" Lucy was sorry and apologised. It was such a beautiful sight, and she was thinking that the fur puller families would never have seen anything like it in their lives around the Borough. Dear Aunts, such good kind folk. How could they conceive of such an existence, a life without crocuses?

She arrived home on Monday morning to find May Abraham's section of the report on the mat, and she gave her own section to May Abraham at the Home Office later that morning. They read and signed each other's papers and handed them to the Chief personally. He nodded as he received them. "Well done. We shall need these any day now. Now then! Miss Abraham! I have a sheaf of Complaints for you to follow up in Liverpool. Miss Deane! Mr Peacock has been gathering up orders for you to go to Belfast and some other places in Northern Ireland to inspect sanitation issues there. Can you plan to be there on Thursday for two weeks? Then you can be back in London in time for Easter."

16

Linen mills and cookery schools

Hye and the Kensington School Board; Mrs Hedingham reorganises Lucy's wardrobe; driving out with Mr Snape; two miserable linen mills; the Grand Central has good bacon; two poached eggs for dinner; losing another umbrella; Miss Barlow and ginger cake; unending laundries; Sprague Oram piles on the pressure.

A note was sent to Mrs Hedingham asking for urgent help to sort out Lucy's clothes for the two weeks in Belfast, and she threw herself into the task with relish. She made lists, examined hems and buttons and pockets, sent Emily out for tissue paper and luggage labels, sent Lucy to the Kensington stores for two new nightdresses and bedroom slippers, and went herself to choose tapes, ribbons, veiling and feathers to smarten up Lucy's serviceable winter hats. Lucy went to the bank, the Home Office, the Finsbury Circus office, seldom used recently except by Adelaide Anderson, wrote countless letters to hospitals, clinics, Evelyn, and hotels; and collected all the stationery to pack into her writing cases, home and official.

Finally she caught the Night Mail to Belfast on Friday at 6.30p.m. from Euston. It was a rough sea crossing, but mercifully she was a good sailor and arrived at the Grand Central Hotel, Belfast, calm and collected at 11a.m., and wired Hye of her safe arrival.

After lunch the District Inspector, Mr Snape, called at the hotel, and took her around the city to inspect several model workshops. She wrote to Hye that evening, 'A typical inspector (of the ungentleman type) with his priorities firmly set on fencing, machinery, safety, and stiff neutrality at all costs.'

A fine, soft Sunday gave her time to explore Central Belfast and go to church and write to family and friends before the inspections began in earnest on the Monday. She drove with Mr Snape to some bleach mills ten miles out and ten miles back in an open trap, the first Lucy had ridden in since a child. She enjoyed every minute of it, and Mr Snape flowered amongst her pleasure, visibly softening and unbending. "Such a capital little horse," she cried, "Goes like the wind and never turns a hair." Thanks to the horse they were able to argue amicably on the appalling and insufficient sanitary arrangements in the mills, and the fearful stench of the bleach vats.

Tuesday, and she set off on her own for Killyleagh on Strangford Loch to inspect two mills there on Complaint from the Home Office. The scenery was breathtaking and the mills were appalling. The sanitation was non-existent, but worse were the demands made of the workers, nearly all women. There were no notices displayed anywhere of the rules and conditions of work, no hours of work, no rates of pay. The women had gone on strike in February against a new rule that the firms required them to sign, which said that 'Double pay would be stopped for any period they were absent without leave.' This had been enforced on two little boys, half-timers. When the women challenged this, the management said the fine was only to frighten the boys and would not be enforced on them this time. The women had given in and signed the forms. The mood in the mills was sullen and the women eyed Lucy with mistrust. They did not want to speak to her at all, and would not answer any questions. Luckily, on the train back to Belfast she got talking to two women who had left those mills and gone to work in Shrigley Mills and they filled her in with much detail and gusto. Lucy was glad she had chosen to travel third class on that journey.

HMI Snape agreed with her about Killyleagh wholeheartedly, and told her of the Strike Action. Lucy wrote to the Chief and to May Abraham, 'If he knew, why didn't he deal with it and why didn't he inform me before I went?'

She travelled to various mills in and around Belfast, and spent a cold uncomfortable two days in a shabby hotel in Newry, with burnt cooking and cold coffee and a stark writing room, though the staff were civil and the bedroom was clean. It was a relief to be back in the Grand Central in Belfast where she wrote to Hye, 'the bacon in the Hotel is GOOD, the ONLY Hotel where I have ever found it so!'

Hye's letter was surprising and disturbing; she had decided she was unhappy with the post with the Kensington School Board, the salary and the responsibilities were not good enough. Lucy was sorry in that it would have meant far less travelling for Hye – she knew to her own cost how tiring and stressful that was; but something in her rejoiced that Hyacinth was looking forward to a more ambitious career.

A letter from the Chief made it clear that on NO account was she to make Complaints visits with Mr Snape. She was to be completely independent in her inspections and her reports. She was thankful that she had gone to Newry on her own. She had visited the flax and linen mills at Bembrook, said to be models of their kind. The mills were certainly beautifully designed, and the atmosphere in the workplace relaxed and kindly. But the sanitation provision was completely inadequate. How can they all be so complacent, she moaned? She spoke to the mill's secretary and told him she would write him an official letter to lay before the Board of Managers. He thanked her courteously. But he seemed surprised.

On one of her return journeys to Belfast she had visited a Roman Catholic Convent school to ask about the practice of half-time schooling, half-time employment in their schools. They told her with glee that they had moved over to an alternate system, every other day and the half day on Saturday, "Oh, it is MUCH better than the half day system." No, they had not noticed the youngsters going to the mills before or after school hours, but they certainly used to, especially last year at Bembrook. Lucy asked them to take note and send word if the young people did work extra time in the mills.

A whole day was spent at a conference of flax dressers at the Trade Union Society. She went with the Flax Dressers Union Secretary and was interested to hear the workers' attitudes to the Truck Act, and to the regulations for deductions of pay and home attendance. Two days later she spent another day with the Secretary and Treasurer of the Textile and Weaving Operators discussing the intricacies of the deductions taken by the mills for thread, for colour dying, and small braid weaving machines loaned to the outworkers. And in between times she spent hours in Ballymena and Ballyclare in the homes of outworkers, watching the niceties of finishing, hand hemming, lace edging, and hand embroidering of fine linen towels, handkerchiefs and napkins.

In Ballyclare she found a most strange little pub run by a tobacconist, John Baird, in two rooms over his shop. He gave her two poached eggs for dinner, a very small, very clean bedroom, and two poached eggs for breakfast. But only 3s 9d, all told.

On the Thursday morning she had a long conference with Mr Snape and then travelled to London by the 4p.m. Mail via Dublin. The weather was glorious and the sea like a mill pond, "and just as well, Hye, as my Office Days began, two days early, so I can rest here at home, comfy and no problems."

However, letters from the Home Office awaited her and she was called there on the Saturday. The Chief greeted her, but was not concerned with the Irish mills. "Time enough for that when I've had time to digest the results with Miss Abraham." He wanted to talk about laundries and about Complaints he had received about restrictions to overhead drying. They all seemed very foolish to Lucy, who said so. Sprague Oram looked stern. "Nevertheless, please look into it at once, Miss Deane. The Complaint has come from John Burns, MP."

"Where's my umbrella, Lucy?"

"Oh, dear!"

"I knew it, you've had it again. Where have you left it this time?"

"I'm afraid I've left it at the Home Office – no, I had it after that – oh, I do hope I didn't leave it on the bus."

"I wish you'd lose your own umbrellas, Lucy, you are truly vexing."

"I'm sorry, I'm sorry. I'll buy you another one."

"Yes, but I'm off to Miss Hardyman early tomorrow, and I'm sure it's going to bucket down all week. I NEED it!"

"Yes, of course. I'm hopeless losing things, I know. I'm sorry."

It had been a gusty, chilly, showery Easter Sunday and the sisters had chickened out of Easter morning church and lit a roaring fire in the sitting room. A ginger cake had just come out of the oven, smelling wonderful, ready for when one of Hye's colleagues, Miss Barlow, arrived to discuss Hye's troubles with the Kensington School Board. The ginger aroma was perfection, but the cake itself had fallen very slightly in the middle, and Hye was consequently irritated, feeling she had let herself down at a particularly sensitive point of time. She was sure Miss Barlow would judge her for it, hence the excessive annoyance with Lucy.

Miss Barlow arrived punctually, wiping her feet thoroughly on the door mat and shaking her enormous umbrella violently before bringing it in. She was an exceedingly cheerful young woman, round and fresh-complexioned, her cheeks red with the wind, her gingery hair curling in wispy tendrils round the brim of her pork pie hat. She looked the epitome of a cook housekeeper. "Ooh, ginger cake," she said approvingly.

"I've just made it," said Hye, "But it's sunk in the middle."

"Ooh, good," breathed Miss Barlow. "I hope it's claggy. I love claggy cake. If I'm at home I take it out ten minutes early, in the hope it will sink and clag – I hope you won't tell anyone at work that," she added hastily.

Lucy laughed and made the guest comfortable by the fire. "Thank you for coming. Hye seems very anxious about her post. I hope you can help her to find a way out of her troubles."

"I don't know that I can." Miss Barlow shook her head, "The two Superintendents are both so set in their ways – very good ways – and they set a good standard for all the students. But Miss Deane has new ideas, and she's had experience lecturing all over the country in different establishments, and giving demonstrations to different groups of people and she isn't interested just in teaching women to cook. It's hygiene and general education and experiments with her as well. Well, that don't go down well with our two old biddies, new experiments don't. No! Cook according to the book, tidy, orderly, get a good hearty meal served, on time, tasty, good quality, keep the accounts, keep your kitchen clean."

"Sounds good to me."

"'Tis good. But no room for experiments, nor foreign recipes nor wines, nor special diets or VITAMINS, not with them."

"Goodness! I didn't realise Hye had such a wide range."

"Oh yes, she's a high flyer is Miss Deane. But there's no scope for her at our School Board. We get in the solid sort of girl who's going to be a good reliable cook housekeeper in a good reliable household and we teach them well, make no mistake."

"Are you happy there, Miss Barlow?"

"It suits me fine at the moment, Miss Deane. I've been there nearly three years, but I shall be leaving in the summer. I'm to be married in July, and I shall be moving to Margate, my husband-to-be's parents run a small hotel and restaurant there and I shall help them until a family of my own comes along, please God."

Hye came in with the tea tray and the offending cake.

"Very nice." Miss Barlow surveyed it professionally. "Not as claggy as I'd hoped. In fact, hardly sunk at all. But perhaps it will be a bit damper under the surface."

When Miss Barlow had gone, replete with cake, Lucy said, "I thought she was a grand person, absolutely clear-headed and sensible. I really think you should hand in your notice, Hye, chuck it, you're a round peg in a square hole and there is no reason for you continuing there. And aren't you the dark horse? I had no idea you were such a culinary innovator. Apply for everything. The sky's the limit."

But Hye was not complimented at all. "Don't say that, Lucy. It's all very well for you, plums just drop in your lap – not into mine. I can't hand in my notice just like that. Where else would I go? What sort of references would I get? Olive Barlow's all right, she's got a marriage to go to – Not me." The tears brimmed.

"Well, darling, good job you're going to Miss Hardyman for a few days, you can chew it all over with her, she'll have some sensible ideas. Meanwhile, I'll buy you an umbrella."

"Oh, damn the umbrella." And Hye flounced up the stairs.

Back to square one, lamented Lucy.

With Hye waved off in the train to Hertfordshire for the week Lucy settled to picking up all the strands that had been collecting while she was in Northern Ireland.

The strands had multiplied alarmingly. The Laundries Bill showed no sign of reaching the House, much less a conclusion, and she found herself inspecting various laundries all over London, and visiting two or three hospital laundries, vast areas full of boiling coppers and steam and heat; but plenty of room to move, and industrial size trolleys and mangles and winches to wheel and wring and hang the sheets and linen, and the working shifts much shorter and with extra breaks for rests. She had a long conference and tea at Kensington Town Hall with Rose Squire, who had been reappointed with a salary of £100 and an upgrade to the full status of Sanitary Inspector. They spent an evening in Rose's house writing a report on small laundries in Acton which she handed in to the Chief the next morning.

He handed it immediately to the office boy to take down to the Secretary's office. "He didn't even LOOK at it!" May laughed when she was told. "This is how he treats us – take it as a compliment." Now that he had got them both together he grilled them on the Northern Irish textiles mills. He wanted the names on HMI Snape's list that had not been visited by either of them. He had heard of disquiet among the fish-curing fraternity in Grimsby, "someone will have to go there," and "poke about." He was concerned about working hours being totally flouted in jam and preserves factories. "Asquith says that's just the way it is! Strawberries all get ripe at once, so you've got to make jam overnight."

"He's not the one making the jam all night, though!" said May Abraham. "He's a good stirrer, though!" said Lucy. Sprague Oram looked shocked. "Ladies, ladies!" He twinkled. He said severely, "Miss Deane, I shall be sending you to inspect small tailoring workshops in Bristol and Bath next week. Miss Abraham tells me they were in total disarray when she inspected last summer."

The two women went off to lunch and to collect addresses and lists of Bristol tailors and dressmakers from Mr Peacock, and to plan Lucy's visit. Lucy told of Hye's problems at the Kensington School Board, and May gave her an introductory note for a Miss Pyecroft at the LCC Polytechnic, so Lucy hurried along to the Domestic Science department there. Miss Pyecroft was friendly but unhelpful. She said that the Polytechnic was much harder work than the School Board and thought Hye's single year's experience there was too little to recommend her. So no go, thought Lucy sadly. She decided she wouldn't even bother to tell Hye she had visited Miss Pyecroft. Still, it had been a useful exercise in one respect. Miss Pyecroft's distinct dark line of moustache made her peer at herself and her own upper lip, and she made a detour to a chemist to buy a bottle of hydrogen peroxide on the way home.

17

Back and forth, back and forth

Sixteen non-existent dressmakers; Aunt Georgie has pneumonia; Bella Brooks cheers them up; boring Bath back streets; charming Mr Maitland; prosecuting Miss Purnell.

She deposited her suitcases at the Royal Hotel in Bristol on a warm, blowy April morning and left her card at the office of the Chief Inspector of the District, Mr Maitland. Mr Maitland was away but she found the Assistant Inspector busy making a scale drawing of a piece of equipment which was to be used for a prosecution the next day. She was filled with admiration for the young man's skill and for the delicacy of the invention.

"I would gladly hang that on my wall at home," she said.

He looked at it critically. "You wouldn't," he said, "It has a fatal flaw. This ratchet here—" he pointed to a tiny section, "has a habit of unhooking itself and flying backwards. It has caused several small accidents and the owners have been warned. Now a man has lost two fingers and the case comes up tomorrow."

Armed with her street maps Lucy set off to visit sixteen dressmakers' addresses on the list that Sprague Oram had given her. Not a single one still existed, and in some cases no one in the street remembered them. Tired and frustrated she walked to the Clifton Suspension Bridge and was rewarded by the view and a lovely sunset. After a good meal she wrote to Hye and to Evelyn and slept soundly.

The following few days she dodged frequent sharp showers to visit dressmakers in Clifton. May Abraham had visited most of them last

September and those seemed to be in good order. The Assistant Inspector, Mr Pendock, who gave her his list of Clifton workshops, said no one had been again to those places since Miss Abraham. It's the same story in all the Districts, she thought. Directly the Lady Inspectors come, they virtually hand over all the workshops to them.

She was struck with the generally short hours in the Bristol workshops, and the little overtime that was done. Saturday half-time often ended at 1p.m. and the general daily hours were between 8 and 7.30 with one and a half hours allowed for meals.

Torrential rain on Friday allowed her to catch up with family letters and letters forwarded from the Home Office from London, Belfast, Nottingham, Leicester, and Lincoln. All of them required action on unfinished business.

Evelyn's letter told of Aunt Georgie's sudden pneumonia, so that she was sorry but Lucy and Hye could not stay there for the weekend, and she showed how frightened they all were for their mother. A letter from Granville Streatfeild commiserated with her over Hye's unhappiness in her present post, and promised to let his aunts know so that they would keep their ears open for possible appointments.

Several Bristol establishments were guilty of not notifying overtime hours and several were grossly overcrowded. She cautioned three and revisited the Alexander Drapery on Saturday morning to read the declaration for a Court Attendance, before rushing home to be with Hye on Saturday afternoon. But she could have stayed in Bath and Bristol, as she found their friend Bella Brooks staying, and Hye happily entertaining her.

Bella Brooks was good for them both, though, cheerful and amusing, a good listener, and a fund of gossip about all their friends. Their cousin, Edith Boscawen, called on Sunday, and the four of them went off to lunch at the Northumberland Hotel. Hye seemed in good spirits and was looking forward to three days of demonstrating plain cake making at a Domestic Science College in Edmonton. "I should be terrified," marvelled Bella, pushing her hands through her shining golden ringlets, "supposing they didn't cook properly, or you forgot something?"

"Oh, I don't forget things. I ask THEM. 'What do I add next? How hot should it be?' Or if I do forget things, they are all really keen to tell me, and they are pleased to know that I know that they know. And I'm pleased to know that they don't know that I don't know."

"And if it really goes wrong you can tell them about the claggy cake."

"Hmm, I should keep that as the last resort."

What am I worrying about, thought Lucy, she'll be fine.

On Monday night Bella took them both to hear Hansel and Gretel at the Savoy with the Carl Rosa Opera Co. Bella and Hye enthused over it. Lucy didn't care for it, though she thought Gretel had a pleasant voice.

Tuesday morning saw them all travelling their separate ways, Lucy to the York Hotel in Bath, Hye to Edmonton, Bella to Berkshire, promising to write to Thomas Cook and ask them to recommend a foreign holiday for the three of them and Evelyn to take in the summer.

Lucy found Bath very frustrating and Bristol even more so. She would have loved the luxury to spend time in the middle of Bath, the sights, the shops, the histories, the galleries. Instead, she spent her days tramping round the outer small streets of the city, searching for the workshops on Mr Sprague Oram's list, most of which, like those in Bristol, were non-existent, and if up and working, had few glaring irregularities. Their main drawback was that they were almost entirely up hill, tucked away in back alleys. She informed Sprague Oram that his lists were no use at all, and he wired back smartly to insist that she go to ALL the places on his list in Bristol and Bath, even though they were blanks.

'They are on MY Register, and I shall report to Maitland, if they prove blanks. Discontinued businesses should not be on the registers and he is to provide me immediately with a correct list.' So Lucy traipsed on, through constant showers, getting a large blister for her pains.

The one bright point in her week was being given an expensive tea in her hotel by Army friends of her parents, Colonel and Mrs Boothby and their daughter Edith. Lucy was relieved that she had got a fresh blouse to wear. They sympathised with her and admired her. "This is a very comfortable, well-appointed hotel, don't you think, Lucy?"

"Yes, it is, and very restful – but it's full of really smart people, or old ladies taking the waters, and they all dress for dinner, such a bore, as I don't have anything but working and travelling clothes. In some ways a commercial hotel suits me better."

Mrs Boothby shuddered. Lucy went on hastily. "I'm truanting

tomorrow. I've told the Chief I'm going back to Bristol, but I shall go home for the Sunday and come back on Monday morning."

In the end the journey back to London was another mistake. Hye had been a great success in Edmonton but was angry because she had been asked by popular demand to repeat two demonstrations on icing cakes; she had done this, but had not been given any extra remuneration for them. Their cousin-in-law, Kathleen, Lady Falmouth, had invited them both to a quiet supper, but Hye would not go, so Lucy felt obliged to go alone, and though Kathleen was charming and natural, her blister hurt and she had caught a cold in the wind and the rain. When she arrived home, as early as she thought was polite, she found that Aunt Florrie and Uncle Murray had called and borne Hye off to a hotel on the Cromwell Road with them. And to add insult to injury, she discovered as she arrived at the Grand Hotel in Bristol that her Office Days had arrived, two days early again. She wired her address to the Chief and went to bed early. 'Very Seedy,' she wrote in her diary that evening.

More visiting of defunct dressmaking establishments was done at Mr Sprague Oram's request. Out of twenty, only two were still running. Mr Maitland sent a note saying he had returned from his break, asking her to call at his office. May Abraham wrote asking whether a Miss Louisa Purnell had been prosecuted yet, as she had recommended six months ago. The Chief sent her Sir Charles Dilke's proposed amendment to the Factory Workshops Act, in which she had suggested the specific requirement that the bedrooms of live-in employees should not be overcrowded, and also that Female Inspectors might enter bedrooms if it was thought that work was going on there.

The Chief asked her to write a special report on the subject embodying her opinions. Lucy happily wrote strongly in favour of both proposals.

Mr Maitland greeted Lucy with a strong handshake and a "Delighted to meet you, Miss Deane," which sounded, surprisingly, to her ears as if he meant it. He told her how much he had valued Miss Abraham's inspections last autumn. "Because of her we managed to clear away a considerable amount of dead wood."

"That was useful." She agreed. "I have been finding a good deal myself with small tailors and dressmakers no longer trading at the addresses on my list. Some of the addresses had never heard of them."

"Really? Are you using our lists?" Lucy said she was using the Chief Inspector's lists. He pulled a face. "I fear that will be the list I inherited from my predecessor when I came four years ago. Mr Pendock has been updating it. My predecessor was here for twenty years, and to tell you the truth, I don't think he ever updated ANY lists. So no wonder you have had a frustrating time. Bad, very bad. I apologise for wasting so much of your time. What can I do to retrieve the situation? Dear, dear!" He looked so woebegone and flustered that she could not help smiling.

"A correct list at the Home Office would smooth the feathers there."

"Oh, help," said he. "But Pendock and I will go through them this very night for you to have tomorrow."

"And the Bath lists too?"

"Bath lists too?"

"I knocked on many dark doors there last week."

"Oh! Oh!" He shook his mane of white hair and spread out his long hands with their elegantly manicured nails.

"I am truly sorry," said Mr Maitland. "We have made so much unnecessary work for you when we need your help with really important issues. Let us look at our list of possible prosecutions, which is definitely up to date, and see how we should best proceed. And then you'll permit us to take you to a little lunch."

Lucy felt it behoved her to act graciously, although she had a strong desire to disbelieve his charm, but he laid out his lists of Complaints for re-inspection, and explained the situations behind them in a perfectly straightforward manner, and listened to the findings carefully, nodding when she spoke of Miss Louisa Purnell's dressmaking premises.

"It is not the first time she will have been cautioned," he said. "She has a very fashionable clientele. I regret that my wife goes to her frequently, and when the balls are held in the season, she has a double overtime permit. She has three separate workshops as well as the main shop for fittings."

"I was only shown one," said Lucy.

"Aha!" said he, "It would be good to bring her into line. But my wife won't be pleased with me. Over to you, Miss Deane."

He and Mr Pendock took her to lunch, and when they heard she was interested in church architecture insisted on taking her to the cathedral.

Lucy was intrigued; such curious stonework in the East window stonework, almost like a true lover's knot. "I don't care for the vaulting in the side aisles, and the gallery runs round above blind arches so the sight lines are often interrupted."

Mr Pendock rose to his cathedral's defence. "But don't you care for the Perpendicular and Early English decoration?"

"I do, certainly."

Mr Maitland regarded them with avuncular admiration. "What a range of expertise you both have!"

"Not expertise," said Lucy, "But interests – plenty of interests. But you do too, Mr Maitland, I'm certain. What are some of your interests?"

He considered. "I enjoy a good concert – not too highbrow, mind. And I play a formidable game of croquet."

Lucy enjoyed the rest of the week despite her bad cold and the chilly and disappointing May weather. She inspected and reported on various workshops, some crammed and airless, some dirty and smelly, and some very poor, hardly more than a front parlour with one machine and the dressmaker employing her mother and daughters. She laid information against Louisa Purnell with the magistrates in Bristol – Mr Maitland chuckled – and against two other firms in Bath, and caught the Saturday afternoon train back to London.

Once again she had an empty Ladies Only carriage, and so was able to spread her papers over the seats and complete a wad of office forms, requests as to cubic space and requirements; she wrote to May Abraham checking on her previous visits to and from places in Belfast, all before the train drew in to Paddington.

She alighted with a spring in her step. It was the first time since she had been appointed that she had felt completely accepted as a straightforward colleague by any of the District Inspectors.

18

Up and down, up and down

Mrs Hedingham dresses them all; Hye studies for an Advanced Science Course; Dr Elizabeth Garrett Anderson; Aunt Georgie convalesces; Louisa Purnell's prosecution; the Lady Inspectors confer again; Birmingham and Wolverhampton; back to London; back to Ireland; Lucy blows up.

When she stepped through the door of 100 Fulham Road, Leah and Mrs Hedingham were there, busy with checking on the Deanes' summer clothes, and jubilant as Leah had just got her first real engagement as a dancer from the manager of a theatre who had seen her private theatricals in Woolwich. Lucy congratulated them warmly. Mrs Hedingham said proudly, "Four weeks! And the last week in Islington, so she can live at home and no rent to pay, and the manager says there's a good chance of a children's pantomime show at Christmas. That would be a six-week run."

"How wonderful," said Lucy.

Mrs Hedingham beamed. "I'm making her some summer dresses – but I'm not deserting you, Lucy." She held up two dresses. "These are no good except for house wear any more – nor your summer work skirts – I turned up the hems last year, they won't stand being turned up any more, much too short. And you really must buy a summer coat, and that means a different hat to go with it."

"Oh, goodness, and I suppose Hye will need the same."

"Well, a pretty dress never comes amiss. But she takes much more care of her clothes than you do. And of course when she's working she has those lovely white overalls. It's the waistlines that take the time. With her I'm always having to let them out; with you I'm always having to take them in."

"Must be very boring. I'm sorry, Mrs Hedingham."

"Not boring at all. I like to turn you out neatly."

"It must be lovely making things for Leah."

"Ah well," and a smile of pure pleasure lit up Mrs Hedingham's large brown eyes. "It really does pay to make things for Leah, there's no doubt. She has a real air about her."

Hye swept down the stairs in her petticoat, carrying an armful of skirts. She embraced Lucy. "Lovely to have you home. There's a great pile of letters for you. We shall have to get a bigger hall table. They keep falling off that one."

"I'll put them in my bedroom. I'm only going to look at letters from family and friends tonight. Oh, but I'd better open the one from the Home Office, I suppose – oh, and here's one from Miss Anderson – and this is Lady Dilke's handwriting."

Hye sighed.

Sunday was restful though, and the weather warm and calm. The sisters walked through Kensington Gardens and marvelled at the spring flowers and blossoms and the bright light greens. Some folk were brave enough to be wearing summer outfits, and the children ran about with no coats, and here and there was a parasol, and a smattering of boaters. They wandered down long beds of tulips, choosing the colours they would like for their summer clothes, and went home via Kensington High Street to look at the fabrics displayed in all the store windows.

They talked about their summer trip to Switzerland, and decided to offer Georgie Dighton and her husband their house for the three weeks they would be away. They talked about Evelyn's letter from Dymock. Her mother was recovering well from pneumonia, and Evelyn would love to see them at Dymock, and hoped in a few weeks to be able to visit them in London.

"You'll have to go there by yourself if you can, Lucy," said Hye. "I can't go till the middle of June – I'm going to take my Science and Physics Advance Exam, next week."

"What!? Hye! When did this come about?"

"I've been going to Evening Classes for a while now. I thought it would give me a step up for a more ambitious job – layouts or kitchens, and things like that."

"You dark horse! Why didn't you say?"

"Because I didn't think I would pass it. I only just passed the Basic one three years ago, and I didn't understand what they were asking, let alone know how to answer it. But when I saw the last year's exam paper I was really surprised. I thought, I could actually do this with a bit of work, and one of the lecturers at the Kensington Board goes through the work with me if I'm stuck. So I thought I'd do it and not tell anyone, and then if I failed, no one need know."

"Hye, you are amazing."

"Don't tell, though."

"No, I won't. But when is it?"

"It's in two parts. Next week is Science and Physics, the following week is Hygiene."

"If you pass, Hye, I'll buy you a dress for Switzerland."

"But what if I don't?"

"Why, then I'll buy you a dress, and one for me as well."

They went home and wrote to the folk at the Boyce to say Lucy would visit mid-week, and to Lady Howard to tell about their forthcoming trip, and to Georgie Dighton.

Lucy rushed about in London on Monday, first to the Home Office where to her relief the Chief was too busy to see her, simply handing her a Complaint for a Baker Street dressmaker, so she had time to buy a small bottle-green boater from the Army and Navy Stores on impulse, before meeting Miss Anderson to plan their prosecution against a dressmaker in Lincoln on Wednesday. Adelaide Anderson lived with her parents in Hadley Wood, but had given Lucy instructions to meet her at her aunt's house in Upper Berkeley Street, Portman Square at 11.30a.m.

To Lucy's surprise Adelaide's aunt turned out to be none other than Dr Elizabeth Garrett Anderson. Adelaide opened the door herself and took her upstairs to a small study. "Angela will bring us some tea and we can talk here as long as we need. My aunt is just going out but she really wants to meet you." To Lucy's delight Mrs Garrett Anderson swept in, a handsome, energetic little woman. "Wonderful to meet another pioneer," she exclaimed, taking Lucy's hand in both of hers, "and wonderful to know Adelaide has valiant supporters like you and May. I hope it isn't too much of a struggle day by day." Lucy told her of Mr Maitland and Mr Pendock and of the pleasure she felt at being included as a colleague. "Oh, how encouraging," said Mrs Garrett Anderson. "Of course, those sort of men are few and far between – but their numbers will grow, they will grow, as long as we stand firm and do a good job. Must go, my dears, take as long as you like with your planning." And she pattered down the stairs as quickly as a child.

Fortified with tea and ginger biscuits they planned their campaign for Wednesday and brought each other up to date on their work. By 1 p.m. Lucy left. "I'm so thrilled to have met your aunt. She's such a beacon for us. She makes me realise how lucky I have been. I've had people backing me, writing letters, encouraging me all the way along. She's had to fight every inch of the way."

Adelaide considered. "Yes, but her father always encouraged her, and her family were all feminists, down to the baby. And my Uncle James fought for her the minute he met her. We're not alone, Lucy, there are a lot of folk we don't know about who wish us well. See you at the station on Wednesday."

Lucy realised she was close to Baker Street and seized the opportunity to visit Mr Sprague Oram's offending dressmaker's premises. She could find very little to complain about except for one very small room, with four women hemming skirts with no windows that would open. She told the proprietress this, who said, "Oh, what a relief! I felt you would be reasonable. I thought an Inspector who came carrying an Army and Navy hatbox couldn't be all bad."

She enjoyed the twenty-four hours with Adelaide Anderson in Lincoln. They stayed at a small hotel at the top of the hill and were able to visit the Cathedral early in the morning before the Court opened. Lucy was only needed to attend as a witness and was impressed by Adelaide's quiet and confident manner. The magistrates were all courteous and she won all six injunctions. They visited a few workshops afterwards and made contact with the Medical Officer of Health over a particularly gross case of overcrowding. He promised to prosecute.

They said goodbye to each other on Lincoln station in the late afternoon and Lucy climbed into the train to Birmingham and thence by stages to Malvern and Dymock.

Evelyn and Horace met her in the late evening dusk as she alighted at Dymock and drove her home through the twilight. She ate her supper on the warm terrace of the old Boyce, with bats swooping for flies over the darkening lawn in the stillness. Evelyn was beside her. There was no wind. Lucy had to listen hard to hear any sound, not even from the farmyard. The kitchen noises were finished, and Aunt Georgie was sleeping in the room above the drawing room, so they spoke little and only in low voices. The relief throughout the house because of her aunt's recovery was palpable. Ginny and Cook walked lightly and greeted her calmly and the family were relaxed again.

"I'm so happy for you all," said Lucy to Mary, who was sitting by a table lamp, marking out a pattern for a lacquer tray.

"We are only just getting used to the fact that she will be well," said Mary, "we've been at sixes and sevens. The dogs weren't allowed this side of the house in case they barked, Horace and Father went up to the lake if they wanted to smoke, Ethel gave up playing the ukelele – she was hardest hit of all, I think. But she'll be able to start again soon – that'll be hard on the rest of us!"

The next day brought more beautiful weather. After breakfast Lucy and Evelyn walked to Dymock and Lucy sent a wire to Hye, swearing Evelyn to secrecy, wishing her good luck for the exam, and another wire to the Grand Hotel Bristol booking a room for the night. When they returned, there was Aunt Georgie being helped into a chair in the sunny morning room, and everyone rejoicing. She wanted to hear all Lucy's news and gossip of family and friends until Lucy was fearful of overtiring her.

"No, no dear, I have been so bored once I started to get better. I want to walk round the garden and they won't let me but I WILL DO it. You and Evelyn must come with me."

"We will, Mother, we will."

"We'll go NOW, Evelyn. No time like the present."

"Very well, but not ALL round the garden, just to the edge of the wood and back." And the slow procession set off, Aunt Georgie between Lucy and Evelyn, with Ethel and Ginny following behind, with a shawl, in case, and a garden chair, in case, and an escaped and joyful dog, and Uncle George, come out of his study to see what the noise was about.

Lucy stayed until after lunch, when her aunt went off to her room for a rest, and then found herself smiling all the way to Bristol.

Prosecutions in Bristol on Friday, prosecutions in Bath on Saturday. Miss Louisa Purnell on Friday and a good result, 20s and 10s costs in each case. The defending lawyer was nervous and Lucy was able to bring in that Miss Purnell had twice been previously cautioned for the same offence of illegal overtime. In Bath she had another successful conviction. Here the defendant's lawyer was very clever, but Lucy enjoyed pitting her wits against his. She told Mr Maitland, "First he pleaded Not Guilty boldly, and then began to lay great stress on Register and Notification and to ignore the records of illegal overtime; I objected; these were not the offences that she was charged with. Still, the magistrates said they would like to hear. Thus, he tried to befog them over precedents in criminal law, where, failure to keep Registers was held no crime etc, etc; I repeated that this was not the offence she was charged with. Luckily, the magistrates were competent and upheld the conviction."

She also discovered several underage girls employed by another dressmaker and cautioned her. As they could not produce a Standard Certificate each she said that the employer must either dismiss the girls, or employ them as half-time school attenders.

Back in London she went to the Home Office to hand the Chief his list of deceased workshops in Bristol, only to be told she was now to go to Birmingham and Wolverhampton for two weeks next Wednesday. She reminded him that she was due for a week's leave in June, and he said she could still take it, and go to the Midlands a week each side of it! "I know the job meant travelling all over the place," she fumed to Hye, "but I wish he would give us all more warning of which and why and where we are sent."

Hye was sympathetic, but upbeat. Her second exam, the Hygiene section, had been easy, and she knew she had done well. So, perhaps she would have passed the whole thing.

Lucy wrote to May Abraham who immediately arranged a meeting for them both with Mary Paterson who was down from the North for a few days. They lunched at Lucas' Restaurant, ostensibly to discuss amendments to the Factory Bill, but then worried over the fact that they had never any regular time to meet as a Department and fill each other in on what they had all been doing. "We MUST meet in conference at set and stated intervals," said May Abraham, "and not allow ourselves to be sent off at no notice, or hardly any notice." Lucy broached her idea of a Female Department 'File' in which the notes of all the places they visited could be placed whenever they were in the Finsbury Circus office, and then, whenever any one of them visited there, they would see what the previous instructions and conditions had been. All thought this was a good idea, and May sent a letter to Adelaide informing her. When Lucy and May went back to the Home Office after lunch, Mr Peacock told them Sprague Oram required Miss Abraham and Miss Deane to go to Ireland together in mid-June. He looked at them oddly when they roared with laughter.

And, as soon as she arrived in the Star and Garter Hotel in Birmingham, she opened an envelope from the Chief requesting her to go to a Complaint, but NOT to tell Mr Hoare, and also requiring a conference with her back in London on the Saturday! Lucy wired 'Do you mean THIS Saturday?' He wired back 'YES.'

Then on Friday he sent another wire. 'Home Office closed tomorrow. Please come Monday instead'. Grimly mollified by the 'Please' she wired back 'Monday. Yes.' And wrote to Hye to say she would be home for the weekend.

HMI Cramp greeted her pleasantly and asked her to inspect several factories for overtime infringements. He invited her to his home on Sunday, and Lucy, taking this as an olive branch, was sorry to refuse. He told her there were workshops in the Hay Mills district that had not been visited for years and years, and asked her to go anywhere there. She told him she had been sent a Complaint by Dr Hill the Medical Officer of Health, and Cramp advised her to send it to the Urban Sanitary Authority.

She travelled to Wolverhampton for overtime evening inspections and found Edwards factory working very late despite two previous convictions; she arrived back in Birmingham on the last train, very tired and dirty, and then went home, with a pile of reports to write up on Saturday morning to find Hye out, organising a grand charity dinner and dance for a Mrs Bosco.

On Sunday they were both exhausted and neither of them dressed until early afternoon.

When she presented herself at the Home Office with all her reports completed Sprague Oram was not in the least interested in them. He wanted to grill her about a question to be asked in the House by Sir Charles Dilke relating to conditions of work among hosiery outworkers in Leicestershire and Nottingham. Lucy racked her memory and thankfully realised the relevant papers were in the files of the Home Office rather than in Finsbury Circus. The Chief seemed impressed. Then he said, "I want to ask you about Mr Hoare in Wolverhampton," and showed her a letter from two men in Stourbridge and Wolverhampton complaining of Mr Hoare's dishonest dealings with the Edwards factory that she had revisited on Friday.

Lucy was shocked. "I think it an outrageous letter! I don't believe it. Mr Hoare may be hot tempered and a real nuisance to deal with for us – us Lady Inspectors – but I'm sure he is as honest as the day is long on any official work."

She showed him the recent Friday night report. He nodded and thanked her and congratulated her.

Lucy was elated by his warmth. She went shopping to celebrate and bought a smart summer jacket in Oxford Street, pale grey piped with green, to go with her new straw hat, and a dark green skirt. "That should please Mrs Hedingham."

She planned out the whole of her week, in and out of magistrates' offices in Birmingham and Wolverhampton, dealing with ignorant magistrates and clerks, attending various courts for various prosecutions and trying to track down wire workshops in Hay Mills.

One morning a telegram was brought to her breakfast table undoing all her plans. 'Secretary of State wishes to see you re Factory Bill. Return by early train at once.' She was annoyed.

"I was looking forward to my poached eggs!"

The waiter was sympathetic. "I'll rush the order through for you. You write out the reply, and I'll see it goes off immediately, and the receptionist will look up the next train to London!"

The manager brought her the eggs himself. She sent a note to Mr Cramp to say where and why she had gone, pushed her clothes into her cases, and caught the 8a.m. train.

As soon as she arrived at the Home Office the Chief swept her into a cab to the House of Commons. Lucy was excited but the adrenalin soon turned to lethargy. The day droned on in a Committee Room about the Laundries Clause in the new Bill, with Mr Asquith, Sir Kenelm Digby, Sir Charles Dilke, Harold Tennant, and Messrs Drysdale, Ibert, Troop Chute and Oram. She was 'invaluable', they told her, as 'their advisor' but the meeting went on and on and no one asked her for any advice.

She groaned to Hye late that evening, "Three mortal hours, debating various amendments; awfully half-hearted and luke-warm. And all terrified of the Irish Party? Why? What had they got to do with anything? Made me angry."

Finally they gathered their papers together. The Chief thanked her fulsomely. "A tower of strength, as always." And as she turned to make her way out of the Commons he said, "Oh, and would you come to the Home Office tomorrow. I am sending you to Ireland with Miss Abraham next week for a few weeks."

"I have several more days' work in Birmingham yet," she said, startled. "And then I am due for a week's leave."

"Oh, complete them, complete them," he said graciously, waving his hand. "Mr Peacock will prepare the necessary travel arrangements for you."

Lucy arrived home unexpectedly to find Evelyn was staying at 100 Fulham Road. Evelyn and Hye got the whole force of Lucy's temper. "He sends me all over the place on a whim. They didn't need me at all. I haven't finished any of my plans in the Midlands and I don't know if I shall be able to do it all. Or why I'm going, or for how long, or when!"

"You shouldn't be so important," soothed Evelyn.

"I'm not important at all. I sat in that boring Committee Room for three and a half hours and no one asked me to say anything!"

19

Mostly Belfast affairs

Juggling the week's leave; with May in Belfast; May annoys HMI Snape; Lucy pacifies him; the magical twilight ride in a jaunting car; Hye applies for posts; the Irish Cottage Industry Exhibition; Claude sets off for India; a momentous meeting; back to Belfast; trotting round linen and rope mills; HMI Snape is reprimanded; meeting the handkerchief embroiderers; the Fearless Four set off on their holiday to Switzerland.

In the end Mr Sprague Oram added the week's leave on to the summer holiday, and Lucy did quite well out of it. But oh! Such a rush back and forth for the next ten days, trying to get the court arrangements and the reports and the packing and all the files and lists for the Birmingham and Wolverhampton Districts up to date; and arranging for Hye to stay with Aunt Augusta in Paddington over the weekends; and finally to travel on the Night Mail from Holyhead to Dublin.

May Abraham met her at the ticket barrier in Dublin, waving a letter from the Chief. "He wants me back in London!"

"Oh, May, NO! Whatever for?"

"He's scared in case I get involved with another case and held up by another prosecution. I've had four since I came and there's another one tomorrow."

"Oh, May, you have to stay for a few days at least! Until I've got my bearings. Where is this prosecution?"

"In Belfast. We'll write and explain it's necessary for me to stay another week. Hurry, there's a train to Belfast in thirty minutes. Let's get your luggage. Here's a porter. I'll fill you in on the train."

Once they were safely ensconced in the Grand Hotel, Belfast, May talked all evening about the state of the Female Department and the best way to develop it. She explained the next day's prosecution. "It's a brute. It's a jam factory. It ought to be closed. Everything's wrong with it. To start with, it's filthy, they haven't lime washed it for years, they say they have, but you can see they haven't. They swear they did it two years ago. Rubbish. But how to prove it unless you have a certificate? Then, they are employing several young people, full-time, and a head teacher will swear they are only thirteen. But here's no fixed penalty for this. Then they don't seem to have filled in their forms for overtime, and the ones they HAVE filled in for this year are recorded on LAST year's forms. It's touch and go whether I can get a proper conviction for any of the counts."

"Oh, dear!"

"We MUST try to get some clauses inserted into the new Bill about keeping a proper Register for employees' overtime – everyone simply does as they please and then pleads ignorance. If the magistrates can get their mates off the fines they will. And I certainly don't want to buy any jam from THAT factory, knowing the state of it."

Lucy accompanied May to the Belfast Court as a witness of her credentials, and sat through the hearing. May Abraham showed no trace of any worries. She appeared good tempered and relaxed, her facts were beautifully organised, she was courteous and charming, but very quick, and when necessary decisive. The defending lawyer stood no chance against her and the magistrates, all obviously on the jam factory employers' side, had no option but to convict. They charged the smallest fine they could and only ten shillings for each injunction. May and Lucy left the court smartly and went straight away to visit Paterson's Match Factory. "Very bad still," grumbled May. "They haven't done anything since I was last here. I cautioned then and I shall have to prosecute now."

They called on Mr Snape who was furious at not having been given personal prior warning of the prosecution that morning. Lucy felt that this was a grave mistake, but May seemed impervious. However, he owned to having received the court certificate, which had been addressed to Miss Abraham, Factory Inspector, opening it, and attending to it without informing them. May had checked on the times and dates with the magistrates' clerk independently of Mr Snape's office.

They wrote the letter to Sprague Oram at the Home Office together, and posted it as May Abraham caught the train to Dublin.

Lucy went to Mr Snape's office the next morning determined to pacify him and certainly he seemed mollified. He handed her several Complaints for textile factories in the surrounding districts and she busied herself with them. He suggested she go to Newcaster, one of the seaside towns in the County Down on the Saturday and stay there over the weekend, and she was very grateful to him. It was a picturesque town and a charming quaint hotel, the Connolly Arms. The weather was beautiful and she rested and wrote family letters and felt at peace.

In Belfast on Monday she extracted the list of Lurgan and Lisburn factories from the office Registers and took two factories at random in Lurgan and two in Portadown. Luckily they were all quite near to their stations and both relatively trouble free. She walked back to the train to Lurgan and as she stepped on to the platform there she met Mr Snape. Why had he come there, she wondered? He knew she was going to inspect there that day. Snape snooping? He covered any confusion cleverly. He was visiting a school, and a parent of an underage employee, a little way beyond the town. He walked along with her chatting amiably.

"I gather Miss Abraham has been visiting Paterson's Match Factory," he said innocently.

"Oh?" said Lucy, as innocently, "That is in Belfast, am I right?" He nodded and raised his hat as she turned in at the gates of the first mill, walking on down the road out of the town.

She was very tired and stiff on her return and realised during the night as the familiar pains gripped her stomach that it would definitely have to be an Office Day the next day. If it had come while I was at the Connolly Arms, I could have coped in comfort, she thought wryly.

There was a letter from May Abraham the next morning telling of her Dublin inspections, and saying that the Chief had a group of places for Lucy to visit in Tuam, in Central West Ireland. 'He is recalling me to London, but these places are small linen mills way out in the county, and he wants you to take them on. Take raincoat and rain hat, umbrellas and stout shoes. If you get caught in rain on those country roads there is no shelter.'

"Help!" thought Lucy. She wired the Chief to say she was on her way.

Mr Snape was dismayed on her behalf. "It's VERY basic out there, and you'll find the accent incomprehensible, and many of the workers will be very rough and wild."

"They can't be all that bad," said Lucy. "What about the hotels?"

"Tuam will be fine – choose an inn near the station. Stick with Tuam – and Mullingar – no small places, whatever you do. And come back just as soon as you can."

It turned out that she enjoyed her three days very much and was fascinated by the area. It hardly rained at all, the hotels were comfortable and the proprietors hospitable and chatty, and some of the small linen mills were producing beautiful tablecloths and curtains with exquisitely woven damask designs. The women, all with stout aprons and clogs and shawls, stared at her with amazement. She spoke to them, but they could not understand her way of speaking any more than she could understand theirs. There seemed to be little overtime being worked. Trade was very slack, she heard, and many women were being laid off.

"What other jobs can they get?" she asked. A foreman shrugged. "Very little. Those out in the country can do farm labouring, piece work, but most of that is just for the family. Some will do home embroidery for handkerchiefs."

Only one mill, out in Dunmore, had to be inspected for overtime infringements, and that not late hours; but it warranted a ten-mile drive out and back in an Irish jaunting car. It was a magical ride back to Tuam in the twilight; Lucy was enchanted.

Mr Snape was genuinely relieved to have her safe home in civilisation, but not so pleased when she opened her pile of letters in his office to find that Sprague Oram had sent her a list with enough tasks to take her another week in his District. Lucy was not best pleased either. A letter from Claude Streatfeild said that he was finally off to India for five years in the middle of July and was planning parties and a day at Henley Regatta to say goodbye, and she must be there.

'I shall be finished here by Saturday and can come home then,' she wrote to the Chief, and wrote to Claude to say she would certainly be home to join in all the festivities. There were two letters from Hye to say that she had applied for three posts, and was hopeful about two of them.

'I do hope you don't have to stay much longer, darling Lucy, it is very comfortable at Aunt Augusta's but I need to be home in the week. Maybe Evelyn can come now that Aunt Georgie is nearly better. Also, Emily hates it when we are not there. I am sure she is looking for another place where she will not be so lonely. I have copied out all your monthly returns and sent them to you. Come home, Lucy. Love, Hye.'

Another wire came from May Abraham and Mary Paterson.

'Conference for our Department next week, if you will be in London. Let us know. We have contacted Miss Anderson.'

There was a letter from a Miss Roberts, a trades unionist, inviting her to the Irish Cottage Industry Exhibition in Belfast the next day, and a letter from Lady Dilke saying her friends Mr Arnold Foster, MP and his wife were in Belfast with Miss Roberts and hoping to meet her. She enjoyed the exhibition, very well presented, but she suspected from her brief visit to Tuam and Dunmore, that the beautifully produced contents of the stalls concealed dark and poverty-stricken secrets, and Miss Roberts confirmed that this was so. She also enjoyed Mrs Arnold Foster's conversation, very friendly and knowledgeable, and the couple were out and out radicals and socialists. The afternoon that they met they heard the news that the Factory Bill had finally passed and they all rejoiced together in the tearoom of the Grand Central Hotel.

For the rest of the week Lucy rushed around to various factories in Belfast, and regretfully uncovered several major infringements, 'which will mean prosecutions – which will mean I shall have to come back here sooner than I want—' she wrote to Hye. But on the Sunday she was able to travel back to London.

She and Hye had hoped for a quiet Monday together, but Claude and Granville banged imperiously on the door mid-morning and took them both out to lunch; and on their return a note from May Abraham asked could she call early evening to discuss the forthcoming conference.

"I can't stay long," puffed Lucy, out of breath with climbing the stairs at Tite Street. "I've got to pack because we're going to Sussex to friends for three days tomorrow early, and I MUST wash my hair tonight."

"We'll be quick," promised May, "Let's plan out our new note and file books ready for the meeting. I told the Chief we were planning to hold it and he is agreeable to it. But he says it has to be next Monday and he won't consider it official, so no expenses will be paid, and we must be considered on leave."

Emily had done wonders during the day, washing and drying and ironing and packing summer dresses in tissue paper. It was late before Lucy's hair was dry, and Hye insisted on putting curling papers in the front, so Lucy was uncomfortable during the night. Hye insisted the green straw hat required 'some tendrils just below the ears.' Lucy surreptitiously brushed them out during the journey, and a helpful breeze made her feel more normal.

It was a bittersweet three days. The old house at Frant sat quietly among its well-kept gardens while the house party played tennis and croquet and chattered and laughed. A distant cousin George Deane, now a solicitor in Kent, and Georgie and Dennis Dighton, and various other friends of Claude's whom they did not know, and all the Streatfeild family were there. George Deane made her laugh. "No, I never come up to London, unless I absolutely have to burrow into my club for a rest. You have no idea the excitements that I have to cope with in deepest East Kent. The ghoulish things I have to attend to in Rhodes Minnis and the Elham valley – sheep rustlers – unnatural death – the garden of England! Hair-raising!"

On the Tuesday they travelled through London to Henley for the Regatta. A hot, hot day and Lucy had a bad headache and felt miserable by the end of the day. Travelling home with Hye and Claude, they said goodbye to him on Paddington Station. They watched his slim white-suited figure disappear up the ramp and felt mournful. "I think half your headache is for Claude," said Hye. They went to Picketts in Oxford Street the next morning to choose gold cuff links for Claude and have them engraved with his initials.

Monday July 15th 1895. The four Female Inspectors met at three o'clock in the Finsbury Circus offices. Lucy had her large suitcase with her, ready to head off to Belfast on the Night Mail to Holyhead.

The first item on the agenda was: How are we perceived?

"It's a very ticklish position. We are hated by the Male Inspectorate, and thwarted at every opportunity."

"Not thwarted, but they are all so grudging," said Adelaide Anderson.

"What is worrying is that so few outsiders know anything about the work we do, or our position. Even the women who run women's unions and societies don't know. We have GOT to publicise ourselves."

"Oh, must we?" said Mary Paterson. "I do dislike feminist militant tactics."

"So do I," nodded Lucy. "And I try not to get caught up in them. But I do agree that now both the Chief AND the Home Secretary will be replaced very soon, our main strength and support will lie in our OUTSIDE influence."

"How to harness it though. There are so few of us, and so much to do. We can't be everywhere at once."

Lucy waved a bunch of women's magazines and papers. "I suggest we publish a series of inspired articles in the women's magazines about us."

"About US?" Adelaide Anderson looked shocked.

"Only very indirectly referring to US. About bad conditions in factories and workshops, and what could be done about them. The articles would show the whole case for needing Female Inspectors."

"The Male Inspectors would smell a rat."

"They would certainly complain to the Chief Inspector's Department."

"And the Chief Inspector might sack us!"

"No, no," said May Abraham, laughing. "Not sack us. Worse, cripple us. Don't look so crestfallen, Lucy. Actually, I think we are very well thought of in the Home Office, and I'm sure any new Chief Inspector will only be appointed if he approves of the idea of Female Inspectors. They are finding us to be a force to be reckoned with, and the tide is already beginning to flow our way." Lucy thought of Mr Maitland and Mr Pendock and was comforted.

"So, what to do?" she asked.

"We should abandon any idea of writing them ourselves under another name."

"You mean, get outsiders to write for us?"

"Yes. But we MUST keep control over what is written. We need to apply to some thoroughly trustworthy organisations."

"And non-political? And non-Party, Miss Abraham?"

"Well, that narrows the field considerably, Miss Anderson."

"There are several admirable people. Various academics."

"What, like Miss Gladstone, Principal of Newnham?"

"My word, that would be a catch. Or Miss Tom, the Moral Science Tutor."

"We need to spread the word around, in the local societies and unions, too. Sensible, interested, literate people with an interest in what's going on near them."

"Well, keep your eyes open and your ears pricked, and make lists and we'll get started on contacts. It's July now, let's try to get the first articles out and about by the end of September."

"The new Factory Bill will give us a jumping off board."

"It's so wearing not having any secretarial help. I can't keep up with all my papers and filing and carrying them around on the trains. It's so heavy. Could we ask for a secretary for the Department, Miss Abraham?"

"Could we STOP calling each other Miss Abraham and Miss Paterson – at least while we are together," said Miss Abraham.

"Oh, yes, please," said Adelaide. "Hurrah!"

"Is that all right with you, Miss Paterson?"

"Why would it not be, Lucy?"

They all looked at each other.

"This is a VERY SIGNIFICANT MOMENT!"

"Yes, it is, Mary. Isn't it, Adelaide. Isn't it, May?"

"It is indeed, Lucy."

"And so can we also ask for a secretary for our own Female Department, May?"

"With a typewriter, for the sole use of the Department?"

"Oh, steady on!"

They all laughed; but it was a serious matter.

May wanted to urge the Home Office to appoint more Female Inspectors, Assistant Inspectors, to be trained, four of them, one to each of the present Inspectors. Lucy wanted them to be Junior Inspectors, to do some clerks' work, and help to search into Special Enquiries, and share the unending workshop visits. AND an extra clerk for May Abraham.

They discussed the rules for prosecutions, so vague, how in so many cases there was no precedent for complainants to follow, and so many different and plausible reasons for employers needing overtime, and all except Lucy agreed that it was in the factories that the greatest evils existed; the workshops, though housed in bad buildings, were not employing such masses, and generally speaking were in a more positive condition regarding sanitary provision and hours of work. Lucy thought of the fur pullers' homes with the anthrax-laden fluff floating into their lungs, and was not convinced.

"Just let me check some of these notes before I write them up," said May, "and then I suggest we all go to a restaurant to celebrate and not mention the word Factory at all." All agreed and gathered round May, the Chair and the Minute-taker.

Lucy looked at her watch. "A quarter to seven! Good heavens! The time! I've missed the Night Mail to Holyhead!"

Lucy was able to wave Hyacinth off to the Cookery College to give a series of High Class Lessons in the morning.

"What are High Class Lessons? Are they learning Haute Cuisine?" Hye looked vague. "As haute cuisine as they are likely to grasp."

"Can we have some here?"

"We can if we get a completely different kitchen."

"Ah! Never mind. It was a nice thought while it lasted."

When Hye had gone, with her bag packed to stay with Aunt Augusta again, Lucy managed to polish off a great pile of office work, and letters to Spinners and Weaving Companies in Ireland before she travelled back to the Grand Central Hotel in Belfast via Liverpool.

She saw Mr Snape and explained her delayed arrival, and set herself to inspecting in the area around – Whitehaven, Brough Monkstown, Carrick Fergus, Larne – and finding frequent infringements. Mr Cooke Taylor was expected in Belfast the next week and so Mr Snape was being particularly punctilious in keeping her informed of Complaints, and dealing with her informations, advising on prosecutions and promising to visit all of them on the Saturday to enforce the laws. He handed her the Complaint of a laundry, which he had apparently attended to himself, and also asked her to call on a tailor's establishment to check out if girls had been secreted in a kitchen at the time of his Assistant's, Mr Pender's, visit. Thank you, Mr Cooke Taylor, thought Lucy. Mr Snape was definitely nervous about his superior's visit, and anxious that his files were up to date and his office running smoothly. He was like a lazy schoolboy suddenly realising that the headmaster was coming down the corridor. His whole demeanour to Lucy had changed and become more like a colleague. Snape and Lucy attended Belfast Police Court together for a prosecution of defective waste cleaning in a yarn mill and of overcrowding. Lucy prosecuted and the case was won. Mr Snape congratulated her on her concise delivery, and they were both pleased with each other.

Then she set out for Bembridge and Lisburn, an adventurous journey. Most of the establishments on her list were some distance from the centre of Bembridge, but the stationmaster sent her to a cheap cabman, Mr Peter Sands in Newry Street, and she engaged him for the day, enjoying his conversation as his little horse trotted down the rough roads to the linen mill and the rope factory. The Millmount Bleach Factory was the principal linen processor in the area, a strange sight with great sheets of linen stretched out on the bleach greens around the town. She thanked him for his company at the end of the day as he helped her to alight at the Downshire Arms, old-fashioned and friendly, and was astonished at his charges for the day. He had driven her the whole day for 10s. Lucy gave him an extra 2s for his trouble, and sixpence for his stable boy, and he seemed delighted.

Lisburn was a very different story. The whole town smelt faintly of sewage and every mill or workshop she visited was defective. SANITATION SHOCKING she wrote, on every form, and in one case there were no WCs at all, no taps for washing, no towels. When she asked a woman in that linen mill what provision was made the woman shrugged. "We go in our privy before we come – or some women go behind that shed in the yard." There was no drainage system anywhere in the town except the very centre. She enquired where she could find the Medical Officer of Health and he proved to be incompetent, lazy and hostile. She visited the Cottage Hospital where she found the Certifying Surgeon, Dr St George. He was surprised to see her, an energetic short man, eager about cleaning and town hygiene. He told her that the chief mill owners were their own Town Commissioners and that the largest factory owner had built his own model village for his own workers and had left the others to it.

"Write to the Town Council," advised Dr St George. "Though I doubt you will get satisfaction. They started on a scheme once, but nothing happened, and now even that has been shelved."

She returned to Belfast full of her findings to discuss with HMI Snape, but he was too upset to listen and could only pour out his own troubles.

Apparently he had been severely reprimanded over his admittedly very lax Register-keeping by the Home Office. So this was the reason why Mr Cooke Taylor had been visiting. They had threatened to remove him. Lucy felt sorry for him. She considered he had not been one whit worse than any other District Inspector, and much better than Mr Connor or Cooke Taylor, and that his District was quite unworkable for one man. He was evidently being made a scapegoat; it was easy for the authorities to pick on him because he tended to fly off the handle and was frequently indiscreet.

So for the next few days she kept her head down and busied herself with constant inspections, visits, warnings, and instructions around Belfast. These resulted in frequent prosecutions in the Police Court, all of which she wrote up at once and sent them to Mr Snape to boost his Registers and Records.

One case dealt with an employer flagrantly employing women until eleven at night despite frequent cautions. A new young magistrate, a Mr Hodder, was being very fair, but his fellow magistrates were of different mettle, and overruled him on all but the most obvious points. One magistrate remarked, "There are hundreds of places where they employ women all night long, and unless they did, trade would be spoilt."

Mr Hodder spoke to Lucy afterwards. "If the Factory Act penalties are as small as these, it will be impossible to enforce the new Act."

She spent her last day in Ireland out in the deep countryside around the little market town of Ballynahinch visiting outworkers of the embroidery trade. Two shopkeepers, Mrs Moffatt and Mrs Dougal ran their shops in the town and were also agents for the Belfast Linens. Their workers were chiefly elderly women, living in tiny one- or two-roomed cottages out in the country, and working exclusively in their own homes. There were no middlemen and no subletting. The women went either to Mrs Moffatt or Mrs Dougal and were handed out the handkerchief squares and told the initials for each set. The pay was occasionally a fixed annual salary, but mostly a fixed commission on the amount done. The price was very low; one woman estimated she could earn about 4s a week. She told Lucy, "My neighbour sometimes earns 10s a week, but she is constantly bent over her needle; and she does very fine work, very fine indeed; leaves and flowers and birds around each initial. And if there is a special commission, a tablecloth or a wedding handkerchief, Mrs Moffatt always gives it to her."

"But you don't do such fine work?"

"No, no, I do the simple initials. She has two daughters to help her with the house and the cooking and the animals, so her hands don't get dirty like mine have to. She has fine fingers, though, fine fingers."

This woman could earn 3d for a dozen plain initials on handkerchiefs, but it rose to 4d a dozen if they were returned to the agent within ten days. Elaborate initial letters could earn 7d a dozen. Children were never given any embroidery, all mistakes and spoiled handkerchiefs had to be paid for, and the workers never gave it to another woman. The trade was pretty brisk just then and they seemed satisfied with the little they earned.

The Chief sent a wire calling her back to London as he wanted to confer with her about Rose Squire. He had been impressed by her contributions to the Laundries Act.

Lucy had a final conference with a chastened Mr Snape. She tried to lift his spirits and they parted on good terms. She had to leave him with plenty of work she had not been able to complete.

She travelled from Belfast to Liverpool and then by the Night Express to Euston and vowed she would NEVER cross that way again. She did not get to London until after midday on August the second. No way to spend her thirty-first birthday!

She took a cab straight to the Home Office to see Mr Sprague Oram. He launched straight into queries about Rose Squire. He had been making enquiries with Dr Dudfield at Kensington Town Hall. He wanted Rose to apply to Sir Matthew Ridley White, the new Home Secretary, for nomination as soon as possible and certainly before Lucy's holiday to Switzerland began in a few days' time. Lucy wired to Rose Squire before she left the Home Office. 'Visit me urgently at home tomorrow before 11a.m.'

Rush, rush, rush to finish the office work and pack for the holiday. Evelyn arrived. Bella Brooks arrived. The tickets arrived. The francs arrived. A letter from Mrs Sidney Webb arrived saying that she contemplated an article in one of the women's monthly magazines on Female Inspectors. May Abraham arrived to exult about Rose Squire and Mrs Sidney Webb's article.

On August 6th the intrepid foursome – Evelyn was inwardly terrified, but smiling broadly, the bravest of them all – set off for their two-week holiday to Switzerland with Thomas Cook.

20

Northern Ireland and Northamptonshire

Back to the grind in Lincolnshire; 'to Londonderry to ferret about'; HMI Snape welcomes her; the Dean's wife and the Archbishop's wife assist Lucy; a weekend with the Gathorne Hardys and Granville; non-existent register for underage workers; Lucy loses holdall on the train; HMI Shaw seems non-existent too.

Hyacinth and Lucy arrived home from the very successful trip to Switzerland early on August the twenty-first. Faithful Emily was there to greet them and they ate their breakfast opening the piles of letters that were piled on the hall table. Hye had two letters regretting that she was not on the short list for two posts ("Didn't want them any way!"), two wedding invitations for the autumn, letters from various aunts, and her time-table for the next term at the College. Lucy's post, apart from a note from Lady Howard proposing to meet her in London at the end of the month, was more prosaic; reports to sign, Complaints to inspect, and a terse note from the Chief requiring a meeting that afternoon, and asking, as a matter of urgency, for Miss Squire's list of laundries at Notting Hill.

"You've only just taken off your hat!" cried Hye.

Emily was stern. "It's slave labour, Miss. I'd tell 'im where 'e gets off."

Sprague Oram handed her another Complaint for the City Road, and one for a mapmaker in Lincoln's Inn Fields, and gave her inspections in Lincolnshire for the next two days.

Back at home Hye and Emily had sorted the washing and laundry, and luckily Mrs Hedingham had come to check the wardrobe – 'and to hear all about the holiday' so Lucy set off for Spalding and Boston with enough clean clothes.

She scurried around cigar factories and featherbed factories, and was out late each evening inspecting for illegal overtime working. In the process she was shocked by the number of 'half-time' and 'underage' children she found at work after 9.30p.m.

Luckily she found that she could lay her prosecuting information by post and so was able to get home by late afternoon on Saturday. Hye had gone to the Boyce, and Lucy luxuriated in a lazy Sunday, washing her hair and writing letters.

"A good job I did."

On Monday the Chief sent her back to Londonderry for a week. "I want you to ferret out conditions of women workers, mostly about restructuring their hours of work. Get as much as you can from actual factory workers, or home workers; there seems to be considerable unrest boiling away under the surface. Exactly what ARE their conditions? What are the wages? How many have been laid off? And the reasons given?"

"You mean I'm to find out through the girls' clubs? The schools? The Trades Unions? The hospitals? Not the actual factories and employers?"

He looked relieved. "That's the ticket. We've had various Irish MPs asking questions. Seems that Irish public opinion is against women working such long hours in factories – not good for home life, sanctity of family, and so on."

"It would certainly be better for home life if the wages were not so pitiful."

"Maybe. Mr Snape has just sent his report on this enquiry. He has a theory the priests are putting the MPs up to asking questions."

"But why?"

"That's one of the reasons you're going. Bit of underground poking about. Miss Abraham's doing the same thing in Dublin. I'm sure you'll be in touch with each other."

Off she went home. She wrote to the Secretary of Textile Operations in Belfast to ask if there was a branch in Londonderry. She wrote to Lady Howard, regretting she would not be in London. She borrowed a book from the Sanitary Institute on Flax Mills. She wired to Hye, to May, to

HMI Snape. She booked her ticket to Belfast via Fleetwood. She packed her various bags. Off she went by the evening train.

In Belfast Mr Snape greeted her like an old friend.

"But why should the employers want to curtail the hours that the women work, Mr Snape? They pay them so much less than the men! I should have thought they would prefer the women."

"But I don't think they do want to curtail the hours, Miss Deane. My view is that neither the managements nor the women are violently in favour of being exempted from those clauses in the 1893 Act. It's the priests who wish it."

"??!!"

"You may well throw up your hands. The PRIESTS wish it because when the girls work at home, or in local workshops, it's far more to the liking of the priests, they can attend services far more than when they are employed inside factories all day and every day. It's the sanctity of the family, the role of the mother, you see."

"Never mind if the poverty of the family that can't make ends meet makes for more hardship for the sanctity of the family, I suppose," said Lucy.

"As usual, Miss Deane, you go straight to the nub of the matter – straight for the jugular! It's the priests put their MPs up to the questions in the House. It's my opinion that whether they are kept hard at work inside the factories or whether, as they are at present, they have less work inside, and are partially in workshops or home working, their monthly hours will work out much the same."

He gave her lists of addresses of Trades Councils, and Church of Ireland clergymen, and she caught the train to Londonderry and booked in at the Palace Hotel. She was greeted there by the manager himself, and given a very attractively furnished room with a small sitting room attached, and she wondered what could have brought about this special treatment until she began to open the letters that were awaiting her. He had seen that one bore the stamp of the Home Office, one the distinctive envelope from Lady Howard in Malvern and one with the seal of the Bishop of Londonderry.

The last one came from the Archbishop's wife Mrs Alexander.

'My dear Miss Deane, My very good friend Lady Howard tells me you are here for a few days. I do hope you will be free to dine with

me and my daughter on Sunday next at your Hotel after Matins.
If you plan to attend the Cathedral Service we could all walk back
together.
I know the Dean and Mrs Smiley are hoping to meet you as well. I
expect they will be in touch soon.
Yours sincerely,
Cecil Alexander.'

Dear Lady Howard. She had eased Lucy's path considerably. Lucy kicked
off her shoes and slipped off her skirt and rested for half an hour in the
charming room; then freshened her face and arms, and sallied forth to a
shirt and collar factory. Then she had a long and helpful interview with
members of the Londonderry Trades Council. They were violently against
employers claiming exemption for women's employment though the
employers were equally anxious for it. Mr Snape's view was definitely
borne out here. She left that office armed with lists of groups to visit and
working women to interview.

Two more days were spent bustling around Derry on the Special
Enquiry, visiting Girls Friendly Societies, and factories, and a Reverend
Egan whose wife ran a Mother's Union on the outskirts of the town. Each
evening she wrote up full notes for her reports.

She went to St Columba's for the morning service on Sunday. 'I shall
wear the green straw hat, but then I must put it away for the winter.' After
the service she was met outside by Mrs Alexander, the noted hymn writer,
and her daughter, two tiny, fine boned women. Mrs Alexander was still
a beauty, her face amazingly free from lines and wrinkles, her daughter a
few years older than Lucy. Lucy noticed that Mrs Alexander had a habit of
stopping every five yards or so to lean on her stick; she would look round
as if she were suddenly noticing something, and Lucy looked around to see
what it could be. There never seemed to be anything particular that she
focussed on, and Miss Alexander never seemed curious.

At the hotel a table had been reserved for them, obviously a favourite
of theirs, and the head waiter was most attentive. Mrs Alexander ate no
more than a bird, but was a perfect hostess. Both mother and daughter
asked knowledgeable questions and were able to give Lucy valuable
contacts both in Ireland and England. Just once, Mrs Alexander stopped
dead in the midst of an anecdote and closed her eyes for at least half a

minute. At once Miss Alexander continued with the story as if nothing was amiss, and Lucy, about to be alarmed and ask what was the matter, was forced to go along with the conversation. Mrs Alexander opened her eyes and smiled at them both with pleasure, "I must get home for my afternoon nap. Such a delight to have met you, dear Miss Deane. I'm sure Mrs Smiley will enjoy you as much as we have, and the Dean too. They are looking forward to greeting you this evening, I hear. We will be sure to put you in touch with people we think may be helpful to you." And off they went briskly towards the Bishop's Palace.

Lucy went up to her room and saw them pausing as they crossed a narrow street that curved around the end of the hotel garden. She watched Miss Alexander take her mother's arm protectively into her own, and the two small figures continue, much more slowly, out of sight.

Mrs Smiley sent a maid to collect Lucy that evening. Lucy was grateful as the Deanery nestled at one side of the Close in a small maze of cobbled streets.

"What did you think of our Cathedral?" asked the Dean.

"I thought it was grand. And the ceiling is magnificent."

"Very striking," he agreed "and not many years old."

They were most hospitable and Mrs Smiley, a member of many committees and a mine of information, provided her with names of various 'women with local knowledge and sensible enough to answer your questions.'

Through Mrs Smiley she met three shirt outworkers and asked about pay and conditions. All were outworkers, two of them machinists, one a 'finisher'. The machinists got 1s 3d to 1s 6d for a dozen shirts, and could make 14s a week if they worked full hours from 8a.m. to 6.p.m. The finishers all took the work home and returned it to the agents who examined it and paid 1s 3d to 1s 6d a dozen. Finishers did the button-holes, collars, cuffs and fronts. They could only make 10s a week and that only by working at night.

On her last day she returned to Belfast on an early train and visited two match factories whose managers said they had not been visited for two years; but when she visited Mr Snape he did not disclose this, simply informed her that, of the three Complaints against sanitary conditions she had made last week, two textile factories had promised improvements within a few months.

Back in London she visited the Home Office and made a verbal report of her findings. She spoke of Snape's neglect of the match factories. Sprague Oram nodded. He had been told that two of Paterson's Match Factory girls were in hospital in Belfast with some infection of the mouth.

Lucy was doubly vexed. "Snape never told me this, though I conferred with him on the matter. So I couldn't make any investigation while I was there, for of course the manager did not tell me, and none of the girls did."

The Chief nodded. "You are surprised?"

"I am disappointed. I had thought we were beginning to be on better terms."

"Ah, it's a slow, slow process. Meanwhile, back to Wellingborough, please, for two days, to finish off those workshops and make sure everyone has an Abstract pinned up on the wall. And that the hours for half-times are underlined."

Lucy felt very tired suddenly. She took a cab home to 100 Fulham Road, as the sun set, and found it cold and empty. Amongst the letters on the hall table was a note from Hye dated that morning.

'I had a call today, Thursday, to go to the Bristol Cookery School for two weeks as their Plain Cooking Instructor has caught the mumps. I have wired to Londonderry but you had already gone. Wire to me when you get this and to the Boyce. I shall go there Sept 7th and 8th. Emily will come in on Friday morning and over the weekend if you need her. I miss you. Kisses. Hye'

Lucy felt cold and miserable. She lit the gas lamp and stood in the empty room. After a little while she opened the other letters. One was from Janie Gathorne Hardy at Benenden Grange – 'do come to stay for a weekend soon, Sept 7th or 8th, or Sept 14th or 15th.' Suddenly she made up her mind. Stop moping. She wrote an acceptance for the coming weekend, wrote a note for Emily, threw her dirty clothes into the laundry basket, repacked her small suitcase and her writing case, turned and shut the door and took a cab to the Euston Hotel for the night, ready to catch an early train to Wellingborough the next morning.

She slept badly. The hotel was noisy and her room gave onto a view of the station with constant trains and shouts and clangings. She made a hurried breakfast, caught the early train and was lucky to have an empty carriage, so she wrote to Adelaide and May during the journey. For two days she went about her Chief's business, uncovering and following up leads on overcrowding, underage employment, excessive hours of work, and making contact with the Medical Officers of Health in the towns from Northampton to Leicester. It became clear that there was an enormous amount of work to be done in the area. Very little inspection had been done in the area's burgeoning factories, and as far as she could see, absolutely nothing had ever been done to check on workshops, or home workers in the outlying villages.

The weather was very warm and by the end of each day her head ached badly. On Friday there was just enough time at 100 Fulham Road to touch base with the long-suffering Emily, write to Hye and the family at the Boyce, pack a fresh suitcase and set off on Saturday morning for the weekend with Janie Gathorne Hardy.

Lady Janie Gathorne Hardy, a distant relation, had been a good friend of Lucy's mother in India and had kept a lively interest in Lucy and Hyacinth. When they were girls the sisters had visited several times and Lucy was looking forward to a calm and sedate weekend in the huge rambling house, and walking in the wonderful gardens and huge park. To her disquiet, at Benenden station two smart traps were waiting, and several young people unloaded a plethora of suitcases, tennis racquets, riding boots, while greeting each other loudly and effusively. Lucy's heart sank. Lady Janie had invited a young house party, and, as was clear by her welcoming greetings, had organised a programme of tennis parties, early morning rides, an evening dance and an evening of cards and music. Lucy wondered whether the pink dinner gown would come up to the mark and whether her two skirts and her plain black shoes could carry her through the festivities. She had counted on a quiet evening with Janie, an early bed time, and a couple of gentle rambles through the park.

"I am so tired," she moaned to herself as the maid unpacked her inadequate belongings. She went down to lunch wondering how to get out of the tennis tournament and bumped into Granville Streatfeild.

"Oh, good, they told me you had arrived," he said. "Are you all ready for the fray?"

Lucy felt light-headed with relief. "No, no, not at all! I was SO looking forward to a nice old ladies' weekend with Janie, and an early night."

"No hope of that," agreed Granville, "But you can partner me for the tennis doubles, and I'll make sure we lose in the first set. Then we can just sit and talk for a bit and you can slope off for a nap."

Her spirits soared. With Granville there she could face the world, and set to the tennis with a borrowed racquet and determination to lose.

Halfway through the match Granville said, "I don't think you want to lose at all."

"Oh, I do, I do! But I don't want it to be ignominious."

"Well, watch it. Put your mind to failing. Because they're not very good! I'm having trouble not getting the ball back."

A short rest and a bath set her up for the evening's dancing and the next morning's amble around the lake at the end of the park with Granville, while another group rode off towards Tenterden, and two or three accompanied Lady Janie to Hemsted church. Granville was full of his architectural plans for the new church in Brighton, and she was interested in the general conversation and amused at the incessant frivolity of a couple of the young women guests.

Back in London on Monday morning and the tiredness swept back and the Office Day seemed particularly painful. She sat in her sad little house in the Fulham Road, trying to concentrate on her Irish reports and Kettering reports. She set out for the Home Office and for the Finsbury Circus office, but felt so faint and weak that she had to sit down at South Kensington and return home to lie down. Emily was concerned. Lucy had planned to visit Adelaide at Hadley Wood but Emily scurried out to send a wire to say she could not go. Slowly as the afternoon wore on, the pains subsided. A persistent thought arose. 'How long can I go on like this? Suppose it gets worse?' But she banished it, and, soothed by sips of hot water, and frequent short bouts of curling herself up on her bed, gradually the pains drifted away for another month.

The rest of September was spent trying to untangle the mares' nest of Disorder in the Northampton towns. The HMI Registers showed that most of the factories had been visited in the past year, though on her re-inspections it appeared that nothing had changed, for better or for worse. Lucy began to suspect they had never been inspected in the first place. HMI Shaw was away for most of September and the clerks in his office seemed nonplussed by her requests for files. Small workshops across the regions had clearly never been visited, and the list in that Register was miniscule.

On arrival in Kettering she visited the Medical Officer of Health. Out. She visited the Public Health Office. Closed. She visited several schools to enquire about the attendance of half-timers. One headmaster told her they had about fifty on half-time. Last year it had been ninety, but this year reduced by the raising of the school leaving age. He told her he knew that several half-timers went back to work in the evenings after their days in school. The headmistress at the Alexandra Street National School said she had few pupils working in the factories. Most of her girls were employed as domestics and many of them were very irregular school attenders, as if they were not in employment, they were keeping house at home while their mother was at work. Both schools provided her with lists of irregular attenders and Lucy enquired at every factory and mill to produce any Children's Worker attendance certificates; the managers found this request universally extraordinary and most simply had no records on file. They were all satisfactorily supplied with plans for Health and Safety, such as machinery guards and fire escapes, but had lamentable provisions, or no provisions at all, for sanitary conveniences, water taps, or any separate place provided for meals and rest times. The small workshops that had made it on to the Registers were in the same parlous state. By the end of the week she found she had Complaints for prosecution on six factories, no workable Registers for workshops at all, and evidence of many children employed under age without a certificate of attendance or employment.

As Hye was still away she stayed in Kettering for the weekend, in an uncomfortable old inn with cheap china and badly sewn religious texts on the walls. She visited numerous parents about Certificates of Standard Education. She made a flying visit to London to ask advice from the Chief, and ask his approval for the prosecutions. He did not seem surprised, but he promised to write to HMI Shaw to await his return from leave and to pressure for the immediate provision of local workshop Registers. Till then he told her she had better make her own register of the factories in Wellingborough and in Rushden!

Meanwhile Lucy had written to May Abraham at her flat, at her family's home in Dublin, and at the Home Office, but with no success, and Adelaide, now inspecting in the Sheffield district, had had no news of her. She should have returned from holiday. Lucy hoped she was not ill. She wondered whether May was taking too great an interest in young

Harold Tennant, now an MP, and his Scottish constituency. On reflection it seemed all too likely.

In Northamptonshire she inspected in Findon and Desborough, relieved to find the factories more regular than further south with regard to underage employees, and she arrived back in Kettering to find she had left her holdall on the train. She left a note to the stationmaster at Kettering and went back in a temper to uncomfortable Angel Hotel.

When she made her visit to the Police Court, the clerks there looked at her as if she was a strange animal and were doubtful of her right to conduct prosecutions. She wired from the court to the Chief at the Home Office to explain on whose authority it should be done. And she enjoyed their great discomfiture when they received his reply two hours later. She accepted their apologies graciously, and managed to conduct the prosecutions that same day. They were all successful for her, and she thoroughly approved of the magistrates and the solicitor, but the late start meant that the court had to sit until after five o'clock.

Exulting, she returned to the hotel and found that a porter had arrived with her holdall, which had travelled on to St Pancras and spent the night in the Lost Property office there. Lucy tipped him generously, and to celebrate ordered herself tea and cakes in the hotel sitting room.

She wrote to the Chief thanking him for his speedy reply to the wire. 'Where am I to go next? There is still so much to be done here, but it is all in such disarray. HMI Shaw has still not returned from holiday and his clerks seem to have no up-to-date information. The Sanitary Inspectors and the Medical Officers of Health seem very tardy to act on information sent them.' Lucy thought the Sanitary Inspector in Wellingborough exceedingly stupid, but thought she had better not say so. She posted the letter by the late evening post.

A day or so later a letter from the Chief said he would see her between 11 and 2 at the Home Office next Saturday. Meanwhile he wished her to make a DISCREET enquiry into the hosiery trade in Nottingham for domestic workers. And he had written to HMI Shaw, and she should be hearing from him very soon.

Friday evening brought a note from HMI Shaw saying he would meet her on Monday. Would she prefer to meet in Kettering or in Peterborough?

Peterborough, thought Lucy. On my way to Nottingham. Then I can look at the cathedral.

The weather changed over the weekend and became cool and grey. Lucy wished she had a thicker coat, and went out and bought some warmer stockings. Her green straw hat was looking forward to being packed away. She looked critically in the long mirror on the hotel landing and thought she was looking rather stiff and severe. Just right for a meeting with HMI Shaw, she decided, when I sail in with the list of all the irregular places I have visited from his Directories.

She took a cab to his office from Peterborough Station. They disliked each other immediately. He saw a tall thin pale woman with sharp eyes and an extremely business-like air. She saw a round balding man with a grey moustache and wide blue rheumy eyes, and a very expensive and handsome suit. He began to talk of his holidays. She said she was sorry but she had so little time, she was due in Nottingham by two that afternoon. She laid out before him the pile of reports she had made, the schools, the factories and the workshops she had visited. She told him how unsatisfactory the Certifying Surgeons had been at the Rushden District. She gave him the list of prosecutions she had made the week before, and a pack of Abstracts to be sent to the relevant factories. He thanked her with a sour smile, they shook hands entirely insincerely, and he helped her climb into another cab and drive away. He was in a bad temper all morning, but as for Lucy, she had forgotten him before the cab had turned the corner and she spent a happy hour in Peterborough Cathedral.

As soon as she arrived in Nottingham she began to settle to the queries the Chief wanted making on the hosiery and laundry trades. At the hotel a packet of letters awaited her sent on from the Home Office, two long letters from Adelaide Anderson, and to her relief, one from May Abraham with helpful addresses of hosiery Unions, laundry women's services, Poor Law guardians and other useful people, Girls clubs, and clergy. There was also a long letter from Hye, returning in good spirits this weekend, a new job in the offing, so much to tell, so much to hear.

'We will sort out our wardrobes, Mrs Hedingham says she is determined to make us as fashionable and as pretty as a very little extra money and her skilful needle will make us. Leah's summer season has been wonderful and she had been given the part of the Good Fairy in a pantomime down on the South Coast. Hooray for Leah!'

Lucy was glad for the Hedinghams as well. Mrs Hedingham had been widowed very young, and she had struggled to bring up little Leah, by taking in mending for various big houses in her neighbourhood. Aunt Augusta Deane had been one of her employers. She was impressed with Mrs Hedingham's constant struggle to remain ladylike and to educate Leah as best she could. From a very early age Leah had been determined to dance and sing, and her dancing school had high hopes of her, placing her as a child in Christmas shows and plays in small London theatres and sending her to auditions as she reached working age. Mrs Hedingham had supported her through thick and thin and now it seemed as if Leah's career finally might be taking off.

21

Laundries, bicycles and dentists

May and Adelaide descend on 100 Fulham Road; Evelyn and Emily hold the fort; Mary Deane's fiancé; Wandsworth is awash with laundries; Lyons' waitresses try to go on strike; Mary Paterson helps with the Laundries Report; Lucy takes bicycle lessons; the Christmas Theatre Outing; 100 Fulham Road stretches to bursting point; inspecting in torrential rain; a lovely Christmas alone; raging toothache.

"You're to bar the door, Evelyn. She is not to go back to work tomorrow. She is not to go near a train for a week. It's too much for her."

"That's just silly, Hye. You know I shall be better by tomorrow. I always am."

"No, not lately. Having to racket about on buffeting trains, having to stay in nasty commercial hotels. It's not – it's not – it's not suitable, Lucy. It's indecorous. It's not good for her, Evelyn."

"I certainly shan't let her past the door tomorrow," soothed Evelyn. "We'll take it day by day. I won't let her go until she's better, really I won't."

Hyacinth swept off to invigilate for three days of Cookery Examinations in Oxford.

"It's ridiculous. I shall be fine tomorrow."

"Then you can sit here and write all your office papers. And get better at your own pace. And if there is anything plain and simple to copy out, I'll copy it out."

The three of them were all relieved. Hye was calmed by Evelyn's presence and knew that Lucy was in capable hands; Lucy was secretly thankful to have an extra day to organise herself slowly; Evelyn was happy to be considered necessary and responsible to look after Lucy.

The morning post brought letters from Adelaide Anderson and May Abraham, both wanting to arrange meetings. Evelyn was dispatched to send wires, and Monday teatime brought both women to 100 Fulham Road for a conference.

"Long, long overdue," sighed Adelaide.

They cleared the table and spread out papers and drew up a rough agenda of needs and requirements.

AGENDA.
We need: a room set aside for meeting with ALL members of the Female Inspectorate at the SAME TIME.
Regular times for meeting with ALL Female Inspectors.
Regular secretarial assistance for the Female Inspectors Department.
An extra member of the Female Inspectorate. (Rose Squire?)
(Preferably two.)
What has each one of us been doing? May, Mary, Lucy, Adelaide.
We need a Junior Inspector under each Female Inspector.

Emily had been doing the ironing in the kitchen when the visitors arrived, and was enchanted by the way May came through and introduced herself and then took over the chair of the meeting.

Evelyn left them to it and came in to Emily.

"Should I make some tea, Miss Deane?"

"Oh yes, what a good idea."

"I'm not sure there'll be enough milk."

"Oh dear, shall I go out to the dairy? Shall I get some cake as well?"

"That would be nice, Miss. And do you think they will be staying for supper?"

"Heavens, Emily, do you think they might?" Evelyn peeped in through the half open door. "It certainly looks as if they've settled in for the evening."

"Then what will they eat?"

"Four of us! And we were just going to finish up your delicious soup. Not really enough for four!"

"No, Miss, but there's some big potatoes and a good fire. If you was to get a good lump of cheese and some more butter, I could bake some

MISS LUCY DEANE.
(From a photograph by G. Glanville, Tunbridge Wells.)

Lucy Deane as Sanitary Inspector for Kensington 1893
"A Sanitary Inspector! Oh dear! Oh dear!" (Prologue)

Lucy Deane 1917. One of the first Women Factory
Inspectors. "We need pioneers like you" (Ch.5)

Lucy's cousins at their home, The Boyce, Dymock, Glos. Squire George and Mrs Deane, Mary,
Ethel and Evelyn (sitting) © All images above in possession of the author (Prologue)

A Family run Laundry 1900. "They slept in the ironing room and the washhouse was the kitchen" © John Brown Collection (Ch.3)

May Abraham, the very first Woman Factory Inspector 1892. "Wonderful young woman, razor sharp and smooth as velvet" © Mary Evans Picture Library (Ch.1)

Sir Charles Dilke, MP Radical Liberal, and Lady Emilia Dilke. She was President of the Women's Trade Union League. © National Portrait Gallery (Ch.3)

The Potteries Stoke on Trent circa 1900. "Soot encrusted houses, strange squat kilns, and a grey mist" © Gladstone Pottery Museum (Ch.9)

'Pit Wenches' in Wednesbury 1890. "That odd pervasive egg-like smell"
© Black Country Living Museum (Ch.27)

A WORK ROOM.

TOP: A Dressmaker's establishment. "An airless room stuffed with 20 women at narrow tables" © John Brown Collection (Ch.2)

MIDDLE: The Frozen Thames 11th February 1895. "The fearful freeze has thrown thousands of men out of work" © John Brown Collection (Ch.15)

BETWEEN THE COURSES.

BOTTOM: The Pink Dinner Dress. "You CAN'T dine at the House in a SERVICEABLE gown!" © John Brown Collection (Ch.15)

Nail- and -chain women workers Cradley Heath. "Wild medieval hovels, slung on the side of beautiful valleys" © Black Country Living Museum (Ch.13)

Artificial Flower Workers. "But they had to freeze because their posies were so flammable."
© John Brown Collection (Ch.15)

Learning to ride a bicycle. "By Saturday afternoon Lucy could pedal unaided"
©John Brown Collection (Ch.21)

Tennis Party. "Don't fret, we'll lose in the first set, then you can slope off for a nap!"
© John Brown Collection (Ch.20)

Women painting plates in the Potteries. "These lead poisoning cases – why are they all so young?" © Gladstone Pottery Museum (Ch.31)

The Jubilee Procession and Illuminations 1897. "It was wonderful, but Hye was too short to see anything" © John Brown Collection (Ch.31)

Lace Making School, Donegal. "Fifteen young girls were already making extraordinary progress" © National Library of Ireland (Ch.38)

The Ardara Hotel, Adara, Donegal 1897. "Oh, this is much the nicest place of all!" cried Lucy.
© National Library of Ireland (Ch.38)

potatoes, and you could have a small portion of soup with the baked potatoes. And I could make some scones as well, while you was out."

"Emily, what would we do without you?"

Emily smiled politely, but inwardly she agreed with Evelyn. "I'll put on the big kettle for tea now, the dairy's only round the corner, Miss."

Evelyn put on her coat and hat and slipped past the three conference holders already engrossed in their plans and note taking.

Emily put away the ironing and took the irons off the range, and filled the kettle and laid the tea tray. She wished it was always like this at 100 Fulham Road, not so lonely, never knowing if either of them was going to be there, sometimes by herself for weeks on end, except for Thursday afternoons when Mrs Hedingham, and sometimes her pretty daughter, came in to mend and press the sisters' clothes.

When Evelyn returned the meeting was in full swing. Evelyn dispensed the tea, and the wonderful smell of baking potatoes filled the house. Emily regretfully went home before her mother began to worry. May had planned out how they were to divide the editing of the new Factory Acts, Lucy had drafted a letter of introduction for Rose Squire to present to the Home Secretary's secretary, Adelaide had planned an entire week of visiting laundries with Lucy in Wandsworth next week, and Evelyn had arranged for Hye and Lucy to spend the weekend at the Boyce.

May and Adelaide left together as the clock struck eight, and Lucy was sent to bed, flushed with firelight, cheerful, and feeling ready to cope with the world again. Evelyn stacked the supper plates in the kitchen ready for Emily to deal with the next morning and plumped up the cushions in the living room.

"You are a brick, Evelyn. Thanks for coming to our rescue." Evelyn's cup ran over.

Lucy set off restored on Thursday to polish off various sock and stocking factories in Matlock, Belper, Nottingham and Cromford, checking particularly on the questions the Chief had given her, and uncovering several inadequacies on the way.

The sisters met at the Boyce in Dymock on the Saturday, a welcome quiet weekend as Uncle George was not well, a small dinner party had been cancelled and the whole family went to bed early. Mary's fiancé was staying as well. Lucy enjoyed talking to him and liked him well enough. He was a tall young man, angular of build and features, a structural engineer about to set off for India to build dams and bridges. He was besotted with Mary's verve and wit, but Lucy and Hye agreed it was an odd match. He seemed kind and capable, but showed no particular need for society life.

"She'll run rings round him," said Hye.

"She'll find him very dull," said Lucy. "He's a homebody at heart."

On the Monday they set off for London and more laundries. Hye was starting on the laundry section of her course in Barnett College. "It makes a change from teaching people good plain cooking." She would be visiting laundries too – "But better than you, Lucy. I get to make starch and light the coppers and wear big aprons."

Laundries, laundries in Wandsworth. Who would have thought Wandsworth could have needed so many. Twelve one day, twenty the next. On Sunday she wrote up all the reports and met with Adelaide to see how she had been coping with her lists. On the Monday she visited laundries in Wandsworth, on Tuesday Wandsworth laundries yet again.

On the Wednesday she went to the Home Office to hand in those reports that had been completed and met Rose Squire there. Rose was very hopeful about her application for Inspector. They clasped hands.

"We all of us want you to join us. If it was our decision you would be here now. You could help us write this Enquiry into Laundries. Wandsworth is awash with laundries!"

"There can't be more in Wandsworth than Kensington. I am a martyr to laundries. I'm going on to a talk given by Mrs Sidney Webb. Come with me. Have a day without steam."

Lucy decided she was justified in going. It was a useful small meeting with an additional lively young speaker, a Miss Seymour, about the Social Democratic Union in Germany. Mrs Sidney Webb was pleased to see them and told them of a new venture, a London School of Economics, which was being formed by the Fabian Society, and promised to invite them to the inaugural session in the near future.

Afterwards Rose took Lucy to a strike meeting of waitresses from the Lyons Tea Company. They wanted to form a Union. The two Miss Tuckwells were there and a woman journalist from the *Daily Chronicle*.

But no other person was there except the twenty or so girls who had struck and already formed themselves into a Union. Hundreds of handbills had been distributed outside tea shops, but the other waitresses were too frightened to join them. Lucy spoke to three girls, dressed exactly as if they were demi-mondes with painted eyes and rouge and lipstick. Lucy felt this would not further their cause. They said they were allowed 7s a week on commission; 5% on what they sold, and earned about 7s a week in tips; that they had to wash up the china and cutlery until midday when the shops opened; that they worked from 8a.m. till 9p.m., Saturday included; that there was no fixed time for meals, they ate when they could; they were provided with a plate of meat and bread for dinner, and a cup of tea and bread and butter for tea; that 3d a DAY was deducted from their earnings for washing (caps, collars, aprons and cuffs) at Lyons' own laundry; that their uniform was sold to them, i.e. they must buy from Lyons four yards of material at 2s 6d a yard – it looked as if it was only worth 1s 6d a yard – and then have it made up themselves. They had struck because they were suddenly informed that for the future they would be paid 2% instead of 5% commission.

"When we complained to the management and said we would strike we were sacked at a minute's notice."

"Right there and then!"

"And heaps of other girls rushed to get our places."

"And now we can't get decent places at Lyons, and we've got a very bad name and no decent place will take us."

Lucy took notes, and so did Gertrude Tuckwell. But Lucy saw they were hopelessly disorganised for a union. Gertrude Tuckwell undertook to approach the Employers of the ABC Tea Stores, or some other reputable company, with a view of allowing these girls to form a union which would have greater weight and power.

"That don't seem likely," said one.

"It might work," said Miss Tuckwell. "These firms are being undercut by places like Lyons who pay wretchedly. They might perhaps consent to a union among their own girls as an advertisement and a check."

They left the poor dispirited girls talking to the *Daily Chronicle* woman, and asked Gertrude to let them know if anything hopeful came of her enquiries.

And then back to the laundries, South Croydon, West Croydon,

Balham, Putney, Thornton Heath, Norwood, Acton Green, Brentford, Ealing, Chiswick.

Arriving home one Thursday evening in the November fog and damp, Lucy found Mrs Hedingham pressing a skirt after patching the hem.

"All this walking is too hard on these skirts," scolded Mrs Hedingham. "I've shortened them as much as I can. And the mud has stained two petticoats beyond redemption. It's no use, Lucy, you must buy some more outfits, and some dresses too, and Hye needs smartening up. You are professional women, you must look SMART as well as serviceable. And look at your shoes, they're worn out. I wouldn't let Leah go out of the door in shoes like those!"

Lucy agreed meekly.

And then May Wilder, an old school friend, came to stay for the weekend riding a bicycle!

"On a bicycle!"

"On a BICYCLE – my dear!"

She had brought it down in the guard's van with her weekend holdall in a jaunty basket on the front. "It's wonderful in Hampshire, saves me hours, and certainly saves money. It's good tempered. It doesn't eat anything. You should get one, really, you should Lucy!"

"Yes, really I should. But I can't ride one."

"Nor could I, so I learnt. Took two or three lessons and a bit of practice round the garden."

"No garden."

"Nonsense. You've got parks."

"It's a wonderful idea. I'll think about it and so will Hye."

Hye did think about it, for one minute, and then rejected it out of hand. "It's a good job you have nursing experience, Lucy. You will be needing it. Not just for the bruises. For the pneumonia you will catch in this winter weather."

But she did agree with Mrs Hedingham about new clothes.

May Wilder took them to see *Gentleman Joe* at the Strand Theatre.

Hye loved it. "It's been a long time since we went to the theatre, Lucy. We should go more often."

"Yes, we should. My word, we are branching out. New clothes, theatres, bicycles."

"Bicycles!" Hye snorted.

However, they made an appointment with Mrs Hubbard, their dressmaker, and bought some fashion magazines; and Lucy went to the Army and Navy for a bicycle. The young man in the Bicycle Department was most enthusiastic, but advised her against buying one until she had had a short course of lessons provided by the Army and Navy. Lucy signed up.

The piles of reports on laundries grew ridiculously high. Mr Sprague Oram said that Miss Paterson had been drafted in from Scotland to help with the final organisation, so Lucy invited her to stay at 100 Fulham Road, and then decided it would be a good idea to invite the entire Female Inspectors Department to a pre-Christmas Dinner and Theatre Outing.

She sent out her invitations, including Rose Squire, and engaged a theatre box for *Squire of Demons* at the Criterion, Piccadilly, and dinner beforehand at the Victoria Hotel, Northumberland Avenue, for the forthcoming Tuesday.

For the next two mornings she arrived at the Army and Navy Stores for her bicycle lessons. A cheerful young woman employee in a red tam o'shanter was her coach, and helped her to lurch around an indoor yard with various shrieks and squawks. The yard had piles of parcels piled around the edges and a constant stream of young store assistants, with sackcloth aprons, came and went, collecting and carrying the parcels out to the delivery cabs. Lucy was treated to broad grins and the occasional encouraging nod. Halfway through her half-hour lesson a man and a girl came to join her, each with their own coach. They had obviously had some lessons previously and both rode very gingerly and without assistance. The girl sat rigidly upright with a fixed expression and her mouth clamped into a straight line. "Oh, isn't she clever?" said Lucy as her coach saved her from yet another lurch over. "She doesn't squawk like me."

"She did yesterday," said her coach. "Split your eardrums till she got the 'ang of it."

By the Saturday afternoon she could pedal unaided.

"Still squawk, though."

"Squawking's natural to begin with."

Elated, Lucy ordered a bicycle, to be delivered after the next stage of lessons – riding amongst traffic. Hye was still very suspicious of the idea, but she was too relieved to have passed, and passed creditably, the Home Laundry section of her course, to give Lucy much attention.

Mary Paterson arrived from Scotland, bringing with her well tried and simplified ways of evaluating the ever-growing mounds of laundry paper. She was amused by Lucy's struggles with the bicycles and went with her to watch the lesson before they set off for the suds and steam in Hanwell.

The dinner and theatre outing was a great success. Hye had been invited but refused. "No, thank you, Lucy. You'll all do nothing but talk factories and prosecutions and Home Office politics. I know you when you all get together. I'll be in bed when you get back."

Sure enough, May wanted extra meetings. She wanted to present Mr Sprague Oram with a definite plan of action for the Female Inspectors with regard to the new supervisions in laundries. They planned a Conference dinner for the next Tuesday. She also persuaded Lucy to go with her to a very elite Brook Street dressmaker's workshop to take declarations of overtime work on a Complaint that work had been going on at 1a.m.

Adelaide came back to 100 Fulham Road with Lucy and Mary to stay the night. It was too late for her to get back to Hadley Wood. Hye was in her own little room, Adelaide and Mary shared Lucy's room with the two single beds; Lucy bedded down in the sitting room with quilts and cushions before the dying fire, and was asleep almost before her head hit the pillow.

The visit to the Brook Street dressmaker was a failure. They found only three girls and the occupier, and the girls all lived in the house. They were terrified and would betray nothing. They all signed declarations saying they never worked before 8a.m. Neither May or Lucy believed them but they could do nothing; however, they decided that it was likely that the dressmaker would be more moderate in future, at least in the short term.

Lucy enjoyed Mary Paterson's company, and Mary enjoyed her time in London with her colleagues. "I haven't been so social for years! Theatre! Hotel dinners! Bicycles!" Lucy learnt a great deal from Mary in her pleasant, patient, measured way of eliciting information from employer and employee alike, and the clarity of her lists, as well as the speed in which she made a précis of her findings with never a superfluous word.

The Conference dinner at the Grand Hotel was useful for all four of them. May was determined the new Laundry Act should be a grand opportunity for inaugurating some special work for the department. And, said Mary, for spreading the rules of the Laundry Act among the laundries, while giving as little power to the employers as possible.

"Yes," said Adelaide, "they have never had formal inspections before, only the checking of their sanitary conditions; therefore, they can't cite the plans suggested to them by previous inspectors by which they could escape the provisions of the law as other factory and workshop employers constantly do. We can, in fact, set our own standard."

"Those are fighting words!" said Mary.

She went back north the next day after accompanying Lucy to the bicycle show at the Agricultural Hall. "A week full of surprises. Thank you so much."

As her train pulled out it began to rain, and it rained in torrents for three days. Lucy struggled to keep her umbrella up as she went from place to place in Wimbledon. On the second day she gave up at lunchtime and hired a cab for two hours, but she got just as wet getting in and out, and so on the third day she hired a cab in Sutton all day and put it down to expenses. Returning home, she discovered she was very seedy, very seedy indeed, took another cab from Victoria station and went to bed.

She stayed in bed over the weekend and to her amazement no cold developed. Hye made a Christmas cake and laced it liberally with sherry. The smell permeated the house and made them feel opulent.

May met her at the Finsbury Circus office on the Monday in order to read through May's summary of their meeting for the Annual Report. This took less time than Lucy had expected and so she went to Peter Robinsons and bought a very jaunty felt hat with cock's feathers, before her appointment with Mrs Hubbard to be fitted for a new winter suit and dress.

Hyacinth did not approve of the hat, and when Lucy got it home, neither did she. They returned it on Tuesday morning and both had fittings for the new clothes before Lucy visited more laundries in Twickenham and Richmond.

She woke in the night with a raging toothache, but decided to hope it would fade away, and went on to make return visits to several fur companies, two of which had had extra Complaints made. The dentist could not treat her until the next Monday, and although she returned to the fur companies she then felt so wretched that she went home and wrapped her poor jaw in shawls. Saturday was a wasted day, a mild, sunny, December day and a perfect day for being out and about, but every step hurt her mouth. She stayed in and wrote to May Abraham. Sunday was truly spring-like. Hye went for a walk across Kensington Gardens to lunch with Aunt Augusta in Bayswater. Lucy fretted by the fire, longing for sympathy, her whole head throbbing.

Hye accompanied her to the dentist. A visiting doctor came to give her gas, and the tooth was taken out. Hye took her home in a cab and Emily fussed around her and put her to bed. She had applied for sick leave for two days, but once the tooth had gone she made a good recovery and had no ill effects. She felt light and easy and clear-headed and when she heard the door bell in the early afternoon came down to find May Abraham. "I came to enquire how you were," said May, "My! What a swollen face! I am so sorry."

"Is it swollen?" said Lucy in surprise. "It feels normal."

She looked in the mirror in the hall at her puffy blotchy face. "How extraordinary! I feel perfectly all right."

"You shouldn't be talking, Lucy," scolded Hye. "That's not good for your poor mouth."

"Don't be silly, Hye. I'm bored up there by myself."

"No, she isn't silly, not in the least. And you needn't be bored. I've brought you the Table of Penalties for the new edition of the Factory Act. I'll read them through to you and then perhaps – only if you feel up to it of course – you could make some notes and suggestions, and maybe get them to me tomorrow."

Emily and Hye looked disgusted. Lucy looked delighted. Emily and Hyacinth went into the kitchen to make tea and listened to May's lilting Dublin accent enumerating fines and deductions, penalties and Complaints.

"How can she expect her to listen to such miserable stuff?" grumbled Emily.

"Lucy would much rather have it than a juicy French novel. They are all of them, those four, distinctly ODD, and Lucy's the worst."

Lucy took the Table of Penalties back to bed with her, and went to the dentist the next morning and he was pleased with her. So she went on to May Abraham's eagle's nest in Tite Street and stayed until early afternoon; she took care to get home well before Hye came back from work, the last day of her Christmas term, and well after Emily, who only worked in the mornings on Tuesdays, had gone home.

By the Wednesday she felt a fraud. She went and had the final fittings for her new clothes at Mrs Hubbard's and then salved her conscience by taking the train to Twickenham.

She ordered a bicycle from the Army and Navy Stores at the weekend and asked that it be delivered to her by Christmas. She was determined that the laundry travelling would be completed by Christmas, and so the last few days before the holiday she went down into Kent around Tonbridge and Tunbridge Wells. She was able to stay overnight with the Streatfeild family, and then with Lina Pott's family when she visited in Hastings, St Leonards and Bexhill. Mr Pott gave her a tour over Tonbridge School, a most extensive set of buildings, and she was impressed with the science rooms, studies, staff rooms, dining rooms and playing fields. She thought about it as she travelled back to London, comparing it with the Parish and National Schools she visited, with their rows of benches and slates and tired schoolmasters and mistresses, and the smells of unwashed bodies.

The Boyce cousins were deluged with visitors for Christmas from home and abroad, so Hye and Lucy spent their Christmas at home, calling on Aunt Florrie and Uncle Murray, going to the *Mikado* together at D'Oyley Carte, writing Christmas letters, sending cards, going to morning service, putting holly over the pictures, eating a brace of pheasants the Streatfeilds had sent up from Kent, enjoying Hye's Christmas cake, and roasting chestnuts.

The Army and Navy did not deliver the bicycle in time for Christmas, and Lucy was disappointed that she could not ride it in Kensington Gardens on Boxing Day. Hyacinth was pleased. She was busy anyway on Boxing Day as the Cookery College had been booked to provide a Ball supper and she was in charge of the desserts. When she returned from Barnet the next day they packed their bags, including their new outfits, and set off for the Boyce for the New Year.

22

Strengthening positions

Rose Squire, the fifth Factory Inspector; Campbell's dressmakers; the Annual Report;
January crowded with requests; the new bicycle arrives; Harold Tennant to the fore;
Hye and Emily are converted to the bike; Sprague Oram's final days; the Finsbury
Circus office takes new shape; a shirt and collar industry report; Lucy's first traffic
outing; hostility at Luton Magistrates' Court; parsnip soup; 'the HORRID Bench';
'the whole article bristles with inaccuracies'.

There was tremendous jubilation on New Year's Day. Lucy saw Miss
Rose Squire gazetted in *The Times* as another of Her Majesty's Factory
Inspectors. She ran from the Boyce breakfast table and brought her hat
and threw it in the air. Mary looked pained and Uncle George looked
bemused. "We are all very pleased for you," said Aunt Georgie equably.
Hye and Evelyn hugged her, but Hye warned her, "Five Female Factory
Inspectors don't make a summer!"

"No, but they make a big difference."

Hye stayed on at the Boyce as the school term did not begin until
the following week. Lucy travelled back to London to a mountain of
correspondence, and found the Chief at the Home Office waving a letter.
"You must all use the Finsbury Circus office more often – the powers
that be are trying to take it away from us – you must establish it as a firm
base; when I have retired you do not know how my successor will want to
rearrange the office space here."

There were various remnants of laundry registers to complete and tidy up, and a few places left to visit in far-flung towns like Reigate and Redhill and Bromley. The lady who had sent in the Complaint about the girls in the Brook Street dressmakers working until 1a.m., a Miss Mainstream, wrote again, saying that after Lucy's visit the girls had been working again until late. Lucy visited Miss Mainstream, whose back windows overlooked the back of the establishment. She said the owner, Mr Campbell, was a horrible man, that the girls were seldom out by 4p.m. on a Saturday half day, were frequently late on other nights, and that no dinner was provided on Saturday, but that he had been scared by Lucy's visit and she thought he would be even more wary in future. She was sure that a top floor tailoring room had not been shown to Lucy and that now he kept a look out to see if the place was watched. Lucy said she would inspect again later, but Miss Mainstream warned that the girls were too terrified to speak to an Inspector. 'It is a very well-known dressmaker. The girls enjoy their status and put up with much inconvenience to stay there.'

Rose Squire invited them all to supper to celebrate. They had a happy evening though Mary Paterson did not come down from Scotland. Rose said Dr Dudfield had looked glum when she told him she was applying. He said he had a gift for spotting high flyers, and he was discovering it to be a poisoned chalice. "I shall have to set my sights lower if I am ever to organise a stable department of my own."

January was Annual Reports. Factory reports, and questions from the House to research and return. Letters flew back and forth from Adelaide, May and Lucy, and they agreed to work at Finsbury Circus as often as was feasible, and put a calendar on the wall there to mark when each one would be there.

January meant a flurry from every other organisation too, and they were flooded with requests for information, conferences, talks, from the National Health Society, from Women's Clubs and Friendly Societies and Women's Union Secretaries. Lucy had a letter from Mrs Sidney Webb asking her to help form a 'Committee of Expectations' which would publish useful information on factory and industrial legislation. 'Lady Cavendish would be willing to write an article on Women Inspectors.' Lucy thought she had best consult May before she committed herself and wrote as soon as she got back from three days in Nottingham.

She struggled round Nottingham and outlying districts in bitter winds and on icy roads, but she was rewarded to find several factories which she had previously cautioned had improved, or were improving, their sanitary arrangements. The manager of the Long Eaton factory anxiously watched her face as she went round the dinner rooms and cubicles. Seeing the pleasure on her face he sighed with relief, and two or three women put down the shoes they were soleing and curtsied as she went out. Lucy laughed, but felt quite tearful inside.

Back in London, Emily told her how the new bicycle had finally arrived in a snowstorm. It stood in the back kitchen wrapped up well in brown paper. Emily was very taken with it. Lucy could see that Emily longed to unwrap it and ride it.

"It's been company for me," she said, stroking the handlebars. "I've been keeping it warm."

"Oh, I'm sorry we are away so much, Emily."

"Well, it can't be helped."

"No, it can't but I'm still sorry. Actually, could you organise a light supper on Tuesday. I've got Miss Anderson and Miss Abraham coming, and Miss Anderson will stay the night. And then Hyacinth will be home at the weekend. Come on, let's unwrap the bike now."

Emily perked up at once.

On Sunday afternoon Lucy went to tea with May at Tite Street and found Harold Tennant perfectly at home in an armchair by the fire. May was looking exceptionally attractive. They discussed Beatrice Webb's proposals and how far it would be wise to get involved. May was not sure about the choice of Lady Cavendish to write the article on Women Inspectors. "It's not that she's FRIVOLOUS exactly but – would she be a bit too dramatic?"

"It mustn't end up deathly dull," said Harold Tennant.

"I know, but – Lady Cavendish?"

"Why not get a man to do it?" he asked.

"Why not? But who would be brave enough?"

"I would be!"

"But we couldn't have you! You're known to be biased."

"I should try George Wyndham."

"Harold! He's a Conservative!"

"He's a sound man. All the better if he would. If he won't, stick with Lady Cavendish."

The next week was completely taken up with their section of the Annual Report. Adelaide had been collating the relevant papers for a couple of months, and so it seemed sensible to do the bulk of the sorting in the living room in Hadley Wood. Adelaide's parents removed themselves to the breakfast room, and their elderly maid kept them supplied with hot drinks and plates of sandwiches, cakes, and fruit at regular intervals. May went back to London each night but Lucy stayed for two nights. They read it through to each other on the Saturday morning, and Lucy arrived home on Saturday afternoon to find Hye and Emily wheeling the new bicycle over Battersea Bridge and teaching themselves to ride in the park. Hye was a complete convert and Emily, though she was very nervous of scratching her employer's bike, was a natural.

Lucy determined not to be outdone and prayed for some fine weather the next weekend. Meanwhile at work they were all pressed into service to complete the Chief's Annual Report and Rose Squire's first few days were spent correcting and collating piles of papers on the tables and carpets of Sprague Oram's solid panelled dining room.

The Chief was anxious. It was to be his last Annual Report and he needed it to be perfect. He wanted the new Laundry Act to have gone through the House before he left at Easter, and he wanted a Special Enquiry on Shirt and Collar Workshops in London. He singled out Lucy to head this, and she was grateful to be on home ground during the winter months. She said so to Sprague Oram and he nodded. He completely understood. He said the great advantage of being the Chief Factory Inspector was that one didn't have to inspect many factories.

Lucy set to work on the Shirt and Collar Enquiry, but she found she was constantly being called away to deal with extras, coping with an indignant letter from the National Health Society concerning 'some little letter in the *Woman's Magazine*. Stupid of them; but a timely warning to check carefully any article to be written about Female Inspectors.' There were plenty of Complaints to be inspected, and plenty of prosecutions arising from the inspections.

The London Superintendent, HMI Cameron was helpful and co-operative and she had a conference with him at Finsbury Circus, which was rapidly becoming much more like a busy working office. Previously it had a dusty and depressed feel with boxes on bare boards under empty curtainless windows, and only one or two tables in use. Now some rugs and curtains had been brought in, each table had been assigned – even

Mary Paterson had her own – photo frames and sometimes a small bowl of flowers graced the tables, extra book cases had been erected and nearly always someone was working there. HMI Cameron told her of the unrest among the South London shirt and collar workers and went with her to three firms in Rotherhithe and visited with her at various home workers' homes. They had signed a petition in favour of 'Homework' i.e. after normal factory hours. Many signers were 'Turners and Creasers', for collars and cuffs, but the majority of signatures were machinists, or forewomen who were obliged to take the work home.

She visited a large shirt factory in Southwark and an overtime tailor's in Woolwich where she was taken round by the Electrical Trades Union Secretary to see the new machines, and had them explained to her by his tailor friend Mr Montague.

Early one February afternoon, soft and balmy, she put down her pen in Finsbury Circus and went home in time to wheel the bicycle to Battersea Park with Emily, and they took it in turns to ride it round and round before the winter dusk closed in. Lucy felt she would soon be confident enough to ride among traffic. Evelyn was there for the weekend and came with them, laughing and applauding.

The problems of the shirt and collar industry ran over into the entire London tailoring industry and not just the East End, though that certainly seemed the area operating in the most overcrowded and insanitary conditions. Lucy and Rose remembered the parlous state of the Kensington and West End tailors' outworking shops.

They took evidence from the Secretary of the Amalgamated Tailors, and May Abraham took it off to a Parliamentary Committee to be accepted, and to have proposals made for extra clauses to be inserted in the Bill. May was off to Londonderry and Belfast to follow up the plight of homeworkers in the linen embroidery there, and Lucy dug out her Irish lists for her.

Harold Tennant had been busy on May's account and had spoken to Sir Charles and Lady Dilke, and they invited Lucy to lunch with Mrs Arnold Foster. Lucy had liked her immensely when they had met in Belfast. Sir Charles was making a probe on permitted fines and deductions in the Shirt and Collar trade, and Mr Arnold Foster volunteered to help.

Over the weekend Lucy ventured into the quieter streets off the Fulham Road with the bicycle, and was pleased with herself. She made an appointment with the coach at the Army and Navy to accompany her on her first proper foray into the traffic. The next morning the young woman came to collect her from 100 Fulham Road. "Where would you like to go?" she asked Lucy.

"Could we go to Finsbury Circus?" said Lucy. The girl looked horrified. "On your FIRST traffic outing?"

"Well, that's where I work." The girl looked even more taken aback. "Are you planning to bike there every day?"

"No, not every day. I'm away from London a lot of the time. But I am planning to take it on the trains with me from now on. It will save me so much time – and money."

The girl looked mystified. "Of course," she said hesitantly, "I will ride with you to Finsbury Circus. But I wouldn't have time to bring you back. I have several customers over lunchtime."

"Once I've been with you I'll be able to come back by myself," promised Lucy.

The coach clearly didn't believe her and was unhappy about the responsibility of leaving a learner in the depths of the City, so they bicycled down to the Embankment, crossed Chelsea Bridge, rode through the warrens of small streets to Lambeth Bridge, accompanied by cheerful rude shouts from workmen on the way, over Westminster Bridge, and back to the Army and Navy.

Lucy felt confident and the coach was impressed. "You'll be fine if you go on being so careful, and make sure you give the correct hand signals. Any sign of a problem – just stop and get off." When she had said goodbye, Lucy rode to Finsbury Circus very carefully, without mishap. Adelaide Anderson was there and was suitably impressed.

She told Lucy that the Chief had asked her whether the Female Department would approve of Miss Abraham being made a Superintendent Inspector instead of Secretary, and to consult with Mary and Lucy and Rose. Lucy thought it an excellent plan.

At that moment May herself arrived and was excited by the bicycle. "I have one myself, it's at the bottom of the stairs at Tite Street, locked in a cupboard, but I can't find the key, so I haven't ridden it in months. I'll search for its key and dust and polish it up. Clever Lucy, it will save us hours and hours. You must learn, Adelaide. Don't draw back like that, it's a great idea. We shall simply fly along!"

"Like witches on broomsticks," said Adelaide.

The next day there was a thick fog and Lucy did not risk the bicycle. She spent the morning at Tite Street with May, who had found the lost key, helping her to draw up a table for the report on white lead, to show the comparative susceptibility of men and women to white lead poisoning.

They had a long talk concerning Superintendentship. Lucy pointed out that there was an immense difference between a Superintending Inspector and a Secretary, and May's present position. First, it placed the entire Female Department in a much better position in its dealings with the rest of the Factory Department and with outsiders. Then, it created the precedent of a woman Superintendent Inspector and consequently of promotions and higher salary scales. It also might carry with it the rule, applying to a Superintendent, that their approval of a prosecution was sufficient without having to refer the matter to the Chief.

Also, now was the time, the only time, they were likely to climb this step, before Sprague Oram retired. It would strengthen them in their struggles with the Male Department. May acceded and saw the advantages, all the while protesting SHE ought not to be chosen. Lucy said "Bosh!" but thought privately maybe that 'the lady doth protest too much.'

That evening May, Lucy and Adelaide were all bidden to dine with Mr and Mrs Sidney Webb to meet Lady Frederick Cavendish and Marion Tuckwell. The dinner was to show them off as harmless, ladylike and tactful, and unlikely to create an uproar in penitentiary laundries if they inspected them. Lady Fred said that she had heard of great abuses in penitentiary laundries, but had not herself witnessed any, and she certainly appeared to have been absolutely ignorant of Asquith's Bill at the time she was pressuring Mr Mathews and Gerald Balfour to oppose the laundry clauses. Now, however, she was keen for an amendment of laundry clauses all round, and it appeared there was some likelihood of this. They talked of her writing an article on the subject, and left hoping they had passed muster.

May was about to set off on her section of the shirt and collar industry in Belfast. Lucy sat up late and sent by the last post instances of deductions for materials and equipment in various factories that might be useful in her interview with HMI Cunningham; and threw in for good measure a Complaint she had received about a collar factory just outside Belfast.

Adelaide had been having a hard time in milliners' workshops in Luton, uncovered many problems, and given many cautions and now was forced to lay information and prosecute. She asked Lucy to accompany her to the magistrates' court to make the summonses. Lucy was shocked by the hostility of the Magistrates' Bench. One was a Mr Cumberland, an auctioneer, "A brute", as she reported to Hye, "but we chose him in preference to another who we met at his bacon stall in the market. At first he refused to accept the summonses at all, thundered at us for making him unpopular and being vindictive. He flung scripture texts at us. We assured him we knew no one in the town and therefore had no personal grudge against the defendants, who had re-offended after a caution had been given."

They went briskly to the Home Office the morning after their return to report on the prosecutions and the hostility they had experienced. Sprague Oram listened, shaking his head gravely, and agreed that it would be sensible to have Lucy present at the hearings as a witness, and that they should have visited as many Luton School Boards as was feasible before Wednesday's hearings.

Adelaide scurried off to Marion Tuckwell and got her to promise to come and report the Luton cases on Wednesday for an article in the *Daily Chronicle* on school attendance.

Lucy went home to Fulham Road, and as it was a singularly mild day, she and Hye went off for a bicycle ride in the early afternoon sunlight in Battersea Park, their spirits lifted by the sweep of snowdrops and aconites glowing between the trees, until, as the sun went down, so did the temperature with a bump, and they spent a cosy evening by the fire. Hyacinth had tried out a new parsnip soup recipe.

"Spectacular!" said Lucy, and they drank great bowlfuls. "Just for us. Only ever for us. There's no halfway house with parsnips. You either love them or you can't bear them. Evelyn loathes them, both the taste and the smell. And you can't serve them at a dinner party. They're kitchen treats. Just for two sisters on a winter's night."

They slept late and planned to have a lazy Sunday, but a worried note from Adelaide meant a hasty tidying up before she arrived in the early afternoon. She was extremely anxious over the Luton court cases on the Wednesday and needed to go over the details with Lucy. "They are such truculent brutes, Lucy."

Lucy sighed inwardly. She assured Adelaide she was there to support her all the way, that Adelaide was more than competent to handle any number of truculent brutes, that the Luton School Boards would be definitely on her side, that the *Daily Chronicle* would be an ally; but her own week's plans would be severely disrupted – meetings to be postponed with the Furriers Association, lists and reports of factories and home workers to be dug out and sent to May in Belfast, sending apologies to Lady Dilke for the Tuesday. Hyacinth did her part in comforting by providing tea and a freshly baked sponge cake, but Adelaide left, only partially comforted.

"I do hope she's not going to fall apart in court," worried Hye.

"Oh, no she certainly won't do that; and she'll keep her temper admirably. But no one likes being hectored by boors. She won't sleep much till Wednesday, going over and over the details. Did you see how drawn her face was?"

Hyacinth agreed. "Yes, her nose and mouth were all drawn. But that was the lingering smell of the parsnips."

Tuesday was the Luton School Board day, and the two young women hired a fly from Luton station, and visited Board School Officers at Langley Road, Surrey Street, St Matthew's, and the School Board Officer. They drove out in the early dusk to Ship End and Martingate.

Mercifully it was a mild grey evening and they garnered a store of useful lists and made contacts, and gained information from School Officers who seemed genuinely pleased to see them. This raised their spirits considerably and they went to bed in the Luton Hotel with Adelaide feeling much more capable to cope with the fray.

Marion Tuckwell was already seated in the court gallery when they arrived. There were three cases and, as Adelaide had predicted, 'a Horrid Bench'. Lucy thought the only magistrate who had any sense was James Higgins, who ran a large straw hat establishment, and the rest ranged from unhelpful to downright obstructive; the auctioneer, Mr Cumberland, was actively hostile. The only successful conviction of the three was of Charles Lawrence for employing child labour, Harriet Scrimmer, a well grown twelve year old, in full employment, after a caution already made some months before. 'And we only got that because Mr Cumberland was not allowed a voice in the matter.' The other two prosecutions, for offences just as blatant, were dismissed, and the costs and fines for the Lawrence case were minimal.

They reported the cases to the Home Office and asked to appeal, but the Chief refused. "Afraid of a fuss," fumed Adelaide. Lucy visited Marion Tuckwell who had travelled back to London on the same train, prudently in a different carriage.

She found she was still in time to make the meeting at Lady Dilke's, although rather late, and found Rose Squire there and a Miss Penrose, the principal of Bedford College for Women. Miss Penrose wanted to make Bedford College the base for a training ground for Inspectors. What, Miss Penrose asked, should be included in that particular curriculum? They suggested Law and Hygiene – always useful – though Rose rather threw cold water on it, but Lucy felt it could work, as a short sharp course tailored to a candidate's existing experience in her particular field.

Early on Thursday she revisited a printing works, to check that the manager had provided the promised warming apparatus for the workers, and then went on to Finsbury Circus to catch up on paperwork, only to find that the great bundle of the proofs of the Annual Report had arrived, and Adelaide already beginning to correct them. Lucy spent an hour with her and then struck! "It's such a heavenly day, and who knows when there will be another one. This warm snap can't last for ever." She caught the bus home and found Hyacinth and Emily and Mrs Hedingham. "Leave it all," ruled Lucy. "Get your hats. Let's go out. You come too, Emily." Mrs Hedingham laughed but stayed sewing. The others spent a happy hour teaching Emily to ride the bicycle round and round Onslow Square Gardens.

Sure enough, the next day it poured with rain. Adelaide arrived at 100 Fulham Road, and they spent the rest of the day correcting the proofs of the Annual Report.

Into the midst of this came a panic stricken note from Marion Tuckwell, and in the middle of the afternoon Marion herself arrived.

"Oh Adelaide! Listen to this. I gave the notes of Luton Magistrate's Court to a friend on the staff of *Pall Mall* for Thursday's publication. I told him NOT to add that Miss Anderson had applied for a caveat as the leave to appeal was refused. But he put at the end of the paragraph. 'Leave to appeal was refused.'"

"Oh, Mercy!"

"Yes, well, I saw this in the first edition so I rushed off and got the last sentence struck out of the later editions."

"Well, that's something."

"I hope it will be construed by the general public that the MAGISTRATES had refused leave to appeal."

"Some hopes," said Lucy.

"It might be taken as a registrar's error."

"But of course, if Sprague Oram sees the first article it will rouse his suspicions after our conversation at the Home Office," mourned Adelaide.

Lucy was cross, reading the article. "It's a great nuisance. And the whole article bristles with inaccuracies."

"I've brought the amended edition. I could put it in the Sunday Times."

"Oh no. Certainly not. Leave it be."

"I'm really VERY sorry," said Marion penitently.

"Well," Lucy pulled herself together. "At least WE, the Factory Inspectors, have committed no error or indiscretion at ALL. The whole thing was public and any reporter might put in what they chose, but it is unfortunate we did not see the notice before going to print."

Later that evening, as they were going to bed, Hyacinth put her arms around Lucy. "There won't be any repercussions will there, Lucy?"

"Not big ones. But it's taught us a useful lesson. Never give journalists any information which they could not have procured by public means."

23

Sprague Oram steps down, Lucy smashes two bikes, Dr Whitelegge steps up

The Lady Inspectors write to Sprague Oram; Lucy smashes the bike; 'nothing but Harold Tennant!'; Dr Whitelegge is appointed Chief Inspector of Factories; Sprague Oram's presentation cigar box; the Luton Court continue boorish; Mrs Moberley Bell and her Good Women; another bicycle; sea gales and steaming laundries in Hastings; Lucy smashes her second bicycle.

The date of the Chief's retirement grew close and the Female Inspectors began to marshal their forces. They needed desperately to meet and talk but with May Abraham in Belfast and Dublin, Mary Paterson in Scotland, Rose Squire still finding her feet, and the others scampering about from the Midlands to Bristol, it seemed an insuperable task. However, the Royal Mail with its frequent and prompt deliveries kept them in touch. Adelaide received a letter from Mary Paterson stating her views of Female Superintendentship and the future of the Department. Lucy didn't agree with them at all and said so in a long discussion with Adelaide one evening. Mary was all for Women Inspectors having their own departments all across the country.

Meanwhile there was a flurry of directives from Sir Martin White Ridley, the new Home Secretary, including a new Parchment with a clause to conduct prosecutions as for the 1895 Act. Lucy decided she would not return her old Asquith-issued Parchment to the Home Office if she could avoid it. The Chief sent round a letter saying that the Secretary of State urgently wanted particulars of fines and deductions relevant to various trades. Lady Fred Cavendish was working on her article on laundries and required information and opinions for it. Rose was in charge of this project and she and Lucy conferred on it. Rose was cynical. "She says she'd be so grateful for our help. Actually she wants us to write the whole thing. And, actually, it would be considerably easier to do. Her style is so turgid." Lucy sympathised. Rose wrote with such simple, graceful clarity. It must be painful as well as requiring great diplomacy to tug Lady Fred's lumbering phrases into a readable order.

And still the monthly accounts and expenses and reports and returns waited for no one.

However, one day in early spring, Adelaide, Mary and Lucy managed to meet in Preston, midway between Scotland and London, to confer. They had a very long talk and found to their relief that they were practically agreed on all fundamental matters. Mary was very strong on keeping in with the new Chief, whoever he would be, and therefore hesitated about the idea of a Female Superintendent, thinking that he would dislike it.

They agreed on a joint letter on the matter, and wrote the following:

To R.E. Sprague Oram Esquire
Home Office, Whitehall
Sir,
We understand that you are shortly to retire from Her Majesty's Factory Department.
In view of change which may possibly follow on this we beg to submit for consideration our opinion that advantages in increased efficiency would accrue to our department if it were organised under the Superintendence of the Senior Female Inspector.
We are, Sir, your obedient servants,
Mary Paterson, Adelaide Anderson, Lucy M. Deane, and Rose Squire.

They all travelled back to Scotland and London on late evening trains, added Rose's signature early the next morning, and handed the joint letter to the Chief. May had just returned from Belfast and was talking to the

Chief. They all went off to lunch and May told them there was a movement to bring in an outsider, instead of Inspector Gould, or Inspector Cramp, as the Chief Inspector. Mr Carter, and Doctor Whitelegge of Bradford had been suggested. Lucy knew little about either of them. May asked Lucy and Rose if Dr Dudfield would apply. "That would be too good to be true," said Rose. "Except all the men would think WE had had a hand in it," said Lucy.

Lucy and May went bicycling to choose a present for the Chief on his retirement and chose a splendid cigar box, which they left in the shop to be inscribed from them all. May wrote to Mary with the news. On the way home a hansom cab edged Lucy off the road and mangled the bike. Lucy had fallen off amongst a group of home-going shoppers, and bags and parcels and people strewed the pavement. Other people helped them up and no great harm was done to any one. The occupant of the hansom got out, annoyed and irritated, and strode away rapidly without looking back. The cab driver stood by the side of his shivering horse. Lucy was bruised and shaken and her hands and face were grazed and bleeding but she was more anxious over a young girl about twelve years old, poorly dressed, who had been knocked flying, and was sitting among the group, very faint and dizzy. A shopkeeper came out and shepherded the girl into his shop, wrapped her in a shawl and sat her on a chair. "I know her, she doesn't live too far away." Kind hands lifted the twisted bike into another hansom and helped Lucy into it. At 100 Fulham Road the driver helped her out and leant the bike against the railings.

Hyacinth was still at the Cookery College and Emily had gone home. Lucy was glad that she could clean her face and hands and take off her torn skirt and muddy coat – mustn't frighten Hye – in peace and quiet. Hyacinth, when she arrived home half an hour later, was perfectly calm and solicitous and sensible, and dispensed hot tea and soothing creams and bandages with no trace of the hysterical weepings and panickings of former years. Lucy marvelled at the change, and was grateful; she was beginning to feel very cold and stiff and achy.

"If you're like this tomorrow I shall telegraph George and tell him you're not well enough to go to the theatre with him tomorrow night."

"I shall certainly go. I'm not missing Mrs Patrick Campbell!" and so she did, and thoroughly enjoyed *For the Crown* at the Lyceum, a splendid tragedy with Forbes Robertson and Mrs Winifred Ewing thrown in for good measure.

By Saturday she felt very sore and her arm ached from where the bicycle was wrenched away from her. Mrs Hedingham dropped in to deliver some mending and shook her head at the sight of the coat. "The state of that! But I can sort that out once it's cleaned. But the skirt – well, there's no hope for that as a skirt ever again." So Lucy limped down to Barkers and bought a neat, dark-grey flannel skirt which only needed the waist taking in and the hem taking up, and took it home with her.

She made heavy weather of climbing the steep stairs to May Abraham's Tite Street apartment for tea with May and Gertrude Tuckwell. They talked, or rather, May talked, almost exclusively about Harold Tennant, his charm, his good nature, his many talents, his aspirations as a Member of Parliament. Lucy listened with growing trepidation. This was not the conversation she had hoped to hear from the future Female Factory Inspector Superintendent. May was her usual vivacious, lively self, but there was no doubt there was an extra sparkle in the eyes. Lucy limped down the eight flights of stairs in a sombre mood and fearful for the future of the department.

Meanwhile the day-to-day work continued unremittingly. She made return visits to various furriers' establishments to see whether their sanitary arrangements had improved. The lists of Abstracts for the offending factories in Luton were sent off. She had a depressing talk with Rose Squire who had had a discussion with the manager of the Fulham Road Laundry. It appeared that many laundries were applying a system whereby each woman AND young person could work for sixty hours each week and were given a system of checks which marked the hour of each one's entry and departure; if they were away or ill one day they had to make it up the next. "That is a FATAL plan," cried Lucy. "If it gets introduced into other industries it means freedom from all control; it will be impossible to administer the Act under such conditions."

March 18th was Mr Sprague Oram's Last Day. A bitter wind and hard little pellets of sleet blew the entire Department except for Mary Paterson into the Home Office. He assured them that Miss Abraham would be the virtual Superintendent of the Department and they were pleased but wary. Virtual? What was 'Virtual'?

The next day they heard that Dr Whitelegge, the Medical Officer of Health for the West Riding of Yorkshire, was appointed Chief Inspector of Factories, and that Miss May Abraham, in consequence of their letter, was now instructed to Superintend their Department. Then they did feel justified in rejoicing and telegraphed immediately to Mary. The Male Inspectors across the country were furious at both announcements which came on them as a sudden shock.

The final Adieu Conference with Mr R.E. Sprague Oram was held at his home in Amherst Road. Only Mary Paterson was not present. He thanked them for the presentation cigar box, and confirmed May was the Superintendent. He cautioned them NOT to visit towns together; it was unwise, in his view, and tended to 'weaken their Department'. Why? they wondered. But later, over a celebratory supper at the Grosvenor Hotel in Victoria, they came to the conclusion that the Male Inspectors would think they could not stand on their own feet, and that in view of the fact that the Male Inspectors were speaking openly against them nearly everywhere, and creating a public opinion against them, their strongest weapon was to enlist as many influential and political people on their side as possible and to speak and lecture wherever and whenever they could.

Finsbury Circus was to become their official headquarters, although all letters were to be sent and collected from the Home Office.

The old Chief Inspector had retired and the new Chief Inspector had not yet arrived. The Factory Inspectors' suite of rooms at the Home Office seemed busy enough, with the clerks processing the forms and the daily post, but of course there were no meetings planned and no decisions being made. One or other of the Female Inspectors collected the post every morning and took it across to Finsbury Circus, but they were returning to their normal pattern of out and about, visiting and inspecting and their report writing was frequently done at home in the evenings.

Lucy girded her loins and set off bravely back to Luton, determined not to leave any more stones unturned than she could help. She made a visit to the magistrates' court to lay information for prosecutions and met Magistrate Higgins there to sign the summons. He made a great furore about signing them and especially the witness subpoenas, and took so long about it that she was obliged to leave the latter unsigned in order to catch her London train. The magistrate's clerk was clearly shocked by this behaviour and promised to send them on to her, and was extremely courteous to her when next she handed him a Complaint about non-existent sanitation in a hat factory in Markyate Street. Heartened by his support she wrote and sent more Complaints to Luton Local Authority and wrote all her reports up to date on Sunday afternoon.

She set off almost at dawn on the Monday to travel to small towns on the outskirts of Luton, and visited workshops in Houghton Regis and Kemsworth in the morning, and dropped in on the Medical Officers of Health, Mr Dunhelm and Mr Woolley, before lunch with her findings. They were impressed and invited her to lunch but she excused herself – she had an appointment in London at four o'clock. This was not strictly true, but she went to Finsbury Circus where she met May, and over tea in an ABC teashop they plotted to arrange a conference between Sprague Oram and Dr Whitelegge about their department.

For the next two days she caught her dawn train to Luton, once to visit workshops and once to go to the magistrates' court to prosecute two hat makers who had been employing children full-time. The unpleasant Mr Higgins was one of the magistrates again, though as his fellow magistrate was the mayor, a smooth, dapper, politic, elderly man, the epitome of calm, she won convictions in both cases in record time, although the fines were minimal. She was back in London by mid-afternoon in time to rest at home and dress leisurely for a social reception at Sir Charles and Lady Dilke's, where she danced with a Comte de Bontamo, the Military Attaché to the French Embassy, and was introduced to Mrs Beerbohm Tree.

Lucy was due for a week's leave in the spring and was expecting to spend it at the Boyce. She mentioned this to Hye, who was very pleased with herself because she had received a minor promotion at the Cookery College. She had been appointed as a permanent examiner for the Cakes and Pastries section of the course, not only for her own college but for four associated schools in the Home Counties. This brought with it a modest increase in salary and a chance to demonstrate in various other establishments. At one of these lectures she had met one of their old childhood friends, Isobel Grant, who had invited them to her family home in Guildford for a week in April.

"Shall we go, Lucy? She does seem to want us to, and they are still in that lovely place near the Hog's Back."

"Why not? How kind of her! I'm sure I could organise my leave to fit in with yours." Again she marvelled. Only a couple of years ago, Hye would have baulked at going anywhere except to the Boyce, or to Bossie and the Aunts, or to Miss Canning and Miss Hardyman.

She went to bed quite buoyed up and slept soundly, and just as well, as the next morning was most depressing. She went with Adelaide to a meeting organised by Mrs Moberley Bell who was holding one of her meetings for her Women's Work Society. There were about fifty earnest women there in serviceable suits and slightly more cheerful hats, all ready to give their opinions on Factory Regulations. Not one of those present had any definite knowledge of Factory Regulations, the main assertion seemed to be 'I rather fancy', and they returned to their prejudices after each argument against them as if to a fort from which they could not be evicted. Mrs Bell thought that the great advance made in the condition of children's and women's work in factories etc, since the 'dark times' prior to legislation, was all due to 'our more enlightened age and greater sympathy' and not at all to legislation; "In fact," she said, "the same good result could have been attained without any restrictive legislation." Letters sent from various sources, replies to papers, and questions on the subject sent out by their Society, were all read out. Without exception they were all in favour of the Factory Regulations; but Mrs Moberley Bell and her Good Women were adamant that 'greater sympathy' was all that was needed. Lucy was bursting with frustration when the meeting was over. Adelaide just laughed.

To put herself in a better mood Lucy went and ordered another bicycle at the Army and Navy Stores, before setting off to inspect laundries in Hastings and St Leonard's for four days. It was cold and very windy, and the sea gales buffeted her unmercifully as she trudged from small laundry to small laundry in the poorer parts of the towns. She gave up her umbrella and tied her hat on with a scarf and was alternately blown backwards and swept forwards by the gusts. Then, after the cutting outside air, she stepped over the threshold of yet another set of steaming, dripping, crowded rooms with the sheets hanging round her like a jungle.

She was told the District Inspector Mr Pearson had not visited at all for years, but had unsurprisingly been round to them all in the last week – "when he found I was coming" – and simply handed out the Abstract Forms for Space, Times, and Rules of Employment, giving the forewomen no instructions as how to fill in the notices, and had told them that each person might be employed for sixty hours a week. So Lucy had to field endless questions as to holidays, mealtimes, cubic space. She returned each night to the comfortable hotel on the sea front battered and dishevelled, and sent her clothes to be sponged and pressed, and ate her supper in her room after a long bath.

And so, as soon as she reached London, she made an appointment with her hairdresser and treated herself to new shoes and stockings, and a smart cream silk blouse to team with her evening skirt, and went with Hye to dine in luxurious warmth and comfort at the Gathorne Hardys' London house.

Easter was early that year and so the next day was Good Friday, with the Three Hour Service in the middle of the day, and then home to Fish Pie and Hot Cross Buns; and on the Saturday she collected the new bicycle from the Army and Navy and proudly rode it home.

On Easter Monday the sisters rode to Barnes Common and back, and on the Tuesday, back at work, she took the bicycle on the train to a group of straw hat workshops near Luton, Ampthill and Flitwick, rounded a country corner too fast and bent the back wheel. Luckily a passing cart rescued her and the bicycle and took her to Flitwick Station.

Hyacinth was unsympathetic. "Thank goodness," she exulted. "Otherwise you would have taken it on holiday to the Grants and we should have had to ride all over Surrey."

"I thought you liked cycling now."

"I do like it, but you always go too far, and too fast, and Izzy Grant is just like you. You overdo things, both of you."

The week's leave began the next day and the Grants made them very welcome; and they rested in the beautiful rectory and its gardens, with the spring flowers and blossom coming out more and more each day.

24

Battles in Belfast and discord in Dublin

take their toll on Lucy

Lucy is sent to Ireland for a month; too many Complaints and prosecutions; workers complain of unfair pay in Belfast; May is engaged to Harold; Lucy is dizzy; major irregularities in Lisburn working hours; aches and pains; Hyacinth has a new appointment; the sewage seepage at the Six Flat Mills; Lucy wins her Belfast court cases; seedy, dizzy and sick; "I will NOT be ill"; the nightmare journey home; an elderly lady takes charge; "I have come home!"

Back in London Lucy rushed around visiting banks and meeting Bossie and trying to get their personal money affairs and the household bills in order before she set off for the month that had been planned for her in Belfast and Dublin.

She was to have crossed with May Abraham to Ireland on the 17th of April, but received a letter from her with news that HMI Gould and all the other Male Inspectors were making a violent effort to nullify May's appointment as Superintendent Inspector, and were also questioning Mary Paterson's powers to lay information for prosecutions with only May Abraham's approval of them. May had found a great deal of underhand dealing going on and Mary had written to warn her. Lucy met May for a conference and then they drove straight to Mr Sprague Oram's house and had a conference with him. He at once went straight to Sir Kenelm Digby at the Home Office. So the journey to Ireland was put off until

Sunday night and Lucy was grateful. She shopped and packed leisurely, collected the mended bicycle, and rode with Hye in Battersea Park. Evelyn arrived to be with Hye for the first of the next few weekends. During the week she would have to return to the Boyce to help with the preparations for Mary's marriage to Archie Mackenzie in June. "Such an ill-matched couple!" sighed Hye. "I can't see what either of them sees in the other!"

Finally, on the Sunday night Lucy travelled with May and with Harold Tennant to Dublin by the night train. He was gentlemanly and kind and competent, but he seemed ineffective besides the vibrant May. She was clearly delighted with him; he was a small thin man, with a pale face and a quiet spare way of talking, and although May was an inch or so shorter than he was, and slim and neatly formed, her personality completely overpowered him, and for that matter, all the fellow travellers on the journey. Lucy thought of Hye's remarks about Archie and Mary, and sighed.

In Dublin May and Harold left Lucy at the hotel and went on to May's family home. HMI Cooke Taylor met her at the hotel and gave her a bundle of lists and addresses. Lucy felt she must make up some of the time lost by her late arrival, and promptly visited workshops and made a full inspection of Paterson's Match Factory.

The next day Harold and May took her to the theatre to see *The Rivals*, and the day after that bore her off to Dublin Races! Lucy felt both guilty and a gooseberry, and, as her monthlies had seized her with a vengeance, would rather have stayed quietly in the hotel and used the day as an Office Day. She made some bets, aided by Harold, and to her amazement made £3 15s 0d, and so invited them to dine with her in the hotel.

HMI Cooke Taylor met her in the hotel after breakfast. He declared he was warmly in favour of Female Inspectors and took up much time going over the same ground yet again. He also told her that the feeling against the women amongst his fellow inspectors was very bitter. He would not commit himself to an opinion about the ventilation in Paterson's Match Factory and when she had her next interview with HMI Bellhouse that gentleman said he didn't consider Paterson's Match Factory needed any improvement at all, and, he said, HM Sanitary Inspector Colonel Meade Tring, HMI Cooke Taylor and HMI Woodgate were of the same opinion. Lucy was sure they were blocking her for reasons of their own. However, she had several pieces of information to lay at the court, besides Patersons, and went to the Dublin Police Court to do so. She found she had to fill in the Duplicate Summons and subpoenas herself and took the various forms away with her.

She was surprised at the number of workshops she found out of order, including those that had had a visit from an Inspector relatively recently. "No wonder the inspectors don't like us," she thought as the train took her to Belfast.

The rain was lashing down when she awoke the next morning. She spent the morning in the writing room sending summonses to Dublin Police Court, four Complaints to Hastings District Council, five to Hastings Urban Council and three Complaints to the Medical Officer of Health in Dublin. Then she made out a complete list of all the cases she was to lay at the Court and sent it to Mr Peacock, the Office Manager for the Chief of Factories at the Home Office, and after lunch when the rain had stopped she went out to visit factories and workshops in Belfast.

She continued in the same pattern for the next few days, revisiting many of the mills and factories she had visited last year, and greatly heartened to see that most of them had made some efforts to improve their sanitation facilities. HMI Snape was surprisingly pleased to see her and shared several horror stories of bad practice with her. He handed her a Complaint from a woman in a collar factory who said there were no particulars of fines for specific mistakes posted up, and a repeated Complaint from a handkerchief maker who had written to him again having also done so the previous year.

Lucy went to visit their spokeswoman, Mary Fairfield, at her home, two rooms spotlessly clean and neat, sparsely furnished and with a small bowl of mixed spring flowers on her white painted window sill. She was a small, quiet, respectable, thrifty woman. She showed Lucy her book detailing her earnings.

"I have worked for Clyne Bros. for ten years," she said. "And they have always been tight employers, but recently they have been imposing fines almost as a matter of course. I am a piece worker and I embroider the handkerchiefs at home in my own time. We are fined if we are a moment late in the morning when we come to collect it – even if the work is so slack that we have to wait for it for three hours."

Lucy saw her book; every other week losing money, fined 1d to 7d a week. "I used to earn 6d a gross as a smoother – pressing the handkerchief hems, and then I earned 14s a week, sometimes as much as 19s. Now I have to work at home to look after one of my children who is lame, and so I am a 'flowerer', I embroider flowers on the hankies, but I get much less – 10s, and sometimes only 9s, and once only 7s. When I worked in the mill I used to take them home in the dinnertime when the firm was very busy and wanted them done at once, and if I was even a minute late in returning from dinner I was fined, even though I pointed out I was doing their work, and that was what had made me late!"

Mary Fairfield took Lucy to the Textile Workers Trades Union weekly meeting where bitter complaints were being made about fines and sanitary arrangements. Two men from a mill complained that false lengths of yarn had been wound onto their beam so that they had woven 110 yards of cloth instead of the statutory 100 yards and therefore their stated output had been lower than usual as it had taken them longer to weave the bolt. Lucy took particulars of this and went to check on it, and cautioned Clyne Bros. and two other firms about excessive fines.

Shuttling back to Dublin for her first court presentation in Ireland, Lucy felt tired and lethargic and cold. The weather was fine and the sun warm, but she shivered as she stood in the prosecutor's place. She obtained the convictions in both cases, but she was aware of the magistrates' hostility, and the fines they imposed were derisory. She wrote to May Abraham and settled herself in the hotel room with hot drinks and set to, catching up on the countless letters, forms and reports. She slept fitfully all night and around dawn fell into a heavy sleep until mid-morning. She dressed and went downstairs asking for coffee and toast which was brought to her; she sat in the sun in the hotel's small garden, and ate a little fish and potatoes at a late lunch, but decided she was feverish and so took herself up to rest on her bed. Then she tried to write more letters, but by suppertime gave up and ordered soup in her room and managed to drink most of it before she went to sleep. "I will not be ill. I will not be ill," she recited like a mantra.

And hey presto! She awoke next morning full of life and vigour and made a good breakfast. The first post brought a letter from May saying she would come and spend the day with her tomorrow, so she decided she must go to the magistrates' court to lay information against George Matthews for overcrowding and irregular working hours in all three of his workshops. The magistrates' clerk was helpful and courteous. Why is it, wondered Lucy, that magistrates' clerks are invariably straightforward and open, but that magistrates are quite the reverse? She had intended to visit HMI Bellhouse after this, but the walk – not very far and not very onerous – had made her feel light-headed and dizzy – so she returned to the hotel and slowly wrote several letters, and went to bed again early, this time sleeping soundly.

When May arrived at the hotel she looked glorious, shining eyes, shining hair, fresh and young. Lucy's heart sank. Sure enough, May had great news to tell. "I am engaged to marry Harold, dear Lucy, we are to be married in July. I know you will rejoice with me."

Lucy congratulated her and they embraced; May was so happy, Lucy could not but feel delighted for her.

"I shall of course be able to go on assisting you all in the department," said May. "Harold never expected me to give it up. And especially since he has been so supportive from the very first, he knows how important it is for me and the department."

"And the country," said Lucy. "You have been the foundation of the whole surge into improvements into women's working conditions. You are the cornerstone."

"No, no," cried May, laughing and blushing. "We are the tip of the iceberg – a living, warm iceberg of fair practice and freedom!"

"Our metaphors are getting hysterical. Let's just concentrate on you and the wedding. Will you make your home in London or in Harold's constituency in Berwickshire?"

May did not know but thought probably London. They sat and chattered and Lucy thought how being in love transformed May. When they arose to go into lunch a sudden wave of dizziness swept over her. May was at her side holding her up. "Lucy, what's the matter?"

"Nothing really. I've been under the weather for a couple of days. It's passing over. I'm much better today."

May was anxious. "You've been doing too much. You always do too much. It's Sunday tomorrow, stay in bed. Should we call the doctor?"

"Of course not," said Lucy crossly. "I'm almost over whatever it was. Let's go and eat."

"Well, if you're quite sure. But I'll give you the name and address of my mother's doctor here. Just in case."

Lucy took May's advice and spent a lazy day on the Sunday writing long personal letters to Hye and to Evelyn. But she wrote in her diary that evening:

'Miss Abraham came and told me she is engaged to be married to H.J. Tennant in July! Such is woman! It's NO good their trying to do any public work unless they are old or ugly or unhappy! She will do good to the Department in one way by this marriage, but after a year when the social duties and her husband's friends and politics, and babies all crowd in, she'll HAVE to drop the Department, and she will sell all the years of persistent work and influence and campaigning which she MIGHT have given. However, she's in love, and poor, and a clever and (rightly) ambitious woman. If ONLY he were a little less unworthy of her!'

The beginning of the week found her much better, and she had a note from Mr Daly, the Dublin magistrates' clerk, about her Summons for George Matthews. When she met him at the court Mr Daly was helpful and heartening. He had been thinking about her summons, he said, and he thought that a summons simply made out for 'employment after legal limit' would be considered too vague by some magistrates, who insisted there must be some extremely definite and tangible charge for the accused to contradict. Lucy thanked him and set about trying to raise a brave witness who could verify the times of the overtime working. She went back to the Textile Workers Trades Union and they promised to ask for support for her amongst their members.

Then she shuttled back and forth between Belfast and Lurgan and Lisburn visiting and inspecting. The half-day hours on Saturday in Lisburn were strange, irregular and illegal. HMI Snape had evidently winked at it. The Damask Weaving Factory in Shankhill had made no improvements to the sanitation since she had visited last year, and its sewage drainage was still non-existent. The damask tablecloths and curtaining it produced were of a wonderful quality. The treatment of the workforce was no better than slave labour.

She visited the Certifying Surgeon in Lisburn, Mr St George, who told her about an accident at Stewarts Mill, which had not been notified to him officially. He said that he was new in the area and was discovering that there were several clauses in the Public Health Act which Lisburn had not chosen to adopt!

The faithful Mr Daly, the Dublin magistrates' clerk, sent copies of the summons again, "so as to be QUITE safe, put 'employed after the legal period of employment, to wit, at 10.10p.m.'"

She smiled to herself as she opened the letter back in the hotel in Belfast. It was comforting to know she was building up allies across the country.

She conferred with Mr Snape over various places and she told him of the irregular Saturday hours in Lisburn, but a 'nice' point had arisen in her own mind, as she had seen that all the working women actually preferred the irregular present arrangement. She decided she would consult with May before she wrote to any of the firms on the matter. Also, that she would write to Miss Cockbill at the Trades Operators Union upon the matter and ask to see her on Thursday afternoon, as being safer to talk than to write.

On the Tuesday she travelled North to Ballymena to inspect the Bridge Rivers Weaving factory. She was much obstructed by the manager, Mr McCallum, on the urging of his superior, who insisted she should not ask the girls any questions except in his hearing. She showed her authorisation and said that if he persisted she should consider it obstruction. She showed him the clause in his own copy of the Act, and he gave way, but said that all the Northern Ireland firms were furious at the innovation; he said, "I have been visited by Inspector Cameron and Inspector Snape for years, and NO Inspector has EVER asked the women a question except in my presence in the office." Lucy pointed out that a Woman Inspector was on different terms to the women than a Man Inspector. He said there was much indignation in Belfast and Northern Ireland at the untruths which the women had told her and Miss Abraham, and that his desires to hear the questions and answers were in order to contradict their lies. Lucy heard in her inner ear the wise voice of Miss Orme, and recalled her walking about her room. 'Don't believe anything they tell you without evidence. Women and girls lie awfully, just as bad as men. Examine thoroughly, inspect thoroughly, the girls AND the managers'. She assured the manager she never asked about the prices fixed for work, but about whether the particular rules, regulations and payments pinned up in the workrooms were adhered to. "It is my duty to ask," she said calmly.

On the train home she worded her complaint to the Ballymena Local Authority and arrived back at the hotel with a splitting headache and feeling desperately seedy. Double seedy. "You really can't be ill," she told herself, looking with distaste at the very attractive supper that had been brought to her room. "You've got to be on top form in court on Friday."

The morning brought a bundle of letters to the breakfast table, and among them letters from Hyacinth and Evelyn. Evelyn's letter bore detailed descriptions of preparations for Mary's wedding, clothes, tempers, trousseau; Lucy saved it for later. Hyacinth was applying for the appointment, vacated recently by an acquaintance leaving to get married, of a Government Inspector of Cookery and Laundry Teachers, and would be also on a Committee of the Council of Education. Lucy was awestruck and then anxious. Only a year ago Hyacinth would not have dared to apply for such a post, but Lucy feared she had not amassed the experience to handle such a highly responsible job. If she got it would she be able to manage it? If she didn't get it, would it knock back her emerging confidence? If she wasn't short-listed for it would she pick herself up? Lucy put it back in the pile to answer that night and made herself eat some breakfast.

She had an interview with Mr Grower, a member of the Belfast Board of Guardians about the Sewage Scheme, or rather, the lack of it, at Ligoniel, a very poor working-class district on the edge of Belfast. It was home to six huge flax mills and when Lucy had first visited Belfast last year she had been horrified by the seeping sewage which ran down the road, the hill, past the rows of rickety cottages. This year, visiting Bodens Mill, nothing had changed. The sewage seeped into the lake, Flaxdam, behind the mills. Mr Grower was resigned to it. It was all the fault of the Belfast Corporation, he said, who would not allow him an outlet for drainage. Whether Ligoniel would be under the Belfast Corporation or Belfast City was dependent on the new Corporation Bill. When was that? That was yet to be decided. What was the date set to decide? No date was yet in view. "So when the date is decided," said Lucy, "it is evident that my first course has to be to petition the Local Government Board to put pressure on whichever body takes charge of the district." Mr Grower nodded glumly. He plainly had no faith in her powers, and she did not feel sanguine herself. Although the meeting had taken place in a clean salubrious office, she felt grubby as she walked down Ligoniel Hill on a bright and breezy May morning.

She had invited Miss Cockbill, the Trade Union Secretary, to lunch with her at the hotel and that lifted her spirits quite considerably. She told

Miss Cockbill of the illegal Saturday overtime in Lisburn, but that the women seemed to prefer it. Miss Cockbill thought it was not a problem. "There is very reasonable surplus labour in the whole of the Belfast area, and the women could get other jobs relatively easily at the moment. If the women chose they could have things a good deal their own way, and their Trades Unions would back them and help to regularise the hours they chose."

After lunch Lucy gathered her papers and clothes together, and left some cases in the Belfast hotel and set off for her three days in Dublin.

She tried to doze in the train, and spent the evening quietly, leaving all her official letters in her briefcase, writing only to Hye and Evelyn, Lady Dilke, Lady Fred Cavendish, and to Marion Tuckwell who was arriving on the Monday for an investigative article. Her head ached, her stomach ached, and she slept badly.

The day of the court case dawned, bright and warm. Lucy felt dreadful. "Don't be stupid," she told herself. "You have conducted dozens of cases. This is no different. And you are NOT ill. Just under the weather. This afternoon it will all be behind you." She took care to dress elegantly, and swept into the court foyer looking calm and composed.

Dear Mr Daly was there to greet her and to show her and the defendants to their places. His manner was impeccably impartial as he shook hands with them, but she knew by his almost imperceptible extra pressure on her palm that he was on her side.

George Matthews seemed extremely confident, flanked by a lean young solicitor with a sweeping moustache and a monocle, and Lucy saw several of the magistrates from former cases ranged in the gallery. "Like spectators at the Coliseum," she thought grimly, and the thought made her laugh out loud. Mr Matthews shot a suspicious glance at her. Lucy was suddenly calm and clear-headed as two people came into the gallery, Miss Cockbill of the Trades Union Council in Belfast, and Mr Whiteside, the head of Larrymore School. They nodded to her. A handful of shabby mothers, with scared looking 'half-timers' in their Sunday best, sat on the benches opposite.

The magistrates came in portentiously, and the Chief Magistrate, a paunchy Mr Bale with an impenetrable Cork accent argued the case for two hours on points of law, frequently interrupting everyone, even the young sweeping moustache, with unnecessary queries and heavy comments. Lucy patiently and simply stated and restated her points, and in the end Magistrate Bale had to concede the conviction for underage children employed full-time. But as a gesture of solidarity to his colleague George Matthews he imposed a fine of only 3s to George Matthews, and costs of 5s to the Inspectorship. However, he had to give the conviction.

Mr Daly was in the foyer as she came out. They looked at each other. "Well held," said Mr Daly and bowed slightly. Lucy walked home feeling dizzy and hot and tired. "There you are," she told herself. "All in the day's work. Nothing to fuss over." She sat in St Stephen's Park for a while and then went back to rest and write her monthly accounts.

Seedy, seedy, seedy, on Saturday, but able to rest. Her stomach ached, she had developed a cough and her headache would not go away. "Only four more days and I shall be home." The pretty little dark chambermaid who brought her some lunch and collected her washing for the hotel laundry looked at her with concern. "Would you like us to call a doctor, Madam?" Lucy shook her head. "No, no, I am just overtired. I'm going out with friends this afternoon."

"We have a doctor nearby we can always call, madam."

"Truly, I shall be fine. Tomorrow I can rest all day."

And she enjoyed the At Home that May's two brothers escorted her to at the Fitzwilliam Club. "Such a clean and tidy place. So civilised. Such a wonderful change from the sewage behind the flax mills." They wrinkled their noses, and plied her with cream cakes and tea, and she really did not want anything at all except her bed.

Seedy, seedy on Sunday, but bit by bit she wrote her many letters. The pretty chambermaid freshened her room and brought her clothes back, clean and fresh, and plied her with jugs of barley water, and posted her letters, and was kind and concerned, and Lucy did indeed feel rested, and slept better than for several nights. Only two more nights and she would be safe at home with Hye.

She caught an early train to Belfast and was at the hotel when Marion Tuckwell arrived mid-morning for lunch. "Why have you come to Belfast, Marion?"

"I've come over to investigate the rumpus about this new 'Housework'

Clause of the new Factory Act. Arnold Foster set it up for me. Apparently a lot of the linen manufacturers have complained against him because he wouldn't uphold their petition. The Act says the employers must pay the same rate to the home workers for handkerchiefs, collars and other work as they do for the factory workers. He agreed with the Act, and the manufacturers are furious and have threatened to kick him out at the next election."

"Goodness!" said Lucy.

"I don't think they'll pull it off, though. But I've got an interview with a trades union man called Sheldon. I invited him to dine here tonight. You'll come too, I hope."

"I'll see. I'm not feeling too bright today."

"No, I can see you're hardly eating anything and you look very tired. But do come if you possibly can. What do you have to do this afternoon? And can I come with you?"

The weather had clouded over during lunch and they were in the midst of a sharp shower. "Well, I ought to go to Brookfield Linen Mills before I go home. Miss Cockbill and the Textile Trades Union have put in a Complaint about Bad Sanitation. I ought not to take you, though."

"Oh, let me come. I promise not to take notes. They can think I'm a Public Health Probationer or something. It's teeming, we'll take a cab."

"Very well, but you might find you just have to wait in the cab."

They set off. The cab jolted over the rough streets and Lucy felt more and more queasy, and the bad sanitation arrangements were certainly VERY bad. She called on the Certifying Surgeon with Marion to report the case, but he was out and Lucy was very thankful, just managing to get back to the hotel before she was sick. Marion and the chambermaid, who was called Harriet, fussed around her, but Lucy was glad when they left her with sips of water and the blessed relief of lying flat, repeating her mantra. "Only one more night, only one more night."

The final morning she felt stronger, but still shaky and weak. The stomach pains cramped her, but not in the same way that she was used to every month, and she definitely had a fever, flushes of hot and then of shivers. She introduced Marion to HMI Snape, and then to Miss Cockbill and left the two women to have lunch together. In between packing she managed two short stretches of lying on the bed and then took a cab to the station, so thankful. The mantras changed, hourly,

"I'm going home. Actually going home."

"I'm sitting on the Night Mail."

"I'm on the ship going home."

It was a nightmare journey, and although the sea was like a millpond, Lucy constantly retched and tried to be sick; but nothing came into her mouth but bile. She was conscious of a family on the quayside at Holyhead helping her to find a porter, and a seat on the London train in the small hours of the morning, but when she roused herself to thank them they had gone, leaving her in a blessedly empty carriage with the blinds pulled down. The guard looked in two or three times, and other people apparently came and went.

At Paddington an elderly lady was beside her, holding her tightly by the arm, and saying firmly, "Walk along with me Miss Deane, don't stop dear, walk along with me."

Lucy could not remember having seen her before. "How do you know my name?"

"I just asked you, Miss Deane, and you told me. I hope it is correct."

"Oh, yes, quite correct. I am going home."

"Yes Miss Deane, we are going to get a cab for you. The porter has all your pieces of luggage quite safe."

The elderly lady went straight to the head of the hansom cab queue, to the annoyance of the whole line, and the porter smartly stacked her luggage.

"Will there be anyone at home when you arrive?" asked the elderly lady.

"Our maid Emily will be there."

"You are sure?"

"Yes, quite sure. It isn't teatime yet, is it?"

"No, Miss Deane, only a few minutes to two. And what is your address?"

"My address?"

"For the cab driver!"

"100 Fulham Road."

"You are sure?"

"Yes, quite sure," said Lucy crossly.

"Off you go, then," said the elderly lady. She rapped the side of the cab and it pulled away smartly.

Lucy enjoyed the ride through London, though occasionally she felt very sleepy, and she wished her stomach didn't ache so. She thought with some perplexity about the elderly lady, and could not remember when she had first got into conversation with her. "And how could I have been so rude not to enquire her name?"

But then, quite soon it seemed, the cab stopped outside 100 Fulham Road, darling 100 Fulham Road, and to her surprise she saw the cabbie spring down from the cab and bang hard on the front door. She saw Emily opening the door, looking cross, and then saw her face change to being frightened, and watched as she ran over to the cab.

"Oh, Miss, what has happened?"

"Nothing has happened. I have come home, thank goodness! I have come home!"

Emily helped her down and into the house into an arm chair, and the cabbie brought in all the luggage. Emily looked in Lucy's handbag – without permission, Lucy was mildly displeased – and paid the driver.

"Everything will be all right, Emily. I am home."

Emily's eyes filled with frightened tears.

"Oh, yes, Miss Lucy. It will all be perfectly all right. You are home!"

25

The lost summer

Lucy has typhoid fever.

Lucy's diary had no entries for the next two months, and then only sporadic notes until October.

Emily and the cab driver set her gently in an arm chair and the cabbie tipped his cap sympathetically and returned hastily to his horse.

Emily smoothed her apron nervously. "Would you like a cup of tea, Miss Deane?"

"Very nice, thank you," said Lucy, closing her eyes.

Emily busied herself with the fire and the kettle but when she returned with the tea Lucy seemed to be asleep and did not answer to Emily's, "Here you are Miss," or to a gentle shake of the shoulder. Emily was terrified. Providentially the doorbell rang and Mrs Hedingham and Leah arrived with a bag of mended clothing. They went straight to the writing bureau to look for the address book, and Emily was sent off immediately to fetch Doctor Thame, while Leah and her mother attempted to rouse Lucy and take her upstairs to her bedroom. This was unsuccessful as Lucy was incapable of standing and obviously did not know who they were.

Hyacinth, returning early to greet Lucy, found them standing over Lucy, having wrapped a blanket around her and were trying to get her to drink sips of water. She was drifting in and out of lucidity and looked apologetically at her sister. "Darling, I'm so sorry. I'm not very well."

Hyacinth was magnificent. "I can see that, Lucy, but thank goodness we have you at home safe and sound. So we shall be together until you are right again."

Emily returned to say that Dr Thame was on his way and would come within the half hour.

When he came he said at once, "Your sister has typhoid fever. I should think she has been sickening for it for some time, perhaps over a week, she has the rosy spots on her chest and her temperature is very high, 103. I'm amazed that she has travelled all the way from Ireland by herself. She has headaches and her stomach must be very tender." He looked sternly at Hyacinth. "Can you nurse her at home, Miss Hyacinth? Not just you of course. She will have to have a nurse with her day and night."

"Oh, I can send for my cousin, she will come. I will send a telegram at once."

The doctor shook his head. "A trained nurse would be better. I can recommend one. Or she will have to go to hospital."

"Whatever you think best – or we could ask the Matron of the Chelsea Hospital. She is a friend of Lucy. Lucy trained with her some years ago."

"If you can contact her immediately. Otherwise I will send a nurse. This fever is already well advanced."

Hyacinth wrote a hasty note to Miss de Pledge and Leah Hedingham fled off with it to the hospital. Dr Thame made a list of medicines, disinfectants and equipment and Emily was sent to the nearest chemist.

The doctor and Mrs Hedingham and Hye helped Lucy to her bedroom. The doctor looked around the room, full of books and papers, clothes and ornaments. "These must all go or they will be infected. Can you clear them out?"

"Yes, yes, of course, into my room."

"Get her into bed first and then make the room as empty as you can. Give her nothing but sips of water, constantly, she must not be allowed to become dehydrated. I will come tomorrow morning early to see how you are faring."

Out on the little landing, he took Hye's hand. "She will be very ill, very ill, for several weeks. Good nursing will pull her through."

"I will do everything you say. Whatever you say."

Leah returned with good news. Miss de Pledge had been in her office and was on her way round at this moment. "She says she will be here in an hour to see what is needed and you need not worry as to nursing care. She will engage someone suitable. What wonderful fortune!"

"Wonderful, indeed."

Miss de Pledge was as good as her word. She came into Lucy's room in the early evening and looked at Lucy, who had just woken up. "Is it you, Matron? Why are you here? Very strange!"

"You are not well, Lucy and I have come to see how you are."

"Oh, you mustn't trouble yourself, I have a bad headache and a stomach upset. I just need rest."

"Quite right, Lucy, and that's what you shall have. Go to sleep, dear."

When she had gone, promising a nurse in the morning, Hye took a cup of boiled water upstairs.

"Such an odd dream, Hye. I dreamed Matron was standing by my bed."

Through the night, Hye sat up with Lucy. Mrs Hedingham and Leah – who were not allowed to go into the bedroom – sent telegrams to the Boyce, and to Bossie and the Aunts, and to Adelaide Anderson, and to Hye's College. Emily was sent home after she had left some soup for Hye and seen that the kitchen was well stocked with coal and buckets of water ready for the kettle; she was back by 7.30a.m. and made Hye eat two boiled eggs and toast, and have a good wash and change her clothes.

By eight o'clock the doctor had returned, and before he had gone, a stern looking middle-aged Nurse Kingham had arrived with a note from Miss de Pledge. She was to be the day nurse and at 7p.m. a night nurse would take over the duty for the night shift. This would continue until further notice. When the stern nurse smiled, which was rare, she looked beautiful. She instructed Hye to help her take down the curtains, and roll up the bedroom rugs and remove all the pictures and sort out bed linen and towels for Lucy's personal use. She hung a sheet soaked in disinfectant across the bedroom door. The dressing table became her medicine station. Then she smiled, and Hye was sent to her room to sleep for several hours.

Evelyn arrived in the middle of the afternoon. Nurse Kingham took over Hye's room and Hye and Evelyn made the attic room comfortable for themselves. The kitchen and scullery were always full of bed linen and towels, soaking or boiling or drying, and both the kettles were always steaming.

From then on, while Lucy drifted in and out of consciousness, the letters began to arrive in fat batches as the news spread through the bush telegraph of friends and relations. Lady Howard wrote to say that she would be underwriting the entire cost of the treatment, and sent a sizeable cheque to 'start them off'. Hye and Evelyn wrote in the evenings to as many as they could.

For a week they were not allowed to enter the sickroom but could only peer for moments at a time through the disinfectant sheet. The night nurse was younger and chubbier and more friendly, but insisted on them both going to bed early; when they woke in the night they could hear her going down to the kitchen for drinks for Lucy, and her soft voice talking to Lucy.

So the weeks progressed, May into June, June into July. Lucy's bouts of delirium abated; the doctor now came every other day, the nurses became chatty and friendly, and Hye was proud to be considered useful enough to be shown how to prepare the minute amounts of beef tea, milk jelly and tisanes that were ready to tempt Lucy's appetite.

And May Abraham's wedding came and went and no one even remembered it.

By the end of June Lucy could sit up in bed for short periods and Hye felt comfortable to go back to college to mark the students on their end of year examinations. The nurses persuaded Evelyn to take Hye to the Boyce for a weekend.

In July the night nurse was no longer required and the curtains and carpets and pictures were restored to the bedroom.

One beautiful afternoon Lady Dilke sent an open brougham to take the sisters for a short jaunt in Hyde Park.

Lucy began to ask for her diaries and report books and insisted they were to be brought back into her room. The nurses protested, but she got her way.

Mrs Hedingham came to check on all her summer clothes.

May Abraham, now Mrs Harold Tennant, visited to tell her all about the wedding.

Adelaide Anderson visited to bring her up to date on the state of the Female Inspectors Department.

The day nurse said goodbye in early August. And the next day the Streatfeild family drove her to Limpsfield for three days.

Then the family at the Boyce rejoiced to have her to convalesce, and she sat and snoozed in a deckchair on the lawn, and one evening Horace and Evelyn rowed her on the lake in the cool of the woods.

Hye had to go back at the beginning of the new term, and so Bossie collected Lucy and bore her down to Kent and the Aunts.

Gradually there were more entries in the diaries.

26

Picking up the pieces

The doctor loses his temper; Hyacinth is an Inspector too; worries over May's inability to lead; Lucy is back in full-time work in October; Hastings laundries; the Women's Emancipation Union; frills and fripperies at the Boyce; Emily gives notice.

Lucy veered from feeling full of beans one day and as weak as a new born kitten the next. The doctor at Frant lost his temper with her – in a most gentlemanly way – one lunchtime in mid-August. "Miss Deane, there is nothing the matter with you that will not sort itself out as long as you REST. Rest does not mean writing letters to other inspectors and mill owners. Rest does not mean walking to Sevenoaks because it is a lovely day. Rest for your personality, I understand, is boring and unnecessary. Rest for your BODY is your lifeline. You are a very lucky woman; only the loving care of your relatives and the excellent nursing you have had wherever you have been staying has kept you alive. To try to push your repair systems too far and too fast is downright selfish of you, and a waste of everyone's efforts."

"Well done, Lyndwood," applauded Bossie. "Quite right. Absolutely the right note. Come and have a drink. I'm going to Kemsing this afternoon, Lucy, and I'll post that letter you are going to write asking for another certificate for sick leave."

Lucy laughed and the Aunts looked relieved. "He was extremely forthright, though, don'cha think?" said Aunt Gertrude, her baby blue eyes anxious in her angular bony face.

"Won't do any harm," said Aunt Florrie severely, patting Lucy's cheek lovingly.

Certainly the next day she had so little energy she could hardly get out of bed, and found it difficult to concentrate on the Aunts as they came in and out of her room to entertain her. The maids brought her tiny bowls of soup and broth, and tiny portions of soft fish and eggs and minced meat. One day she had no appetite, the next day a craving for fruit, apples, plums and pears, ripening in the orchard, all of which were forbidden her. Dr Thame sent more medicines from London, and the doctors at Seal and Frant and Limpsfield or wherever she was staying dropped by to check up on her, and gradually she felt her strength returning. Finally, in the first week of September, rambling round the Streatfeilds' wonderful garden in Limpsfield, Lucy knew she was ready to pick up the reins again. She felt strong and able to cope with the responsibilities.

Arriving back at 100 Fulham Road after a full month staying with the various friends in the country she caught up with Hye who had, in her absence, applied for and won the Government Inspector's post for Cookery and Laundry Training and had begun on September 1st, 1896.

Hye had changed. She was thinner, though not so thin as Lucy, and her whole demeanour was older and stronger. There were new lines on her forehead, and her girlish gaucheness had gone. She carried her head high and looked the world in the face instead of dipping her chin and eyes downward when newcomers came towards her.

"I can't tell you how proud I am that you've got this new job," said Lucy, as she lay in her bed the first evening back at home, and Hye sat by her side. "I didn't even know you had applied for it until you told me your interview was settled."

"I nearly didn't apply for it at all. I was so worried over you. And the College had given me leave of absence at the end of term, I thought – we thought – we were going to lose you." Hye's face looked ready to crumple. "But Evelyn said I ought to."

"Good old Evelyn."

"Yes, she is a brick. Scuttling back and forth. She really couldn't have cared less about Mary's wedding, you know. She would happily have forgotten all about it. But it wasn't her who made my mind up for me; it was Matron."

"Really? Matron?"

"She was wonderful – sent a day nurse and a night nurse as soon as she heard – Lady Howard took all the cost – and one day she came – you were very bad, and she stood at your door, and looked at you, and then she said, 'She'll do!' And she said, 'I hear you're going to be an Inspector too.' And I said I didn't think I had the heart for it any more, and she said, 'Why this is what you've been working towards all this time, growing up from a scared little girl to a frightened young woman, and you were so brave, and kept going, and everything was so much harder for you than for Lucy. If you don't apply for this you'll regret it all your life. What have you got to lose? You've got a good job already. If you don't get the post, you've still got a good job. If you do get it we shall cheer to the roof top.'"

"Good old Matron. I'll cheer too." And Lucy cheered and waved her arms.

She spent the next few days going through all her papers and reacquainting herself with the tasks and organisation.

Then Adelaide Anderson and Rose Squire came and had tea with her to bring her 'au courant des affaires' said Adelaide. Rose went off at five o'clock, but Adelaide stayed on for a long private talk from which it appeared that Mrs Tennant – "I can't get used to her married name," wailed Adelaide – "simply cannot do the superintending work efficiently under the present circumstances."

"He wants her at home?"

"Of course he does."

"She has got a household to run."

"Of course she has."

"And his little boy to get to know."

"Of course. And he is very delicate, I hear."

"And Harold's social life—"

"Yes, yes—"

"And Harold's work in the House!"

"Oh, Lucy, she WANTS to do our work. But her attempts are completely unsatisfactory!"

"Maybe Mary Paterson should take over. She has years more experience than you or me."

"Maybe. But the Home Office wouldn't accept Mary as Superintendent owing to the feeling against her – I don't know why that is. And she just hasn't got the necessary diplomatic flair."

"In that case," said Lucy, "the only hope is to let either you or me DO the actual work for Mrs Tennant, and let her simply sign the papers and be the figurehead. Her personality and influence are still extraordinarily useful to us. There is so much we still need, like a proper office, and a clerk, and a special honorary post for Mrs Tennant. I can see no way out of the deadlock about the Superintendentship at the moment owing to Miss Paterson's disfavour at the Home Office."

After Adelaide had gone Lucy sat reflecting, playing with her pencil. Very soon, she must see Mrs Tennant and talk everything over.

The next day she went to Finsbury Circus to look round. The Office looked uncared for, not exactly untidy, but with piles of papers on the tables awaiting filing and a general air of depression. She wrote to Mr Peacock, the Head Office Manager, to send her letters to 100 Fulham Road; Adelaide and Rose had dealt with nearly all of those that were in the office, and she wrote to May to ask if she would do some of the routine writing for her.

The other Female Inspectors were as supportive and thoughtful as possible. Rose had invited her to a hotel in Eastbourne for the following weekend, and Lucy was touched by the gesture.

On Sunday she mounted her bicycle for the first time for ten weeks and she and Hye had a short ride which both of them enjoyed. Hye had her first inspection at a College in Cumbria the next week and had arranged for Lucy to stay with Miss Hardyman in Sunninghill. "Someone needs to be with you Lucy, for the next month or two."

Lucy would rather have stayed home, it was a chore to pack and repack, but she said nothing, and Miss Hardyman was easy going and glad to be of service. So in effect she had another week's holiday with the old lady, and then a comfortable seaside weekend holiday with Rose.

Emily looked glum when she heard that the house would be empty again. She had been by herself most of the summer while Lucy was convalescing in the country.

October approached and the end of Lucy's sick certificate; and she felt strong and ready to hurl herself back into the fray. Gertrude Tuckwell invited her to dine, à deux, at Lady Dilke's house, 76 Sloane Street. Letters wanting information began to arrive and leave again; Mary Paterson wanted notes for a paper on Women Sanitary Inspectors. Lucy wrote to the Medical

Officer of Health in Leicester to ask about Women Inspectors there. She went to the AGM of the West London Branch of the Co-op Guild and was struck with the eagerness of the women there to acquaint themselves with business procedures and habits, and to learn to express themselves appropriately.

At last May Tennant came to tea and they had a long talk. She evidently wanted to keep on the Superintendentship though she indicated that most of her family objected, and she knew that the authorities were doubtful of the possibility of her doing it. She thought that at any rate she could make it certain that her own post continued as a permanency. Their great standby would be Sir Kenelm Digby. May considered Sir Martin Ridley, the Home Secretary, practically indifferent as to whether the Female Inspectorship continued or not.

"Women Inspectors are not HIS fad as they were when Asquith was around, and although he acquiesces in principle 'to please the people', he is not keen to help the Women Inspectors," stated May.

"And Doctor Whitelegge?"

"Dr Whitelegge is feeling his way very cautiously. He is frightened of the men under his charge and eager to keep in with them."

October the 8th. Red Letter Day. Lucy's sick leave ended and she had her first meeting and interview with Doctor Whitelegge. He had been going through the prosecutions taken by all inspectors for the past year and considered that the case against George Matthews in Dublin had not been conducted properly in May. He required her to state her case again clearly and to write a report. The Certifying Surgeons in Dublin had not been signing the requisite forms concerning the age and health of underage workers. He said he had found many cases where Certifying Surgeons had not checked, and even more in factory accidents where various reports had been missed or lost. He also asked her to complete her lists of Complaints in Hastings laundries, which had been waiting since May! And finally, he asked her to inspect in the Stroud and Wolverhampton Districts.

Lucy reported all this to Hyacinth and Evelyn over the evening meal. Hye had made a lamb casserole and an apple charlotte, and laid the table with the best blue Indian place mats, and Evelyn had brought up some of the last pink summer roses from the Boyce garden. Evelyn was shocked and huffy at the amount Dr Whitelegge had given Lucy to do. "He had no business piling it on like that so soon. How can he call himself a doctor? You must be exhausted!"

"On the contrary, I feel exhilarated," said Lucy.

The weather in Hastings was bright and breezy and Lucy enjoyed being back among the Hastings laundries, and the evenings she spent in the almost empty hotel, writing up her notes on her lap in solitude in front of a roaring fire in the lounge.

Back in London she addressed herself to more correspondence, particularly to gathering more information about the lax Certifying Surgeons. Amongst her files she looked up a letter from Mary Paterson, complaining, over a year before, of cases where they had passed children as suitable for employment without even seeing them or checking age or schooling. She and Adelaide discussed this at the office in Finsbury Circus.

"What's to be done?"

"I suggest WOMEN Certifying Surgeons as the men are so useless," said Lucy, as they set off for the Marlborough Police court for a case against a firm of fur retailers. Adelaide won the case easily with 23s costs.

"Let's go shopping, Lucy," begged Hye, back from four days examining at a Domestic Science College in Cumberland. "It was so depressing. All the young women looked about forty. Everyone wore thick hand-knitted cardigans!"

"Well, it's cold up there."

"But they'd all knitted their own – and all grey – or dark brown – or bottle green – or black – or dark blue – not a proper colour among them, and all their hair scraped back in a bun – and they weren't required to – not required uniform or anything – just DEADLY."

"You're very harsh, Hye."

"They looked so boring, and they could have looked attractive. I kept thinking what Mrs Hedingham would have thought of them. Let's go and buy something frivolous, please, darling!"

"Oh, Hye, I've promised to go with Adelaide to a conference of the Women's Emancipation Union at St Martin's Town Hall."

"Lucy! Yeuk!"

"We have to go in our capacity as Factory Inspectors. They are a well-meaning bunch of women."

"They are always a well-meaning bunch of women, that's the problem."

"It's about the factory restrictions."

"Lucy! More yeuk!"

"I know, I know, but these women are less woolly than most. And it's useful for us Inspectors to know which of them could be useful to the cause or not. But I'll come away early. We'll go this afternoon. Come and collect me at St Martin's Town Hall."

The Women's Emancipation Union audience was composed of women's trade union members and working women, and their main fear was that the Factories Acts and Restrictions would turn women out of work. Their great activists were Isabella Ford and Elizabeth Wolstenhome Elmy. Their work was mainly amongst northern textile workers but many other trades were affiliated, and Lucy thought the best talk of the morning came from a woman compositor in the printing trade, where women had been turned off because of restrictions as to their light work.

"Well, was the morning worth it?"

"It was. But they are too vague. It makes me realise how much they need us, to set things out, and push things into Parliamentary Committees, and keep checking and gathering evidence, checking and gathering evidence. Where are we going now?"

"We are going to look at FRILLS, Lucy."

"Oh do we have to, Hye?"

"We do! And FEATHERS! And Fripperies!"

The frills and fripperies had a relaxing effect and Lucy was glad of it; her following three days were smelly, muddy, dreary, in dirty mills, overcrowded work rooms, noxious and disgusting sanitary arrangements, grey-faced workers and unpleasant factory owners. The hotel at Stroud was very commercial, dirty, and noisy at night, and Lucy was thankful to arrive at the Boyce on Saturday teatime in pouring rain, for a hot bath and a clean set of clothes. Evelyn made sure there were always enough of Lucy's clothes ready and waiting for whatever season she stayed there. Hye arrived on the evening train with two hatboxes full of hats and the fripperies, and as it continued to rain, Evelyn and Ethel joined in, and they spent a happy Sunday morning redecorating their hats for the winter.

"Another two days in Stroud! Such a dispiriting place!"

After the Stroud visit there were a couple of days in London writing up all the reports and countless letters. She worked at the Finsbury Circus office, and in the evenings sitting writing close by the kitchen range, as Hye was off again, this time to Chester.

And then, Emily came in gravely, to give notice.

"You've both been very good to me, Miss Deane, but you're both away so much, and it's very lonely, here by myself all day often."

"You've been very good to us, Emily. We shall miss you very much. Have you found another post? We shall give you first-rate references."

"I think I have. I'm looking for a place where they have more staff, a cook, and other maids, probably a place where I'd live in, where there's more company – we'll see. I've been thinking about it a lot, and I would have gone in the summer, but I couldn't possibly have left you then, with everything so up in the air."

"You're a real friend, Emily. Thank you."

The door closed on the London fog as Emily went home, and Lucy felt sad. Hye would be sorry too. And they would have to reassess their needs.

27

Rough diamonds in the Black Country

HMI Jackson is straightforward; the long fustian cutting mill; 'I walk from here to Manchester for 15s a week'; the breakfast meeting in Manchester; penny for the Guy in the next street; final amendments signed at the Women's University Club; Lucy loses her pocket book; the Walsall courts run as smooth as butter; the breeze washing banks; 'that odd egg-like smell'; could Evelyn replace Emily?

There was no time to reassess their needs at 100 Fulham Road that week, though. Lucy set off the next morning for the Black Country and checked in at the comfortable Walsall George Hotel. Despite the industrial smoke and the crowds and the rough clothes and cold draughts round the corners of the streets, her spirits rose. There was a different feeling in the air among the throngs of Black Country folk. The people, young and old, were rough but straight; there was a confident, pugnacious, but good-tempered air about them. They looked her in the eye, and their Black Country humour delighted her. She had a long meeting with Inspector Jackson about the proposed report the Home Office was setting up on the use of lead in industry. Lucy read him the plans she hoped to carry out about visiting lead works, and lead workers, and he listened and made suggestions.

"Did you know that Balfe and Jordan's Enamel Plate Works have given up using lead in their works since March?"

Lucy gazed at him and her mouth dropped open.

"That's what they SAID, and Cramp and I believed them. I sent a special report to the Home Office on the subject; but then there were three more lead poisoning cases in June."

"Oh?"

"But Dr Smith the Certifying Surgeon thought that might be owing to the lead having already been in the patients' systems a long time, and more especially as one of the girls had been recently at the chrome works in Wolverhampton. She was discharged from there as being ill with it."

"Do they insist on them all using respirators?"

"There ARE respirators. They MUST provide them. That's universal. But a lot of the workers just don't use them properly. We find it difficult to insist, as they claimed they WOULD use them, DO use them and can prove it."

"Can they?"

"Hmm. If any of us go in to visit, they are all wearing respirators. When you go in, they will all scuttle about and they'll all be wearing them. However, it is improving, Miss Deane. The sanitation of Walsall is much improved since your visit when HMI Sedgewick was here. The sanitation authorities are waking up."

Armed with comments and suggestions from the HMI Lucy wrote to Adelaide Anderson and Mary Paterson, asking for an urgent conference on planning procedure. It was one of her Very Seedy days, and so she stayed in the Walsall hotel doing office work. To crown it all she woke with a sore throat and a stuffed up nose. "You are a lucky woman," she told herself, "You are in a warm place, with people to look after you, you have warm clothes and enough money and a loving set of friends." She looked at herself in the mirror. "But you just look a fright."

That evening letters arrived from Mary and Adelaide, agreeing to meet in Manchester. Lucy caught a late morning train to Manchester and snuffled her way through a meeting with the Manchester Medical Officer of Health who kept determinedly and courteously the other side of the table from her throughout.

She trailed over to Warrington to a fustian cutting works and was appalled at the work carried on there. She was taken into a vast room with benches 150 yards long, set three to four feet from the floor, and with the fustian stretched tightly along them. To begin with she was pleasantly surprised. The room was brightly lit and there was hardly any sound of machinery. The workers were mostly women quietly walking up and down, up and down the frames. The fustian was woven from linen and hemp, a rough-backed material but with extra looped wefts. When the loops were sheared and cut with special knives and the pile on the other side had been side brushed the result appeared as corduroy, exceptionally durable and hard wearing. But the best quality velveteen needed forty cuts per inch, and a two-yard length of cloth two-foot wide would take about an hour to finish.

On and on walked the women, lightly bent, concentrating on the task; any tiny nick in the material was penalised, and every woman had her own sweeping movement, so a break or a change in the cutting changed the pile, and too slow a sweep lost money. One woman said, "I reckon I walk from here to Manchester every week for 15s a week." Her daughter Margaret was working for nothing for the first four months. Her mother had high hopes for her. "She'm a beautiful shearer already. They'll have her on velvet, mebbe."

She paid a visit to the Certifying Surgeon and Medical Officer of Health in Warrington and then thankfully took the train back to the Manchester hotel to deal with a deluge of letters. May Tennant sent a thick packet to be discussed at the meeting with Mary and Adelaide on the morrow, and said she would be over from Dublin to London soon to consolidate the Factory Bill arrangements.

Mary arrived that evening and Lucy found she truly valued Mary's clear head and grasp of a situation. Mary's stance was decided and uncompromising, but always carefully thought out. She would never jump to conclusions, but having decided, she was unshakeable. This had its drawbacks; but at least you always knew where you were with Mary.

Adelaide arrived by the early train the next morning and the three young women shared a happy breakfast. Lucy could not taste any of it. She might have been eating brown paper. But the coffee was hot and it was good to be among friends.

After the main substance of the Lead Report had been dealt with, the subject of May Tennant's Superintendentship came up. It was becoming increasingly clear that the present arrangements could not continue. Adelaide was reticent but the others felt she would have to take the lion's share. Mary was very unwilling to move to London, and they all agreed they must stay under the protection of the Home Office for the time being. They made a list of suggestions for a draft report.

They saw Adelaide off on the afternoon train to London and then Lucy and Mary went together to the Medical Officer of Health in Salford because of various Complaints. They visited some steamy laundries, where, despite the cold outside, the women worked in petticoats and shifts because of the heat.

Mary took Lucy as a treat to the Prince's Theatre to see Beerbohm Tree and Miss Baird in *Trilby*. That evening there was dense fog and the mist had got inside the theatre and gently wreathed itself around the Upper Circle and gallery. Lucy longed to be in bed with lemon and honey linctus.

At the weekend she arrived home at 100 Fulham Road. Emily was there to greet her and Lucy found a letter for her from the housekeeper of a large house in Ebury Square asking for Emily's references. The coalman came with a ton of coal and Adelaide came and spent the night with her. Adelaide had walked from Victoria and had been waylaid eight times on the way by groups of street urchins asking for 'Penny for the Guy.' "I always gave them a penny – if I could see the Guy! But if they said the Guy was in the next street, they didn't get the penny!"

On Friday afternoon they met at Mr Asquith's house, 20 Cavendish Square, with May Tennant, Adelaide, Rose Squire and Mr Asquith's secretary. The suggestions they had made in Manchester were accepted substantially, though as they thought it best to give clearer reasons, Lucy engaged to redraft the report and meet them with it again on Monday. Adelaide and May took the original to the Home Office to show the chief, Dr Whitelegge.

Hye came home weary from her week Cookery Inspecting in Carlisle and Chester, and they sat companionably at the table by a cheerful fire writing their various reports and discussing what they should do to replace Emily. Rose Squire came on Saturday evening to help to redraft the proposed amendments, and on the Sunday, as Hye's cold developed and Lucy's receded, they hibernated by the fire. Lucy wrote countless letters, returns, and slips, and Hye began reading a novel – "I haven't opened a novel since September. I intend to finish this by Christmas."

The Female Inspectorship met in civilised surroundings at the Women's University Club and they all signed the final draft of the proposed amendments, May signing for Mary Paterson. Lucy left them to make a quick visit to Stroud to lay information to prosecute three tailoring establishments in the town. To her astonishment the court was extremely helpful and speedy; Mr Winterbotham, a banker, signed her summonses within three quarters of an hour of her getting off the train, and the deputy clerk made them out for three days later, on Friday at 11a.m. Lucy was taken aback as she had expected at least a ten-day time lapse, but was determined not to postpone any of the dates. She wondered aloud if she could get from Walsall to Stroud in time for the 11a.m. court, and the clerk sent an office boy running to the station to find out.

As everything had happened so promptly she felt it behoved her to visit several other tailors' firms which had notes beside them in her diary. She left her pocket book in Slad Road in the afternoon without noticing, and a policeman cycled up to the railway station to return it to her as she walked up to the station platform in the dusk for the train to Birmingham.

"I didn't even know I had mislaid it!" she said.

"You soon would have if you had tried to get on the train, Madam. Your ticket was inside it."

The Walsall hotel gave her the same room she had had two weeks before, and treated her like an old friend, sending her a complimentary cup of hot chocolate, and biscuits, and a hot water bottle.

Lucy could not believe her wonderful smooth day and marked it with two little flags and stars in her diary.

Life went on being remarkably smooth. She laid information for prosecutions at the Walsall magistrates' court where the Magistrate, a boot and leather manufacturer, signed them most civilly and the cases were set to be heard, again speedily, in a week's time. While she was in HMI Jackson's office, looking through his lists and directories and maps, working out her next week's plans, she mentioned how smoothly the Stroud and Walsall courts had been arranged. "In both cases the system spread around like warmed butter on toast – no hassles, no arguments!" Inspector Jackson was amused. "I think the word is getting round, Miss Deane, that the Lady Factory Inspectors are not going to go away. While you were ill in the summer we had two visits from your colleagues, Miss Squire and then Miss Anderson. You all seem to be cast in the same mould. And I, for one, hope there will soon be several more of you. Meanwhile,

I hope you have strong boots and a waterproof coat. The Black Country is hard and unforgiving terrain in the winter."

He was anxious that he should take her to some of the breeze washing banks in Wednesbury and Tipton and Moseley. "Some of the dreariest and most difficult ways of earning a living you can find, even worse than going down a pit. And even here you'll find a camaraderie and a loyalty." A breeze washing bank in Wednesbury was certainly as unpleasant as any place Lucy had visited. This was the term used for the conversion of coal into coke for use in the iron and steel smelting foundries. There the burnt coke was 'washed' to remove the impurities and produce pure coke and anthracite which burnt clearer and at higher temperature. The coke came out of the coke ovens, was washed in the deep 'baths' and then sent off to the steel mills.

Sited not far from a pithead, it was a large rough building, with great furnaces and baths like black swimming pools. The air stank of gas and fumes, the steam and the smoke swirled around the great halls, the temperature veered from tropical to arctic; as the water ran out through the bottom of the baths, dirty men and women with their hair wrapped in coal-matted turbans, supposedly to protect them from the coal dust, clothed in great sleeved overalls, heavy clogs on their feet and leather gloves on their hands and arms, broke up the larger lumps of coke and anthracite. They were a very rough lot, laughing and joking with each other, and they looked at Lucy with interest and disbelief. There seemed to be nowhere to sit down, or to eat, and the sanitary conveniences were as black as they were themselves. Every ten minutes or so great sweeps of winter air rushed in as the trucks of 'breeze', damp coke and anthracite were pushed out of the building to the waiting coal carts and the huge cart horses, four to each load.

Beer was in ready supply and the foreman seemed to be a favourite. He shouted at them and they shouted back, with the men shovelling coal into the furnaces and the coke into the trucks, and the women filling and emptying out the baths of foul water.

"It's back-breaking work," gasped Lucy. "How can the women stand it?"

"The beer helps," Mr Jackson assured her. "And the pay is good. 21s for a man, 18s for a woman."

However, the next day, at another breeze washing bank, it was a different story. The halls were leaky and the floor flooded, draughts blew the flames out of crevices in the furnaces, and there was an overpowering smell of rotten eggs as the coke and anthracite cooled in the breeze washers. There was an aggressive surly feeling in the workplace and the women seemed oppressed and almost silent.

"Is it because I'm here?" wondered Lucy.

"Could be," said Mr Jackson. The workers took their lunch break in shifts and she tried to talk to them but they clammed up completely and tried to shun her. She asked if they had anywhere to sit and they pointed to three or four rows of benches.

"And where are your sanitary conveniences?" They looked blank and then they laughed in her face.

"Why would way need them? If way need to shit way goo THAT side" pointing to one side of the building. "The men goos on t'other." They looked to see if she was shocked.

"You deserve better," said Lucy.

"All way deserve is more money," said one, swigging beer.

Mr Jackson and Lucy walked back from the pit head down the rough road towards the rows of dark cottages. Even in the November drizzle washing lines with grey and bedraggled garments flapped in the yards.

"Well, there's a letter to be written to the Local Authority, certainly. I'll do it as soon as I get to Stroud tonight. I'll be back on Tuesday."

He nodded cheerfully. "You'll enjoy writing that letter, I can see."

All the way in the train to Stroud she smelt coal on her clothes plus that odd egg-like smell, and she knew the others in her carriage smelt it as well.

The court cases against the three tailors proceeded with despatch and Lucy won all three convictions with reasonable fines and costs. The magistrate, a Mr Holt, stated 'any more cases of the same kind would be much more severely treated' and the deputy clerk was clearly delighted with the result. She swung out of the court at lunchtime and visited two textile mills. Both were examples of Bad Old Mills, crowded with machinery and mill hands running into each other. Lastly, she visited the three small mills belonging to Evans and Co. where the sanitary arrangements, though they did exist, were deplorable, and the smell so strong that her own coal-flavoured coat faded into gentility.

With relief she arrived at the Boyce on Saturday night. Everyone wrinkled their noses. Ginny positively ran up the stairs to run her a hot bath and carried all her offending garments away, including the waterproof coat at arm's length. At dinner that evening the family drew in relieved breaths, and Horace sniffed round her first tentatively, then appreciatively, before offering her his arm to lead her in.

"Horace, don't be so crude!" said Aunt Georgie, shocked.

"You didn't have to sit next to her in the dog cart, Mater. She certainly advertised her presence!"

"I don't know how they can all bear it, day after day, Aunt Georgie!"

"Will you have to visit the washing banks again, Lucy?"

"I'm afraid so – they're all over the Black Country. They are all built on such rough ground near the pits, and the rows of their houses come up so close. It can't be healthy for any of them."

"You will have to save that outfit for such visits and buy another for more normal inspections."

"I can't do that Aunt. I would need a cabin trunk for every foray. And a personal maid and porter."

The subject of No Emily was broached and well aired. "The problem is that the Fulham Road house is so often empty like now. I'm away from it for two weeks and Hye is usually the one who has to come back to live in it alone. It's often empty for several days at a time, and then it's cold and uninviting."

"And waiting to be burgled," said Uncle George.

"Possibly. It needs someone to go in and get some food prepared for when we DO arrive, and see to our laundry. Not every day – certainly someone who doesn't mind being on her own. Someone capable of sending on letters, too, that would be a help."

"She would have to be absolutely trustworthy!"

"Of course. Mrs Gates runs a very good agency nearby, she will see us right. But Emily goes at the end of next week and I haven't even been able to interview anyone yet."

"Hye could do that for you both," said Ethel.

"Oh—I—" Lucy stopped. Once again it had not occurred to her that Hyacinth could take on such a responsibility. Ever since her mother's death she had sheltered and carried her nervous, unhappy little sister. But the little sister was burgeoning.

"Very possibly," she agreed. "I'll write tomorrow morning. She'll be home Tuesday."

Evelyn was very quiet throughout the meal and the evening. Lucy went to bed early and Evelyn knocked on her door.

"Lucy, I could come next week and be with Hye, if it was any use. I could come any time if it was any use. I could come ALL the time come to that. I'm not needed here at all. I don't mind being in the house in Fulham by myself. I'm no good at housekeeping, but you don't need much. I could be there when the maid or the cleaner came, I could send on the letters, I could do a whole lot of copying out for you while you were away when you needed it. I could be of USE. Think about it, Lucy!"

They embraced. "I will, Evelyn, I will. I'll write to Hye in the morning. It might solve several problems in the short term anyway. And in the long term the three of us must sit round the table and decide what will be best."

The family drove to church at Dymock in the dog cart on a cold, frosty but sunny morning. Lucy and Evelyn said nothing about the last night's conversation. Evelyn looked radiant. Lucy spent the sermon organising her letter to Hye and trying to lay out pros and cons in her mind. In her letter she asked Hye if she would take on the initial meetings with the domestic agency, and also whether she would mind if Evelyn came down to stay for a few days. 'I have another ten days in the Black Country with these noxious breeze washing banks, and iron and steel works and clothing mills and clothing workshops.'

She walked up with Evelyn to the post box in the pale afternoon sun, muffled up against the cold and with their hands in rabbit fur muffs. Evelyn was full of hope.

"Don't get too excited Evelyn! Coming to help us out would basically be very dull. To begin with we're so often not there, and you'd be lonely."

"I've got friends in London. And there's Aunt Augusta in Bayswater. And I'd be back and forth to the Boyce, of course."

28

From Wednesbury to Wigan and
cold comfort for Adelaide

Hye engages Mrs Anstey; the new London School of Economics; Mrs Anstey settles in; Adelaide summoned for assault; Lucy supports Adelaide; Lucy loses the Official Postal Book; bitter, beautiful wintry Lancashire; Christmas with Bossie and the Aunts.

Lucy enjoyed her two weeks hard working and hard walking back in the Black Country. True, it was dirty, rough and cold, but an air of honest self assurance pervaded it, from the factory owners to the shop keepers, the church groups, the rowdy pubs, the housewives washing their front steps, the working women in their shawls and clogs, the noisy school children corralled on Sundays into Sunday best Eton collars and polished boots, or serge dresses and white aprons, the men with their flat caps and stringy greyhounds. The clerks and inspectors and trades women expected to take a pride in their official capacities, and they expected her to uphold hers with the same pride. They were not deferential, they always called a spade a spade, straight speaking for sure, and in their own way they were caring and generous.

Night after night she returned to the George Hotel in Walsall tired out, and sat in the little writing room, filling in her reports.

Hye had sent a telegram on the Monday, promising to deal with engaging a new servant, and Evelyn had gone to London mid-week to give moral support. Letters flew backwards and forwards and Lucy was heartened. Hye had been delighted to have been given the task, and the London Aunts and Lady Howard and Miss de Pledge at the Chelsea Hospital were all being admiring and, said Hye, clapping on the side lines. Evelyn sent on any letters immediately so, what with the Home Office packets as well, she was deluged with reports and correspondence. She was quite glad of her Very Seedy day to catch up quietly in the hotel, writing letters.

At the end of November she travelled down to London, and changed for the first time for more than a month into her silk blouse and velvet skirt to attend a reception at the new London School of Economics. There she met Mrs Sidney Webb, Miss Payne Townsend, Gertrude Tuckwell, Miss Collett, and a Mr Vaughan Nash.

Hye was still up when she got home.

"Did you have a nice time?"

"Yes, I did."

"Was there dancing?"

"No, of course not."

"Why of course not?"

"It was all very earnest. Don't sigh so, Hye. Nice food, though. And everyone was so CLEAN! Makes a great change!"

"What did you talk about?"

Lucy considered. "Mostly Workmen's Insurance and Employers' Safety regimes, I think."

"Lucy, you are hopeless!"

"Yes, but I was telling Gertrude Tuckwell about our servant problem. She has flat trouble too. She is by herself now in the flat she shared with May Tennant and she wants to move out. She suggests we all get a bigger flat together."

"What, all of us?"

"It's a thought."

Hye looked black. "I hope it's only a thought. I don't think I could live with Gertrude Tuckwell."

"No? Why?"

"Gut feeling. We're all right where we are."

"This house is very small though, especially if Evelyn is going to be here more often."

"It's just right, when we've reorganised the attic room; it's a nice space. I'll move into it. Evelyn can have my little room. It's our home, Lucy. No one else's. And the domestic agency has given us three names and you are to say when they are to come for interviews. They are all middle-aged ladies who live nearby."

Lucy was impressed and they fixed Wednesday morning, early afternoon and teatime for the women to come. "And I'll tell Gertrude it's no go."

Evelyn came to London on Monday and accompanied Lucy to look for patterns and styles for a new winter outfit, suitable for Ordinary Inspections and not Smelly ones. Evelyn always thoroughly enjoyed the shopping excursions, a new world for her, particularly the fabrics in the Kensington stores, and the long counters piled with pattern books. She went back to Gloucestershire armed with various patterns and fabric samples to mull over, for herself as well as Lucy, and looked forward to returning the next week to stay with Hye while the new servant, Mrs Anstey, settled in.

Mrs Anstey was a small, quiet, neat widow in her late forties. Her own three children were all in work, one an apprentice hairdresser, one a live-in shop girl, and the boy, aged fourteen, apprenticed to a plumber in the Cromwell Road. She had arranged with Hye to come in on Mondays, Wednesdays and Fridays. Monday would be the day to do the general cleaning, take the sheets to the laundry and do any washing of smalls. On Wednesday she would clean each room thoroughly on a monthly rota and do the ironing. This was usually the day when Mrs Hedingham came in to do any mending or sewing. Friday she would do any shopping from lists that had been left for her, prepare any simple meals for the weekend, fill up coal scuttles, lay fires ready for the weekend and make beds ready for any guests at the weekend. Hye seemed delighted with her, and with herself; the references from Mrs Anstey's chapel minister's wife had been more than adequate.

Lucy was knocked sideways on the Monday morning when she arrived at Finsbury Circus to find that Adelaide Anderson had been summoned for assault. Adelaide was white and strained.

"What? Where? How?"

"By a wretched worker at a tailor's factory in Leeds. Last Thursday."

"Whatever happened, Adelaide?"

"I wanted to ask her about overtime employment, and she didn't want to say anything. She was terrified. I put out my hand to reassure her and the forewoman accused me of hitting her cheek."

"My God! What a miserable condition the poor woman must be in to do such a thing to please her employer. What does Doctor Whitelegge say?"

"He says he's very sorry and he will do what he can. He says he hadn't thought of me being a tiger before. Actually, I think he wanted to laugh!"

"I'll 'tiger' him."

The two of them met together that night at a small supper party at 5 Hyde Park Mansions to meet the suffragette activist Isabella Ford. Lucy had been introduced to her some weeks previously at a Women's Emancipation Conference. Miss Ford had not thought much of the Conference or the Union. She was full of humour and practical enthusiasm. She gave the impression, without actually saying so, that she had little time for women Liberals, that the Women's Emancipation Union was neither emancipated nor united, simply a flock of woolly bleaters running this way and that. She thought that the Heather Biggs and the Fawcett schools of industrial theories were dying out. She laughed happily at Adelaide's description of being summoned by workers for assault in Leeds and gave examples of her own exploits on and off platforms and marches around Britain. "I think Leeds is the very worst and most miserably sweated town in England. The tone, the conditions and the morale are so bad."

Gertrude Tuckwell was at the supper as well but very flushed and feverish. She excused herself and went home in a cab early. Lucy was worried as Gertrude was alone in her flat and up all those flights of stairs. She went round in the morning to see how she was and found her very low. "Come and stay with me and Hye." But Gertrude wanted only to stay in bed. Lucy made her promise to come on Sunday lunchtime and stay until she felt better, and went to collect her in a cab after the Advent Sunday morning service. Gertrude lay gratefully on the sofa in Fulham Road swathed in shawls and blankets and drinking copious cups of lemon and ginger, and filling Lucy and Hye in with all the London gossip. She assured them that the scandalous charges that had been resurrected concerning Sir Charles Dilke's first marriage breakdown were absolutely false (Lucy was troubled, but was not comforted); of the great hopes they had all had of the Labour

Party; of how those hopes had been dashed; of how it had failed to do anything definite either in the Factory Bill or the Truck Act – or anything else; that it had simply TALKED Socialism vaguely and ubiquitously; that Keir Hardie was regarded a failure in the house.

Lucy felt she should stand up for the Socialist ideals. She said that the 'simply talk' was at any rate educational and that both Conservative and Liberals were steadily becoming less shuttered and more tolerant of democratic views. And they discussed May Tennant's probable future with the Labour Party now that she had married.

May herself arrived in London to stay with Gertrude on the Tuesday for a few days, and to conference with the Female Inspectorate. She very wisely discouraged all plans of visiting Leeds in force to support Adelaide, and laid plans to get the Home Office to take up the case, and to get evidence of the complicity of Sunderland and Wetton, the employers. She talked a little with Lucy privately over her future, whether she would stay in her present post or not, but no decisions were made.

Lucy had not intended to go to Leeds with Adelaide, who had laid information with Leeds magistrates' court against various tailors on illegal overtime and overcrowding issues. But, despite Adelaide declaring herself not worried in the slightest, the slur on her reputation was deeply disturbing, so Lucy decided to accompany her to Leeds for those court hearings, before going on to her own ten-day programme in Wigan, Burnley and Rochdale. Hyacinth and Evelyn were violently against it.

"It's too much, Lucy, you forget that you were seriously ill in the summer."

But Lucy was determined, and she and Adelaide caught the midnight train to Leeds. Those cases passed off smoothly. No news of Adelaide's mishap seemed to have reached anyone in the courts and she obtained convictions both for Messrs Greenstein and Rothfeld, although both cases were conducted with great difficulty owing to the perjury of the witnesses. The Stipendiary Magistrate, Mr Atkinson, was scrupulously fair, and secured the claims.

Mary Tennant had been writing on Adelaide's behalf and had set up a meeting for them in the afternoon with a Miss Agnes Clove, the secretary of the Leeds Tailoresses' Union, and a Mr Shaw of the Trades Union Council. They met at the Independent Labour Club. This was a fine new building, and its secretary, a very keen young Mr Bennington, took them on a tour pointing out its glories, and provided a large tray of tea and sandwiches. Miss Clove and Mr Shaw showed no surprise and every sympathy for Adelaide's predicament. Mr Shaw remarked that it was "par for the course for Sunderland and Wetton's," and planned with them how to get evidence of the instigation and connivance of the firm in the summons that had been taken out against Adelaide. They were supportive and positive. But when they had taken their leave Adelaide shook uncontrollably and wept bitterly, the first tears she had shed. Lucy persuaded her to go home on the late afternoon train, and after she had waved the train out of the station discovered to her horror that she had lost her Official Postal Book.

She must have left it either in the Labour Club – ignominy – or in a cab. In the end she booked into a Leeds hotel, wired to the Wigan Hotel, and to two people she had arranged to meet in Wigan the next morning, and took herself round to the police station. They contacted several cab firms, and the Postal Book was returned by a cabman that evening.

Because of this, most of the morning was spent in the train chuffing across the moors to Wigan. Lucy watched the wind blow the dusting of snow across the landscape and was glad of her two pairs of woollen stockings inside her sheepskin-lined boots. A Miss Silcock, secretary of the Wigan Women's Weavers Union was waiting for her in the hotel, and over a bowl of steaming oxtail soup, laid out for her a collection of Complaints from home workers and small workshops that she had amassed against the Co-operative Company around the Wigan area. Lucy was surprised and dismayed, as she had always been a great champion of the Co-operative movement, but she promised to investigate, and set up several meetings with milliners and workshops for the morrow.

Sunday in Wigan was bitterly cold and she was glad of the chance to rest up in the warmth and to catch up with a plethora of letters.

Monday was too cold to snow.

Tuesday was not too cold to snow. She spent the afternoon on two slow trains, chugging this time rather than chuffing through the white moorlands to Manchester and then from Manchester to Burnley. She arrived in the dark, thankful that she had booked in at the Station Hotel and had no distance to travel.

Wednesday the snow was driving hard and was several inches deep. HMI Platt arrived during breakfast and advised her against visiting anywhere except Fenton's Mill in the centre of the town. Lucy took his advice and was glad to be back in the warm hotel by teatime.

On Thursday the snow had stopped and the centre of the town was a grey slush. The trains at the back of the Station Hotel hooted and clanged cheerfully enough. The stationmaster assured her she would get to Rochdale without trouble, and he was as good as his word. She sat gazing out of the window at a winter wonderland as the little train bustled south through the forest of Rossendale, past frozen lakes and bleak moorland, all transformed by transient gleams of sun. A young mother and her son, about seven years old, bundled up with shawls and scarves and mittens sat solemnly in the opposite corner. At Rochdale she took a cab to two mills to investigate Complaints and arrived back at the hotel with her feet quite numb, despite the boots, and her briefcase like a ton of bricks. The hotel manager welcomed her in, took her coat and scarf and sat her by the fire in a small parlour room. "You are welcome to use this, Madam, all our commercial gentlemen have gone home early for Christmas."

"How wonderful," said Lucy. "Could I have a hot drink, please?"

"Certainly, certainly – but could I offer you a brandy, on the house – you look fair clemmed."

Lucy accepted gratefully, took her meal on a tray in the snug little room with the firelight flickering, and, warmed inside and out, went up to her room where a small fire had been lit, and a stone hot water bottle had been warming her bed.

She had been planning to visit HMI Wright but her breakfast table had a note to say he would not be in his office. Thank goodness, she thought, and caught the earlier train to Manchester and the fast train home to London. In London, no snow, only slush; but it felt colder than ever it had been in Lancashire, and not nearly so beautiful.

However, here she was in London, in good time to shop and prepare for Christmas. She met friends, sent off Christmas cards, bought pearls and shoes for Hyacinth. She and Hye called on Lady Howard who had come to visit her family in Portland Place. They casually mentioned that they might move to a larger house. Lady Howard did not favour the idea. They dropped the plan.

They spent Christmas in Kent with Bossie and the Aunts at Flammswood. Georgie Dighton asked her to be godmother to the twins and Lucy accepted. Lucy and Hye went to the theatre with friends and particularly enjoyed *As You Like It* with Julia Neilson Terry. They sorted out their personal accounts and asked Bossie to invest a little money for them. They ordered new clothes for day and evening, and bought accessories in the sales, Liberty scarves, handbags, gloves; and Lucy could not resist a wildly extravagant, ravishing, wide black grosgrain evening belt that made her waist look even smaller in the velvet evening skirt.

29

Everything needs conquering at once

Bookbinding and fish; Lucy stays with May Tennant in Berwick; HMI Jackson is not so straightforward; Bolton factory conveniences are disgusting; HMI Birtwhistle is helpful; writing the Annual Report at 100 Fulham Road; Belfast Textiles ask for a permanent Woman Factory Inspector; fish curing on the Isle of Dogs; an unreported factory accident; Sir Charles Dilke faces an adultery trial; why are the book binders so ill?; Lucy loses the theatre tickets; little Charles Tennant dies; more unreported accidents; Sally Army's dubious hymns; 1896 Truck Acts flouted.

Monday January 3rd, 1897, and for Hye the Cookery Term began all over again, and the Lady Inspectors found a range of new and unfamiliar trades and infringements to conquer.

The first to cause concern was the outwardly respectable bookbinding trade in the centre of the City; dozens of small workshops, many of them in the basements of Holborn and Saffron Hill.

After that Doctor Whitelegge received several Complaints from workers in fish working firms, some in London, but more particularly around Lowestoft in Norfolk. It appeared that the famous fish retailers, the Maconochie Brothers, were working their staff all hours, as long as they chose. As soon as a catch arrived in Lowestoft it was shipped to Billingsgate by train, and then the firm claimed it had to be cured and processed at once. Lucy was detailed to find out what was done to the fish at Lowestoft before it caught the train.

"What ought to happen to it?" asked Lucy.

Doctor Whitelegge looked blank. "There must be a circular about it somewhere I suppose."

Lucy and Mr Peacock and the useful young Ibbotson, whose voice had now broken, unearthed Circular Four, Fish Curing. Lucy took it home to read and could not understand it.

But both these new challenges, Bookbinding and Fish, had to take a back seat, while she was sent to Bolton after a letter from Adelaide Anderson disclosed that a much greater proportion of factories than usual had been gravely flouting the overcrowding, ventilation and cleanliness requirements. Adelaide felt that the District Inspectors had, even on the most generous assessment, fallen behind on routine inspections; there seemed to have been no inspections of small workshops, and no lists of outworkers at all; and she strongly suspected that inspectors had been conniving not to lay any derogatory information against factory owners.

Adelaide's case in Leeds was to be heard the next week and May Tennant would be present. May sent Lucy to Bolton, but invited her up to her new home, Chirnside, near Berwick on Tweed, where Harold Tennant was the Member of Parliament. "Come for a few days and we can discuss business in comfort. We shall be coming back down part of the way with you anyway on Harold's route for Cardiff and then the Dangerous Trades Committee, and then I'll go back to Leeds to be with Adelaide. While I've got you we can begin to plan out the Annual Report, and go for lovely walks if the weather allows."

Hye was ambivalent. "It's miles and miles out of your way – and it's in the middle of nowhere. And it's Arctic. And you're not strong enough to go to Bolton, let alone Berwick."

Lucy wanted to go, though, to see where May was now settling and the places where her future life would mostly revolve. So she took the night train towards Edinburgh and was collected from Berwick by a smart carriage which took her the eight miles to Chirnside Hall, a warm and comfortable Borders small mansion with spectacular views.

The weather did allow short walks with May and her little stepson, and the air was like champagne. Charles was a friendly little boy of eight, but painfully thin and pale. Two days before they arrived he had learned to play chess, and easily beat Lucy, to her chagrin.

Margot Asquith, Harold's sister, arrived with her friend Violet Little and even May was put into the shade by her spirits and fun. Margot was much younger and prettier than Lucy had expected and quite clearly adored her young nephew.

Lucy enjoyed her four days, the good food and the pampering; May ran her house as capably as she ran the Superintendentship, and the staff were attentive and very friendly.

When the adults set off for London, Cardiff and Bolton, the little boy waved wistfully from the schoolroom window.

The arrival at Bolton hurled her back into a harsher, rougher, more aggressive world. The first meeting in HMI Jackson's office turned into an incoherent tirade against Women Factory Inspectors; he thought they all ought to be under Superintendent Inspectors and should definitely not be permitted to prosecute. He was so apoplectic and red-faced that Lucy wondered if he was drunk; and was so voluble that she speculated that some sort of indignation meeting had been held in the area before her arrival. She realised she must play strictly by the book and wrote to HMI Birtwhistle in Blackburn to announce her arrival three days hence.

The five factories she inspected in Bolton, on Complaints sent to the Home Office, were certainly very bad. Three had no doors and no proper flooring whatever in the women's lavatories, and when she reported this to the Medical Officer of Health for Bolton, he shook his head resignedly and said that the manufacturers were determined to resist doors in sanitary conveniences for females, or the women sat in them too long! Lucy urged that this was frivolous and disgusting and probably illegal. She pointed out that the North End Company had insufficient lavatories as well. They had assessed the standard two for the first fifty workers and one for every fifty thereafter. Lucy said the Home Office had a much higher standard. He said he had not heard of a Home Office Standard before.

The staff of the Swan Hotel Bolton were polite, but icy. It was as if she was a completely new type of animal; either that or news of her arrival had been filtered through by the factory owners to other business owners in the town. She wrote and made an appointment with Doctor Whisher, the Medical Officer of Health for Heywood and went to visit him after visiting Highfield Mill and Rosehill Mill. The sanitary conveniences there for women were in earth closets in draughty sheds outside in the yard, and no water in sinks for washing hands at all. Dr Whisher seemed discomfited to be told this, and said he would try to get water piped in. If possible, he amended.

The next day she presented herself at HMI Birtwhistle's office in Blackburn and he at least was helpful and pleasant. He gave her lists of places and maps for factories in Accrington and Blackburn, drove her to Clayton le Moors as the weather was atrocious, and back to the Old Bull Hotel where he insisted on buying her a brandy. He tipped her off that it had come to his notice during the past week that the trustee for the Clayton and Company Mill, being on the Sanitary Committee, had stopped and suppressed the notice sent last summer by Miss Anderson to the Clerk of the Sanitary Authority.

Sure enough, when she visited Dr Tattersall, the Medical Officer of Health, the next morning she found there was no knowledge and no record of any notice. She visited two small factories in Accrington, and then climbed with relief into a train to Manchester and home to London, where Evelyn and Mrs Anstey had made Fulham Road cosy and charming with warm fires and sprays of perfumed winter jasmine brought up from the Boyce.

The whole of the next week was spent sorting out the papers and writing up the Annual Reports from the Female Inspectorship. Hye was away in Wakefield for the week so boxes were stored in her attic room and all meals were eaten on trays before the fire, as the table groaned with the precious papers and files. Adelaide and Rose came from Monday to Thursday and Evelyn was in her element, copying and recopying out lists. "You have no idea the value it is having you here," cried Rose at the end of Thursday. "If only we could have a secretary – preferably a stenographer – at Finsbury Circus – how much more we could get done!" Evelyn was pink with pleasure. Because of her neat writing and clear headings, and the fact that she did EXACTLY what was explained to her, the Report took shape smoothly, and by the next Monday, when Evelyn left, and Tuesday when Hye returned home, Adelaide and Lucy were ready to begin to write it, incorporating Mary Paterson's stoutly wrapped packages from Scotland.

That week Doctor Whitelegge informed them that they were to be moved from the premises in Finsbury Circus and it seemed a good time to press for an office in Westminster, close to the Home Office, even if not actually in it, and May drew up requests for a permanent stenographer and a filing clerk.

Lucy met with May and Adelaide to confer on this and also to talk about a letter they had received from the Textiles Operations Unions in Belfast. They were asking for a permanent Female Inspector in Northern Ireland, on the grounds that the present inspections were too short, and too uncertain. The three women decided that a permanent Irish Female Inspector would be at a great disadvantage, and, among other things, raise political difficulties and jealousy between Northern and Southern Ireland. The Inspector concerned would be isolated from her colleagues and out of May's or the Superintendent's control. May thought the most likely outcome would be that she would work with Mary Paterson, under the male Scottish and Irish Superintendents. On the other hand, they acknowledged that the problems of the women textile workers in Ireland were certainly diffuse and legion. Lucy suggested that one or other of the inspectors should spend six months of the year – two months at a time – in Ireland, and said she would be willing to do it.

They decided to put this suggestion to Dr Whitelegge. Lucy asked leave to go to Ireland, armed with Special Instructions to deal with the fines and deductions problems over which the men were currently striking. They all agreed that NOBODY must go without specific support from Dr Whitelegge, on account of the distrust and jealousy for the Women Inspectors.

Fish Curing raised its unpleasant head again, this time at Maconochie's Food Processing Factories in Lowestoft and also on the Isle of Dogs. The factory on the Isle of Dogs produced cans of fish, and meat, and stew, and canned vegetables and jars of potted meat and fish pastes. The work force was overwhelmingly female and classed as unskilled. All the produce was highly perishable and had to be dealt with fast, and so the hours were long and unremitting, and the Maconochie Brothers flouted the overtime rules, and abused the special permissions that they had been given. The firm had crowds of girls waiting outside hoping for casual work. It was difficult for them to get off the Isle of Dogs to find other work, often the bridges across were raised for hours at a time to allow boats to enter or to leave the docks, and the lines of carts using the bridges made it impossible for omnibuses to keep to any timetables. The wages were pitiful, but one worker complained "if the girls complain and ask for higher wages they get the sack, and there are plenty outside waiting and anxious to be taken on."

Lucy travelled home from the Isle of Dogs several days running, having braved the journey in sleet and snow, and sick to her stomach with the sight and smells of fish and meat preparation. "And just think, Hye, I can come home into the warm and the quiet, and they are there fourteen hours a day, and never free of it."

She also spent time in the East End visiting Ritchie's Jute Mills in Stratford East because of two Complaints. One was from a trades union secretary complaining that some girls were being given excessive fines for problems with their work, and the other telling of an unreported accident. She spoke to the girls but could do nothing for them, as they were terrified of losing their jobs if they gave their names. All she could do was to caution the Mill for the future and file a slip to report in case of other irregularities.

In the case of the unreported accident, a Mrs Waller had been hit by a flying shuttle and injured her arm. She had been discharged by the West Ham Hospital and was now at home. Lucy collected details from the hospital and went to the Medical Officer of Health about the factory. He said it was the first he had heard of the accident. She took the chance to inspect Ritchie's thoroughly, and asked the reason for not reporting it. The foreman said it had only been a slight accident. Lucy said of course she understood that shutter guards must be formed in such a way as not to hinder the work, but in this case it was patently possible. He seemed unconcerned and Lucy felt snubbed. While she was at it she told him his sanitary conveniences were insufficient! She wrote and asked HMI Vaughan to go to the Jute Mills with her.

The next day was a Very Very Seedy Day and she was at home doing Office Work, but bounced back and was able to dine at the Cadogan Hotel with Gertrude Tuckwell and her new flatmate, Miss Edwards. They went on to a reception at Sir Charles and Lady Dilke's, and while they were there Lady Dilke took her up to her bedroom and told her the details of the rumours that Gertrude had told Lucy about previously. Sir Charles was having to face a retrial for adultery – committed with a chamber maid – against his former wife. He denied the charge. The marriage had been a disaster for years and his wife's affaires were common knowledge. The wife had died several years after the divorce and Sir Charles had had to fight hard to retrieve his reputation. Lady Emilia had been a great friend and supporter throughout this time and when her own first husband, the Master of Lincoln College Oxford, died she and Sir Charles had married. Lucy was very angry for Lady Dilke, and even for Sir Charles. It was a tragedy blown up to discredit Sir Charles in order to muddy both their names and discredit the valuable parliamentary work they were both doing.

On Sunday, May Tennant came with her to West Ham Hospital to collect a certificate from the house surgeon of Mrs Waller's incapacity for work. They came home tired and footsore and Lucy sat down for a nap and woke up at bedtime.

She spent three days concentrating on the bookbinders working in their homes in the Clerkenwell area. She visited between ten and twelve homes a day, and was distressed by the unprecedented cases of coughs and asthma. Why? It could be just the damp basement rooms; it could be the February winds and rains; it could be the damp washing and family cooking smells mixed in with the bookbinding glues and the dust from the cloth book fabric. The workshops seemed on the whole much neater and more orderly than most workshops. Could it be the bronzing powder, liberally applied over wet ink to give a gold effect to book titles, and a glossy finish, that got into the lungs? What was it composed of? None of the women had any idea.

She went to St James' Theatre and bought five tickets for a Pinero play as a treat for Adelaide, Rose, Hye, Evelyn and herself. When she got home she found she had lost them on the bus. Hyacinth erupted. "You do this ALL the time! You lose your pocket book, you lose your umbrella! You lose MY umbrella! You leave your luggage behind in the hotel, you lose the Official Postal Book. You're a joke! You do too much. You MUST rest."

Lucy apologised meekly; but the next day she went back to St James' Theatre to explain and found someone had posted the tickets back to the theatre. Hye was cross all over again. "You don't deserve it! Why should people be so nice to you?"

February ended with a great blow. May Tennant wired to say she had to return to Berwick. The wistful little boy at the window had had yet another bout of bronchitis and was now dying of pneumonia.

March definitely came in like a lion; winds and squalls of icy sleet. Lucy gave up all hopes of an umbrella and resorted to a voluminous rain cape and a sou'wester hat purchased at the Army and Navy. The cape flapped about her legs and irritated her, and the hat, though the saleswoman had assured her it was the latest fashion in women's rain gear, did nothing for her sense of style. Whitechapel was depressing as she plodded round on her bookbinding and artificial flower inspections and the workers seemed as damp and dejected inside as she felt outside. The artificial flower makers were cold as well; they dared not heat their work rooms because of the methylated spirits they sprayed on the flower stems and posy clusters. They sat, freezing, in arbours of icy, stinking beauty.

Every evening she returned home cold to the bone and heavy at heart. On March the third the news came that little Charles Tennant had died, a brave boy. The thought of him tugged at Lucy's memory and her heart strings. The sight of his lonely face waving at the window brought back to her the misery she and Hye had had to cope with when their own mother died, and they were much older than Charles and had each other to cling to; there were kind and loving relatives all around them; but there was ever present the nagging fear, buried deep, that nobody would ever again actually want them for themselves. She hoped that he had not had to carry this fear.

Hye had a fearful cold and could not go amongst her students in the kitchens. The little house in the Fulham Road was permeated with eucalyptus and steamy handkerchiefs boiling. They sat writing their reports, blankets around their legs, shawls around their shoulders. Lucy wrote the Special Reports about Ritchie's Jute Mill and the Maconochie Bros. Fish Factory and sent the prosecution reports in duplicate.

Hye filled hot water bottles and blew her sore nose. "This is the life!" she proclaimed. "Full of adventure and gay abandon."

On Wednesday Lucy visited the East London Children's Hospital in Shadwell to get particulars of a young apprentice whose hand had been hurt in an accident in a toy factory. Then she tracked down the home of the child, one room in a greasy, littered side street in Whitechapel. The tiny mother, Mrs Butwell, said the hand was too bad for the child to work at all for five days and the nail was still black. The accident had happened on January the 16th, the same day as the jammed shutter case in Ritchie's.

In both cases the overseers had alleged the accident as 'too slight to report' though in both cases the wound was still not healed.

On her way back to the City she passed the Whitechapel Salvation Army Women's Shelter in Hawley Street and made herself known to them. She found a rough good-natured Sally Army Captain and several women in sacking aprons, sorting great piles of blankets and singing hymn tunes lustily. The words of the hymns were distinctly un-hymn like, but they did not stop when she came in, and were not stopped by the Captain. She gave Lucy a great mug of strong sweet tea. Lucy thought it was ambrosia.

On Thursday she trailed off to Luton for yet another inspection of a particularly recalcitrant factory. "They are simply being TIRESOME over their illegal overtime, a five-hour spell one session!" She could not reach a satisfactory conclusion. "It will have to come to a prosecution. I cannot get them to see reason."

On Friday it came as no surprise that she was struck down with gastric flu and had to stay in bed, trying to write letters and her weekly returns. But after the weekend she had to send to Dr Thame, who gave her a Medical Certificate and a prescription, and she slowly recovered with the help of spring sunshine and Mrs Anstey's bland and comforting presence around the house.

The first morning she went back to work she had a very disagreeable meeting with HMI Cameron at the Home Office about Fire Wings and Safety Fencing which had arisen over the Ritchie's jute factory incident. He insisted that all safety fencing issues should be relegated solely to him, and he was very disinclined to deal with the hand press issue in the toy factory, but nor would he let her take charge of it. Lucy relinquished it, simply to prevent a rupture. He wanted to take the matter of the Fire Wings out of her hands as well, but she refused point blank, and when she heard that no notice had been sent in on either of the cases she had mentioned, she said she would send the notices herself. She also asked him the outcome of the overcrowding notice she had served on Cohen and Winns in Hanbury Street. He said he would write to the Junior Inspector who had visited there after her and ask him. Lucy stipulated the reply should be forwarded to her, and that she should write to Cohen's on the matter so as not to have it snatched out of her hands.

She boarded the afternoon train to Wolverhampton in a bad temper and had the same battle the next morning with HMI Jackson about appalling sanitary conditions at a baker's in Bilston. She refused to let him take the prosecution out of her hands, and was heartened to find that a diplomatic letter from HMI Cramp had been sent to him advising him to leave the matter with her. In the end she visited the baker's with HMI Jackson and the Medical Officer of Health, and the District Surveyor. They all agreed to press the matter with the Sanitary Authorities, that HMI Jackson should answer them in his own and in her name, and that if a case were brought, she would attend and give the required evidence.

She also visited the Balfe and Jordan factory with him, and returned to London late on Saturday mentally exhausted but defiant.

May Tennant called a meeting of the Female Inspectorship and attended in deep mourning looking very drawn and ill. All the inspectors were present, even Mary Paterson, on one of her rare journeys south. They had all had cases which worried them, particularly excessive fines levied on employees for minor misdemeanours, and wanted to form a fairer policy. All had come across numerous cases of workers being fined, and deductions being made for lateness or carelessness, or damage to work and equipment. Many factories were obviously unaware of the directions set out in the 1896 Truck Acts. They went through all the points and cleared up a number of vague descriptions and listed them.

1. Any deductions or fines for employees which cannot be posted under the 1896 Act cannot be legally charged under that Act.
2. The word 'Register' applies only to the clause about fines, but if a reduction, or payment from wages, is made for damage or injury which is LESS than the actual cost of same to the employer, then it may be considered in the light of a disciplinary fine, and must be entered as such in the report.
3. No fine in EXCESS of the cost of damage is permissible at all.
4. If the damage is accidental, then to be 'fair and reasonable' the deduction must be small in proportion to the wages. If the damage is due to negligence only, then less small, in proportion to the wages formula.
5. The deductions in respect of cleaning are to be based on:
    a) The amount paid to the cleaner
    b) The number of girls on whom the toll is levied.

6. The occupier (employer) has a right to deduct for time lost, and if he has a system of locking out, he does not have to allow for time lost owing to this, but not for any time in addition, IF he locks them out.
7. The wages book becomes a factory document if it is also noted as a fines Register.
8. The Fines notice MUST begin with a preamble setting forth that it is in accordance with the 'Terms of the Contract.'

When this had been checked and agreed on, May told them that although no decision had yet been made as to where their specific office would be situated, they were to be given a part-time stenographer, Miss Palmer, and a part-time filing clerk, Miss Mandrill.

"Only part-time!?"

"Well, it's a start anyway," said May. "They are going to begin next week at Finsbury Circus."

The meeting finished with them all discussing the new Home Office regulations in relation to General District Inspectors and what this might mean for their emerging Department.

Lucy and Adelaide met again that evening. They had been invited to a reception at Sir Charles and Lady Dilke's, and so they had decided to dine at Frascati's before they went. To their surprise they met Mary Paterson at the reception. "You didn't say you were going to be here!"

Mary looked shy. "It's the first time I've been invited. I was wondering if I would come. I thought, I shan't know a soul and I haven't got the right sort of clothes." She was wearing a plain dark blue woollen dress with a red merino Paisley shawl.

"You look absolutely right. Couldn't be righter."

Mary looked relieved.

"If we'd known you were to be here you should have dined with us as well. We went to Frascati's to make a night of it."

Mary looked uncertain. "Not my usual way of spending an evening."

"Nor ours, I assure you, but we like an occasional treat."

"Oh, so do I, so do I. But I usually choose a concert or a play."

They introduced her to as many people as they could and Mary enjoyed herself. She was self-possessed and well able to hold her own in the throng, but she had no airs and graces. Her simple smooth hair style, her freckled complexion, and, Lucy had to acknowledge, her height and her large hands and feet set her apart from the over-confident and slightly artificial manners of Sir Charles and Lady Dilke's usual guests.

"Let's strike while the iron is hot," urged Lucy as she discovered Mary had only one more day in London. So Rose Squire, Lucy, Mary and Hye all dined together at the Cadogan Hotel and then went to see *Sweet Mary* – "What better?" – at the Court Theatre in Sloane Square.

30

The enquiry into lead poisoning

Lucy loses her Official Notebook again; HMI Walmsley says the Special Rules are a farce; Mary and Lucy are shocked by Hanley Potteries' laxness; defective shutter guards at Ritchie's; fish-curing conditions become insupportable; the hotel organises 'an office'; visiting the girls in hospital with lead poisoning; lead poisoning and personality changes; Hye has the flu; May plans to retire in May; 'we are drops in the ocean'; helpful Temperance Hall ladies; the lead poisoning tea parties; a magical drive to the Staffordshire Moorlands; back to London.

May Tennant wanted the Home Office Special Enquiry into Lead Poisoning in the Pottery Trade to be put under way as soon as possible, and asked Lucy and Mary Paterson to go to Staffordshire to gather information on how best to set up the Enquiry. They decided it was best to go the very next day and for Mary to travel back to Scotland via Staffordshire. So letters went off to various Staffordshire Pottery Firms and to Her Majesty's Inspectors, and then Rose, Adelaide, Mary and Lucy went off to have supper at the Victoria Hotel. Lucy managed to leave her Official Pocket Book in May Tennant's house. May sent it in a cab to 100 Fulham Road, and Hyacinth was cross with Lucy again when Lucy arrived home.

Mary and Lucy arrived in Stoke on Trent in the early afternoon and went straight to HMI Walmsley's office to check on the Special Rules and Directions for employees exposed to working with lead. They told him they had come about the Special Rules for workers and employers using lead products. Were they observed? No, said Mr Walmsley. What effect did they have? None, said Mr Walmsley. Were they useful? Not at all, said Mr Walmsley. They were a dead letter; that, owing to their wording they were not enforceable; and if enforced they were no good; that the workers could not be bothered to wear the protective clothing even if the employers had provided it; that the potters' grievances were largely their own fault; that there had been no diminution in the lead cases since their promulgation; and that he was strongly on the manufacturers' side! Lucy laughed, and sympathised, and put him back into a good humour.

They visited one of Minton's factories and found that the Special Rules were certainly a farce (and that, incidentally, the sanitation was bad). A visit to the local Sanitation Authority offices was hopeless. Mary Paterson said bluntly as they went back to the hotel that they were a farce as well.

At half past five they dropped in on the offices of the Women's Pottery Union. The secretary, Mrs Goodwin, was just putting her hat and coat on, but quickly took them off, welcomed them in, and gave them the names of two of Minton's workers who had been laid off sick with lead poisoning; she promised to collect a list of employees to be interviewed for their next visit. She upheld Mr Walmsley's view that no positive effect had resulted from the Special Rules.

The next day they inspected together – May Tennant had permitted it – in various Hanley potteries and were shocked by the general bad conditions and laxness. They visited the ex-employee of Taylor and Tunnicliffe whose name Mrs Goodwin had given them, and they visited the Certifying Surgeon to the Medical Officer of Health, Mr Clare, in Hanley. He promised to make a list of lead poisoning cases over the past year, and seemed keen to assist them.

They parted on Stoke on Trent station platform having parcelled out the reports to be written. Mary went off to Glasgow, and Lucy thought, as she travelled back to London, how much she had enjoyed her time with Mary, and how greatly she always valued her solid measured judgements and carefully thought out opinions.

Back in London, shutter guards, shutter guards appeared to be on every other piece of paper on Lucy's desk; and all defective, or renewed, or renewed and still defective. And all at Ritchie's Jute Mill. It seemed that Ritchie's had installed new shutter guards on the machinery, cheap and shoddy ones, and that now the workers were on the verge of strike action. Sir Charles Dilke himself had been to talk to the workers, and had urged them to keep quiet until he could get better ones installed. May Tennant said that Mr Norton, the secretary of the Trades Unions in Stratford East, had written to her complaining and making impossible suggestions. He is a fool, she told Lucy, confer with him and any others, and try to keep them quiet until the better shutter guards arrive.

She fixed a meeting for the Wednesday morning to meet Mr Norton and some of Ritchie's Jute weavers. Mr Norton was doing his very best to milk the situation and make it worse. Everyone was objecting strongly to everything and were busy writing petitions and collecting signatures. Lucy urged patience and consideration as to petitions, saying that the factory had ordered new, more suitable shutter guards, and she fixed a meeting with HMI Vaughan to recommend suitable guards and have them made up. She wrote to several firms herself. When the time came for her meeting with Mr Vaughan she discovered he had not recommended the first set of new guards, but neither had he asked about any others, nor taken any trouble over their installation.

Meanwhile the storm clouds of Maconochie's fish-curing problems were gathering in Millwall and on the Isle of Dogs. Conditions for the workers there were becoming insupportable.

Yet more shutter guards were fitted at Ritchie's. They still did not fill the bill. Mr Ritchie declined to do anything more about either guards or ventilation fans and Lucy felt considerable sympathy with him! She sent a note to May Tennant – who had gone to the country for a few days' rest – went home to write full reports, and sent them in typed by wonderful Miss Mandrill and Miss Palmer. Then she wrote notes to everyone to say she had done it.

It was almost a relief to arrive back in Stoke on Trent and settle into the hotel there. Mary Paterson had come the day before. The hotel had given them adjoining rooms. Both women had brought boxes and bags of papers as well as their suitcases, and as May's room was larger than Lucy's they went down to ask the manager if they might have a second small table in her room. When they explained that they were making a Government enquiry into lead poisoning the manager was very much interested, and said he had a small room at the end of their corridor with an entrance through a bedroom. "We occasionally use it if a family come to stay with a child – but that doesn't often happen." For a minute sum he was willing to let them use it as a small office. "We can light the fire there if you need it in the evenings." So Lucy moved into the room with the little study attached, and Mary kept her bigger room. They were very grateful and everyone was pleased, and they spent the evening planning the next few days and setting up their 'office'.

Mary had fallen and sprained her ankle quite badly a few days previously and needed to rest it, so they spent the next morning sorting and examining a thick parcel of lead poisoning reports that had been sent to the Home Office in past months from doctors across the whole Potteries area. They sent circulars to various small china factories in the Black Country too, asking for any reports, and letters to all the main hospitals in the region.

Lucy called on the various Medical Officers of Health in Hanley, Stoke and Tunstall, and told them of the forthcoming Enquiry, and the next day she and Mary visited the Staffordshire Infirmary together. The Matron took them into wards to see four young women suffering from lead poisoning.

Eliza Whittaker was 21 years old, a majolica painter at Brunt's in Hanley. She had been painting crockery there for four years. She had been ill before and been off work for seventeen weeks, but had not been to any doctor, and then returned to work feeling better. But after a month or two she was ill at home for another 9 weeks and then had to come to the hospital quite paralysed and with severe stomach pains. She had been in the hospital since the end of January. She could not understand it; her mother and her mother's family had worked at Brunt's for 24 years – "and all the folk on my mother's side – and they ent none of 'em suffered." She suffered very badly. She said she did not do the skilled painting, Brunt's workshops turned out very cheap ware painting, the more you could turn out the more you got paid. Lucy asked what the washing and cleaning facilities were like. "Yow could never get the paint off yower hands, not completely. No, the pottery had no towels provided. Yow just wiped yower hands on yower overalls, before yow ate yower meal middle day."

A girl two beds further down from Eliza was called Gertrude Lambert. She was just seventeen and had only been at Ridgeways in Hanley for eight months. She had been a dipping hand, cleaning the plates and bowls after their painting. She had never been ill before, never ill enough to be in bed like this, certainly. She had been 12 weeks in the hospital with partial paralysis and blindness. She too said that her sanitary conveniences had no towels, and everyone simply wiped their hands on their overalls.

In another ward a young married woman, Jane Pendleton, had just been brought in. She was 20, with a high fever, and partial paralysis. She had worked in the dipping mill with the lead glaze at Milton and Holmes in Stoke. She was half unconscious and too ill to give them any details.

In the last ward they visited they talked to Cecily Withington, another young married woman. She too had only worked for a few months before arriving a month before from the Stafford Infirmary. She too was partially paralysed and her eyes were affected. She could not understand it – her father had worked as a dipper for 22 years, and although he suffered chronically from the lead, she kept saying "But not like this! Not like this!"

The Matron made an appointment for them to see Doctor Allerdyce, the house physician, the next day. It was Palm Sunday so they both went to church in the morning, and then to the hospital in the early afternoon.

Dr Allerdyce was extremely interested in the Home Office Enquiry and set himself to be as helpful as he could be. In his opinion the lead cases had not diminished either in number or in severity since the introduction of the Special Rules in the District. On the contrary, he thought that, although they were not more numerous, they were certainly more severe, and he did not know why this should be. Quite recently there had been three cases of blindness due to lead, one of temporary insanity, and several cases of convulsions; such cases had not been seen before.

He felt that there should be regular inspections at all potteries, and that yearly, or three-yearly, certificates should be issued. And if a significant number of infringements occurred then the Medical Officer of Health should have the power to suspend, and if necessary to close down permanently. He would definitely prohibit Young Persons being employed in ANY dangerous processes ANYWHERE until 18–20 years old as in his experience Young Persons were much more susceptible to convulsions.

He was aware of there always being a very large number of outpatients – but no record was kept of those; and he did not hold out much hope that their own doctor, even if they had one, which he doubted, would have anything but the most rudimentary records. Only very, very severe cases were brought into hospitals.

He promised them he would send them a statement the next day of the number of lead poisoning patients at Stafford Infirmary over the last ten years, and he was as good as his word, adding a small list of his own of general practitioners who he thought would be sympathetic to the cause. Lucy and Mary parcelled them out between them and made appointments with several. Lucy visited a Doctor Philips in Jasper Street, and a Doctor Mistry at the Church Mission Room in the High Street. Dr Mistry had a theory that prolonged working with lead had a definite effect on personality changes. He had noticed that sufferers from lead poisoning became much more bad tempered, irrational and aggressive, picked fights with strangers, and that the men who worked with lead were more likely to beat their wives and families for no apparent reason. He had no conclusive evidence, but he felt it was too frequent to be mere coincidence.

They began to visit their way through the long lists of home patients that their general practitioners had provided, choosing first the women's names, but then found that the men of the house were in worse case than the women, and were more likely to struggle on with worse symptoms for months longer than the women. The woman of the household, who had all the housework to do as well, after her twelve-hour shift at the factory, often collapsed quite quickly.

On the Wednesday in Holy Week Lucy went back to London and Mary to Scotland. Lucy carried with her the first drafts of their reports to talk over with May Tennant and Doctor Whitelegge the next day. She found Hyacinth in bed with flu, and Mrs Anstey coming in late evening and early morning to light fires and provide hot drinks and nursing care.

Lucy worried about leaving Hye while she went to the Home Office but Mrs Anstey assured her she would stay, so Lucy carried her reports to Westminster, only to find that May Tennant had gone off to the Tennants' new home in Kent for Easter, and had forgotten to write to Lucy to say the meeting had been postponed. Lucy was furious. Doctor Whitelegge was in his office, but had other appointments. He apologised to Lucy and made an appointment for after Easter. "But, really Hye, it was not HIS fault. May simply hasn't got her mind on the job at all. She simply can't go on, she's turning into a disaster."

She wrote May a very stiff note; when she reached home and began to pay attention to her postbag she discovered a letter from Rose Squire asking if she could check on two laundry Complaints before Easter, as the list that May had sent Rose was too long for her to complete before the holidays. Fuming, she went and inspected them – old Complaints, still nothing done about them.

She came back to poor Hye quite worn out. But at least they were able to spend Good Friday and Easter together, alone and quiet.

As things turned out they had a whole week together and they made the most of it. Hye recovered slowly and steadily, and a telegram from Mary Paterson said she was laid low herself, and was not able to meet in Stoke until the week of April 26th. Thankful, Lucy spent her days catching up with the reports, Complaints, visits and letters that had been piling up for weeks. She met up with Rose Squire, also grateful for a plain sailing week. Rose had been carrying the Laundry Enquiry to all intents and purposes alone, as Adelaide was increasingly taking over the planning and administration that May Tennant could not complete. May herself, torn in too many directions, assisting Harold with his parliamentary plans, nursing the little Charles and then coping with his death and funeral, was dropping the reins of the Female Inspectorship almost completely, and Adelaide was trying to pick them up and do her own detective work with the Dangerous Trades of fur pulling and bookbinding.

Lucy had a long interview with Dr Whitelegge about the Potteries Enquiry. He allowed that it would be a good thing to bring in statistics regarding the number of men ill with lead poisoning, to compare them with the women. He agreed that she and Mary should work together, visiting and collecting material. He was very interested in it all, and said that it must be done thoroughly, and soon.

As she left he gave her a ticket for a seat along the route of Queen Victoria's forthcoming Jubilee Procession, and said he would get her another if her sister would like to go; but Hye had said she would much prefer spending the day at the Boyce in Dymock and join in the country festivities there.

The extra days in London permitted her to tie up the final ends of the flying shuttle factory incident, and the case for compensation for the toy factory apprentice.

Hye's summer term at the cookery school began again, and she and Lucy had a shopping day together buying household goods for 100 Fulham Road, and planning additions for their summer wardrobes.

Lucy dined alone with May Tennant, and May told her she was retiring at the end of May. "You are right, Lucy, I cannot do this job satisfactorily and support Harold as I should. I really don't know who will follow me. It should by seniority be Mary Paterson, but I'm doubtful about her doing so. She is sensible enough – too sensible – but the men who want to bring us down will run rings round her. I am sure Doctor Whitelegge will not choose her."

Lucy said if that was so, Mary should certainly be alerted as soon as possible on the state of affairs. "I heard her wondering if she should be moving south; she didn't want to; and she was suffering unnecessary inconvenience because of the uncertainties."

May nodded. "And also, we all have to put up with so much unpleasantness in the course of our daily work."

Lucy considered. "I find quite often these days that I am not regarded with such horror and resentment as I was when I first set out. Sometimes I feel that I am actually being seen and treated as a colleague. I still find that amazing!"

"One of these days it won't be amazing at all!"

"One of these far-off, far-flung days, yes. But then I come up against an Inspector or a magistrate who looks at me as if I were some sort of weird witch, to be vanquished and made invisible, and I realise how far off it is. The reasonable men are drops in the ocean."

"Well, WE are the drops in the ocean, Lucy. There are only five of us in the country, the whole country! If each one of us was ten people – we would still be only drops in the ocean. However, as I am the one who is leaving the Department, I think it might be possible for me to represent more openly to the Home Office the disagreeable attitude of the Male Department."

On the 26th April Lucy and Mary met in Stoke again and set up 'shop' in the little room at the end of the hotel corridor. They decided to interview as many people as they possibly could during the next two weeks.

Mary went and engaged a room in the Temperance Providential Hall in Hanley for four evenings and they hand-delivered sixteen letters to women and girls who had attended as patients of Dr Philips and Dr Mistry.

The Temperance Hall organisers were very interested and undertook to find two ladies to dispense tea and sandwiches.

Lucy delivered by hand the lead reports to HMI Cramp. "This is as far as we have got." He looked at them sourly. She told him of the forthcoming tea parties. "Good," he said. "But don't be surprised if not many of them turn up. They'll find it daunting."

"We'll try not to daunt them. We've said they are welcome to bring friends with them."

They took a cab in pouring rain to Stoke Infirmary and spoke with a Doctor Moody at length about the Special Enquiry. He was very anxious to take part, and his assistant, Dr Foley, explained the procedures of the hospitals when reporting cases to HMI Cramp and also to the employers. Young Dr Foley wrote them letters of introduction to local doctors and to the local workhouses.

The first tea party was useful. Nineteen women attended, but only eleven had had lead poisoning. The others were friends. Mary and Lucy sat at small tables and wrote down as many details as they could, and the Temperance Ladies bustled about making a fuss of the girls and making them feel at home. Six girls had 'recovered' and gone back to their former jobs. "It's a case of having to, Miss." Several of them asked if their friends could come to the next tea parties. Several asked if their brothers and fathers would be allowed to come too. It was clear that they were going to be deluged with names and details. The Temperance Ladies were more than equal to the challenge. "Way might 'ave to borrow the tea urn from the Ladies Sewing Circle. Down't yow fret, Miss Paterson, yow jest get on with the lists, way'll see yow straight!"

Each day they scurried round the Five Towns. May visited and inspected the factories and the workshops, Lucy visited the homes of sick employees and the doctors' surgeries. Several doctors had looked up their own reports of their own patients and copied them out for the Enquiry. They both visited the outpatients department at the North Stafford Infirmary.

The lists grew longer and longer: Mrs Meek of Lichfield Street, Mr and Mrs Bennett and Mr and Mrs Taylor, all lead dippers; Florrie Simpson, Clare Road, George Smith, Gruntling Street. Then there was the Eugenia Porcelain works and Grimwade Bros; both their sanitary arrangements were very bad, in Grimwade's case practically non-existent. Mary went to various magistrates' courts to lay informations on four horrendous breaches of regulations.

The piles of papers on the table in the office room at the end of the corridor grew higher and higher. They went together to Stoke Workhouse, a huge, infinitely depressing place, where the workhouse manager showed them first the sections for the elderly men, and then for the elderly women, and promised them a census of the inmates over 60. The Manager was resigned. "Nearly everyone here has been a member of the 'Potters' Army' and all have been wounded by the pottery trades, whichever Department they have worked in. If it's not lead, it's clay, lugging huge weights of it around – or the damp – or the heat – or the dust – ! But every house in the land needs plates and bowls and cups! What's to be done?"

They called on the Co-op Society and various Trades Union folk, and alerted them to the ongoing Enquiry.

For the second tea party thirty-two women arrived and two men with their wives. Twenty-two were or had been affected by lead poisoning, twelve had returned to their work. The final two tea parties had fifty people apiece and the Temperance Ladies had recruited several more volunteers and were a welcoming and comforting presence, encouraging the women to add little details and keeping everyone well provided with jam and meat paste sandwiches. Lucy asked for the bill at the end of the four sessions. "Yow just pay for the hire of the hall, Miss Deane. The Temperance Society will be proud to support yower cause."

On Saturday afternoon the usually stolid Mary struck. "Lucy! You are not to go into that little office. We will not even open the door! We will both have a long bath and change our clothes, and we will take a cab and go to the theatre! I have booked tickets for *Harbour Lights in Hanley*. It was not very good, but Lucy enjoyed it. Mary slept peacefully through the first act.

Luckily Sunday was a rainy day; they settled to the piled up table and managed to bring it into some sort of order. By late afternoon the rain had stopped, the sun was brilliant and the skies beautiful.

They went into the hotel lobby where the manager was at the reception desk. "Ah! Ladies! I hope you have had a restful day."

"I'm afraid we haven't. We've been trying to catch up on our paper work."

"ALL DAY!"

"Pretty much. But it seems a lovely evening. We thought we would go for a walk to stretch our legs. Is there a little park not far from here – some grass – some flowers?"

The manager laughed and shook his head. Then he said, "Oh, we can do much better than that. Would you permit me to call a cab for you? Then you can go for a drive and it will take you so quickly out of Stoke and into the country. In only a mile or so you are in the Moorlands and it is so wild and open. This evening after the rain will be grand. I would instruct the driver to bring you back for dinner at whatever time suited you."

"It sounds wonderful. Is the countryside really so close?"

"I assure you! You will be restored!"

They rushed for their hats and coats and within minutes he had summoned a small neat carriage and a dapper bay mare, and they were off.

"Way'll head for Wetley Rocks," said the driver. "Way won't get there all the way, but you'll see the glory of 'em in the distance."

Sure enough, within ten minutes the dark reddish black kilns and streets began to thin out and in half an hour Lucy and Mary exclaimed with pleasure. The little horse went at a spanking pace, and the Moorlands rose up before them. They could not believe they should see sheep grazing so close to Stoke, lifting their heads from the tough turf to gaze at the young women gazing at them. They trotted through the hamlet of Hulme and towards the grim outcrop of Wetley Rocks, where the driver pulled up for a while.

"If way'd had the whole day I'd a taken yow to Ensdon where they have the well dressing – and way'd gow to Brown Edge, a truly pretty place. But no time, no time."

"It's so beautiful, so strange," said Lucy.

"Yow aven't seen even the tip of it," said the driver. "I was bred in the Manifold Valley. Now, there's real beauty for yow." And he turned the horse's head back towards Fenton and Stoke and the dirty mist, that even on this perfect spring evening still drifted above the low streets.

Monday morning brought the usual packets of letters for them both. Lucy's contained a letter from May Tennant recalling her to London.

Lucy was annoyed. "Does she want you to go too, Mary?"

"No, nothing."

"Then why does she make it out to be so urgent? We shall be finished here at the end of the week."

"I suppose it is because she is retiring in just over two weeks."

"I know that. But we shall ALL be in London that week, of course. And we have FIVE court cases this week, and the Grimwade one is going to be tricky, we both need to be on our toes about that one."

"Don't go then," said Mary placidly. "Tell her you'll be there on Monday next, unless it's really urgent."

"I think I'll do just that," said Lucy, "because I could see my way to going to my cousins in Gloucester this weekend. And after May has stepped down we shall all have to pool our resources and help Adelaide until Dr Whitelegge decides how we are to go forward. What a calm steady influence you are, Mary!"

They spent the week revisiting the hospitals, the HMIs, the Medical Officers of Health and the general practitioners. They prosecuted five firms and won all five cases with very little trouble. They cleared the little room at the end of the corridor and sent packet after packet of reports by Special Delivery to the Home Office.

They thanked the hotel staff for their care very generously, and the hotel manager seemed genuinely sorry to see them go. Finally, they clasped hands on Stoke Station and went their separate ways. "But only for two weeks – see you at the Home Office."

Evelyn stood on Dymock station with her arms stretched out. "Darling Lucy, are you still alive? You don't look as exhausted as I was expecting."

"Well, all things considered, I have 'the satisfying feeling that my duty has been done.' But I tell you, I shall sleep well tonight."

31

The Female Department on tenterhooks

The new office in Great George Street; back to Stoke and the Lead Poisoning Enquiry; the Stoke doctors turn up trumps; Adelaide calls a breakfast meeting in Bradford; Hye enjoys copying out lists; the hotel staff keep an eye on Lucy; the Jubilee illuminations; the Lady Inspectors demand more office help; Evelyn is drafted into the office; Scottish lead poisoning problems are added onto the pile.

While Lucy had been away an office had been procured for the Female Inspectors' Department in Great George Street, and Rose Squire and Adelaide had been busy removing all the papers and files from the Finsbury Circus office and setting them onto their new shelves. Miss Palmer and Miss Mandrill, the part-time secretaries, had been invaluable; they had discovered for themselves ways of filing and cross-checking trades, towns, inspectors, reports, correspondence. May Tennant had asked the Home Office for extra hours for the secretaries, and was hopeful that this would be granted, her last achievement before she retired.

All Lucy's London problems with ventilation and accidents had simply piled up. She went to HMI Vaughan the East End of London District Inspector with her sheaf of related correspondence.

"I know," he said. "They are dragging their feet. I told them what ventilation ducts would be the best for them months ago. Leave it to me."

Lucy handed the folders over to him with relief; she was not going to be able to remain in London long enough to put it all right at once. And when she discovered that Rose Squire was investigating yet another ventilation mishap she was able to hand a second folder over to Rose, a great load off her mind. She spent a light-hearted morning in the Great George Street office tidying and passing on relevant papers to Rose, and, as the appointment May Tennant had booked for her never turned up, she was able to go to the Army and Navy Stores on her way home to buy a new, much lighter suitcase.

Bright and early the next morning she set off for Nottingham where she spent three days inspecting shirt and textile factories and visiting them after hours. She caught several girls still working at 8.45p.m. and a group of them were taking work home from the factory to finish. There had been two Complaints that a Mrs Coble, who ran several shirt finishing workshops, was working her girls illegal overtime; but Lucy went to all of them between 8 and 9 at night and found all the premises dark and closed.

She also found the Factory Inspectors' office closed at 11.50a.m. the next morning, and only a small office boy there, who said that both the Inspectors had gone on a fishing holiday from Friday to Monday. "Back Tuesday morning early."

Lucy had to acknowledge that it was perfectly beautiful weather. She would have liked to go fishing too.

She caught the train from Nottingham to Stoke and met Mary Paterson at the hotel. They were greeted by all the staff as old friends. "Will you need your little office room? It's free for you. No charge."

On the Friday night they opened packets and packets of mail. The Potteries' hospitals, doctors and workhouses had been as good as their word, and lists of patients soon piled up on the office table.

"Lucy, what do you think of this Medical Report from the Certifying Surgeon? It's shoddy, it's badly spelt, it gives no medical details. When you put it beside these from the hospitals it's dreadful. And his handwriting is all over the place."

Lucy perused it. "It's useless. He's just thrown two or three facts together. He's a SCAMP!"

Mary looked at it again. "I should say he was a drinker."

However, apart from the local Certifying Surgeon, they had been sent a huge amount of useful facts and reports. They visited three factories in Burslem on the Saturday morning and then drove out again in the smart carriage with the bay mare, through Caversall to Cheadle to see Pugin's extraordinarily extravagant church. The driver folded back the roof and they exclaimed with pleasure all the way there and all the way back. They insisted that the driver should share their tea table in a Cheadle tea shop, and returned to the hotel, rosy and warmed through by the sun, to sleep soundly.

To make up for their excursion they visited six lead poisoning patients in their own homes on Sunday afternoon, and wrote up their reports in the evening.

At breakfast on Monday morning a letter addressed to them both arrived from Adelaide. She was inspecting in Bradford.

'I am inspecting in Bradford. You are in Stoke. Rose is in London, but due to go to Bristol. No one is in London. May has resigned. No one is Superintendent. No one has yet even begun to consider appointing her successor. No one is in the office regularly to forward our mail or to liaise with Dr Whitelegge as to where we should go next or why. This is a Bad Situation and we must have an urgent meeting. I cannot leave Bradford (court appearances until Friday). Can you all meet me here at the hotel on Thursday lunchtime?'

"I suppose we must," said Lucy.

"Better to meet in London," said Mary. "I'm going there Wednesday week anyway to meet with Dr Whitelegge AND Adelaide."

"Oh, are you? But surely we must all have got together before that meeting. We must be able to present a united front."

"I suppose we must." said Mary.

The letters flew back and forth and the lead poisoning visits and evidence grew apace. The doctors in the hospitals were a mixed bunch. Dr Griffiths was a Fool, Dr Allerdyce was Very Helpful, Dr Davis did not Appear to Exist, Dr Tibbets sent Useful Records, and the Workhouse was a goldmine of information. Doctor Fred Arlidge took the trouble to come to the hotel especially to see them. Mary thought he was a Humbug, but Lucy thought he could be very useful and invited him and his wife to dine at the hotel early the next week.

They caught the milk train to Bradford at dawn on Thursday and all met at the Midland Hotel for their emergency talks. Rose reported that the two part-time secretaries were turning out to be worth their weight in gold. "If one of them could be given the responsibility of opening the letters and forwarding them when necessary it would ease the situation considerably. Some can just wait until we get back there; but if we're away more than a few days it's hard to remember the details and your evidence slides away."

"But even a secretary worth her weight in gold can't make the decisions of parcelling out the work. WHO are they going to APPOINT?"

"And WHEN?"

They marshalled their ideas throughout the lunch and Adelaide waved them all off from Bradford Station.

Mary was very quiet on the journey back to Stoke, looking out of the window, and frequently closing her eyes.

Lucy knew she was only pretending to nap, and felt sorry. She wants to be given the Superintendentship, thought Lucy; she is the most senior among us, after all, and has most experience, and she can see Adelaide's vibrancy and quick grasp of situations, and her unaccountable passion for reading and writing reports are a great threat. It's almost certainly going to be Adelaide, thought Lucy. Rose is too new and it won't be me. I put paid to that with the typhoid fever and even if I hadn't caught that, my monthlies have put paid to it! They know I have one or two days a month when I'm often confined to my room, sick and dizzy, and only able to cope with routine letters. It's not fair. I should be SO good at it. Still, I haven't done so badly. In the top five! The first top five! And she turned herself comfortably and closed her own eyes for a while.

Hyacinth arrived in Stoke on the Saturday morning for the weekend, bringing Lucy's bicycle, and her own bicycle, for Mary to use if she wanted. "You said what a nuisance it was trying to get from factory to factory."

Lucy was delighted and Mary was somewhat taken aback.

"You don't have to use it, Mary, I can just take it home with me, if you don't ride."

Mary could ride, but was rusty, she said. So Hye and Lucy bicycled out to Fenton to various small workshops in the morning and then on out to the countryside near Brown Edge on Sunday morning.

After tea, while the two Factory Inspectors worked on tabulating the lists of lead poisoning cases, the cookery inspector busied herself counting and reading the names on the lists and the ages and sex of the afflicted workers.

"They are all so YOUNG, Lucy, it's terrible! Far more young ones. Why don't the older ones get it?"

Lucy considered. "I don't know, Hye."

Mary looked up. "I suppose the old ones who got it died when they were young."

Hye said, "I've been counting up. More than 350 cases. That's since the Special Rules Act in 1894."

"And a whole lot more in these folders," said Mary, waving them. "Well over 400 cases."

"It's prodigious, this paper work!" Hye was shocked. "Isn't there anything I can do? Copy something out for you tomorrow while you're inspecting?"

Lucy hesitated, but Mary jumped in. "Oh, yes, there is if you would really like to. These tables, names, ages, address, dates of first symptoms, doctors attended, length of employment."

So on the Monday while Lucy pedalled round Fenton, and Mary went to Longton in a cab, Hye sat happily in the office room making out two or three of the interminable lists, and in the evening Mary took them as a thankyou to the play, *Within sight of St Paul's* in Hanley Theatre.

On Tuesday Hye, and Hye's bike, went off to Grimsby to inspect at the Cookery College there, and Mary set off for London for the meeting with Dr Whitelegge and Adelaide.

Lucy spent the rest of the week cycling round the Potteries inspecting and visiting Borough Surveyors, Miss Bidnall of the Women's League for Stoke, other Trades Union Secretaries, Hospital Matrons and Registrars.

Dr and Mrs Fred Arlidge came to dine with her at the hotel on Friday night with young Dr Allerdyce who had been beavering away so industriously. The dinner party was a pleasant and useful occasion. Both doctors knew each other from their work at the North Staffordshire Infirmary, and their wives had met socially many times. They were both friendly practical women, big bosomed and high coloured; they silently appraised Lucy's pale colouring and slimness, and laughed at her accounts of bicycling round the Potteries, though Dr Arlidge gave her useful warnings of areas not to approach at night. The conversation centred on lead poisoning, of course, although Mrs Arlidge and Mrs Allerdyce had plenty of anecdotes of working women, and of pottery life and conditions. Lucy tucked them away in her mind, and prayed that she would be able to remember them and write them down before she went to bed.

The moon was full that Saturday evening, and when her guests had departed, and against the evident disapproval of the hotel manager, she rode off to Trentham on a Complaint for illegal overtime inspection which was spectacularly successful. She found a small tile factory with two rooms of workers busily painting tiles at 9.45p.m. They were amazed to see Lucy alighting from the bicycle; so much so that the factory owner was positively pleasant to her. She waited until the last worker had gone and the employer was locking the door and then, calling out "Good night" she cycled back through the dirty moonlit country lanes into the rough cobbled streets on the outskirts of Stoke, to the brilliant electric light of the hotel.

She paid for all her exercise on the Sunday with excruciating stomach pains that arrived two days earlier than expected, and spent most of the day in bed, being brought hot water bottles and warm drinks by her friend the chambermaid.

"Yow'm got no one but yow to blame for this, Miss Deane. Just plain foolhardy. Too far to ride and us with no notion of 'ow we could find yow if yow' had a accident."

Lucy said meekly she was sorry, but it was her job.

"There's ways to do a job," said the maid severely, plumping up Lucy's pillows, "And there's ways NOT to."

Lucy struggled on with letters and reports for the next two days. She wrote to the Stoke Sanitary Authorities and compiled a draft of the report for HMI Walmsley who spent all one afternoon with her at the hotel. The hotel manager made it quite clear that he did not think the little room at the end of the corridor was a suitable place for a young Lady Inspector to receive a Senior Male Inspector, and provided her with a downstairs writing room with a Do Not Disturb notice. Lucy meekly complied. She realised that the hotel staff regarded her with a proprietorial air, and they felt that she Needed to be Kept an Eye on.

She had discovered during several inspections that HMI Walmsley had turned a blind eye to many infringements of the previous Special Rules from 1892 and 1894. She pointed these out with as much diplomacy as she could muster. He saw that she had not included them in the reports, but he knew that she knew, and she knew that he knew that she knew. She felt that was the most positive thing she could do.

Back in London Mary and Lucy drafted countless letters from Great George Street and the two secretaries tapped away happily. Lady Dilke immediately invited them both to dine to bring her up to date on the Special Enquiry. Lady Dilke would have liked to press Mary about the new Female Superintendentship, but Mary politely blocked all Lady Dilke's moves.

"I hadn't anything definite," she said later. "There ISN'T anything definite. They are just taking an unconscionable time testing all the waters. I don't think Sir Matthew Ridley or Dr Whitelegge have the faintest idea what to do with us all. I think they would just like us to evaporate."

"Maybe they would. Maybe the Male Inspectors would. But think of those armies of working women, trade union women, girls' clubs. They depend on us fighting for them."

"But is fighting with words enough?"

"They're a start. And we're a start. Don't go back to Scotland yet, Mary. Stay with Hye and me. She was going away over the Jubilee holiday, but she's changed her mind. I'm going to Nottingham tomorrow for three prosecutions, and then we're going to ride on the buses and see all the Jubilee illuminations all over the city. You come too."

The illuminations were wonderful and the crowds in full jubilee mood. They sat on the top of an omnibus as it inched its way through the centre of London for hours, finally getting off at Knightsbridge and walking home to Fulham Road in the small hours. But Hye insisted on their being out bright and early and making their way to Whitehall. They took picnic food to the office at Great George Street where Miss Palmer and her young brother, aged 14, were waiting hopefully, and then pushed their way into the middle of the crowd to watch the soldiers and the horses and the bands clatter by. They could tell by the tremendous crescendo of the crowds further down the street when the State Coach was passing by. Mary was sure she caught a glimpse of the Queen herself. Lucy saw a coachman. Hye and Miss Palmer were too short to see anything, but the young brother valiantly lifted them, one after the other, in case they could get a few inches higher, and they all saw the tops of hundreds of busbies and the odd plume.

All five were deafened by the shouting, and hoarse with hurraying, and stiff with waving, and aching with standing.

When they finally reached home, exhausted and starving, Hye produced a large cold ham, a bottle of champagne, and a small iced fruit cake with '60' surrounded by white flowers.

June 23rd 1897, and the country settled down again after the celebrations. The office at Great George Street hummed with letter writing and requests for interviews for every kind of trade. The Home Office sent over a file of Complaints regarding irregular procedures at factories all over the country. There were requests to speak at conferences at Women's Leagues and pressure groups, dates to be set to lay information for prosecutions in magistrates' courts.

Rose Squire came back from three weeks inspecting in the West Country to be given a sheaf of slips requiring her to inspect the Northamptonshire Brick Industry for another two-week stint. She came into the office flushed and irritated, and looked with horror at the piles of letters on her desk.

"What's to be done with these? My mother has gone out this morning to buy me two new sets of underclothes and more blouses as there's no time for our family to get the others laundered before I go!"

Miss Palmer hurried across with a letter opener and a pad of paper for lists.

"Sit down Rose, sit down Miss Palmer," said Mary. "Rose! Lucy and I have a conference with Dr Whitelegge in an hour about the Lead Poisoning Enquiry. Before we start we will say that we need more secretarial help, and a regular space in our diaries when we are ALL in this office together to plan out our journeys and meetings."

"In the immediate short term I'll send a note to my cousin Evelyn," said Lucy. "She has no training, but she is a careful and obedient office boy. If she can come she will, she has often done copying for me. We're off, Rose. Miss Palmer, if Adelaide comes in tell her of our plight."

Dr Whitelegge went through the information they had collected and was much concerned at their findings. "It's clear that factories have not been paying attention to the Special Rules from the '82 Act."

"Nor have the inspectors been reminding them."

He raised an eyebrow. "We will send a circular to all the Staffordshire potteries requiring the return of numbers employed. Miss Deane, you will draft it. I am anxious that the report gets to the secretary as soon as possible."

"However, Dr Whitelegge, our diaries are full of inspections of other Complaints. I am visiting Retford, Derby and Burton on Trent tomorrow, and all four of us still have unfinished business in London. New urgent cases come in daily."

"I am well aware of your prodigious workload, Miss Paterson."

"Miss Palmer is excellent, but 24 hours a week is not enough for us. She and her assistant both need more hours. And a permanent presence in the office is becoming an imperative."

He nodded. "I will consider it speedily. But, ladies, this Lead Poisoning Enquiry is your overriding priority at the moment, and I propose to widen its remit to the Scottish Potteries around Edinburgh and Glasgow as well."

They gazed at him in disbelief.

"I should hope that as it is a much smaller industry than in the Potteries you could complete your enquiries within a week. That would give you time to incorporate them into the wider report and you could complete the whole document by the end of July."

They walked back along Whitehall to Great George Street, watching the men dismantling the bunting from the Jubilee celebrations.

"London is getting back to normal."

"But shall WE ever get back to normal?"

"Lucy, this IS normal for us."

Friday, many many letters.

Saturday, long train journeys to Derby and Burton about Complaints for Saturday afternoon overtime visits. Both factories were firmly closed so she was able to get home by early evening and found an ecstatic letter from Evelyn, to say she was more than happy to help, and did not care 'how boring and prosayic (sic) the tasks were.'

Sunday, glorious weather. Hye and Evelyn went to Battersea Park while Lucy drafted out the circular for the Potteries in Staffordshire and made out the list of all those who had had lead poisoning cases in the past year 1896 – 1897. It took her the whole day.

Monday, many, many more letters. Evelyn and Miss Palmer were charmed with each other and settled down with Rose to deal with as much of her correspondence as they could. Mary Paterson set off back to Glasgow with a suitcase of Special Enquiry papers and another one full of her own dirty washing. "Wonderful to be able to get it done at HOME for a change."

Tuesday, Evelyn went back to Dymock, gratified. Lucy and Hye sorted out household bills and letters and finished the Jubilee cake.

Wednesday, Lucy and Miss Palmer and Miss Mandrill sent off all the newly printed circulars from Dr Whitelegge to the pottery firms, and she travelled to Edinburgh by the night train.

Mary met her train in the morning and settled her in the Royal Hotel in Princes Street, and walked her around the centre of the City. They met with HMI Bellhouse, and for the rest of the week they shuttled back and forth across the region in Edinburgh, Glasgow, Alloa, Dunmore, to several infirmaries and general practitioners, and a handful of sad families where a lead poisoning victim was struggling at home in poverty and distress.

HMI Wilson was a good friend of Mary, and he and his wife came and dined with them at the hotel. They were a homely, cheerful, dumpy pair, full of good sense and good will.

On the whole the Scottish Potteries were small and well run and the days in Alloa and Dunmore not too taxing. HMI Wilson gave them a list containing pottery establishments, which he had rated from excellent to execrable, and sent them off to a group on the edge of Edinburgh in Portabello. He was also anxious to take them to a linoleum factory. "While you're up here ladies. It's a chance you'll not have for a while." They travelled over the Forth Bridge. Lucy thought the journey exhilarating and the linoleum factory a shambles!

"Thought you would, thought you would," nodded HMI Wilson. He thought the factory time sheets were very erratic. Lucy and Mary could not see that there were any signs whatever of any sanitary conveniences; whereas the jute factories that had been bitterly complained of in Dundee that the District Inspector wanted them to see, and which meant an overnight stay in a hotel there, seemed of more than passable standard throughout. And when they said so, the Inspector seemed surprised and relieved.

"Why was that?" asked Lucy, relating the story to HMI Wilson.

"I expect you had been set up," he said, nodding at them, "to see whether you were fair and reasonable, or whether you were a pair of busybody women sent up from London to cause trouble."

"Oh dear! The truth is we are frequently both. We just have to get used to it!"

He laughed. "So do we."

HMI Wilson accompanied them out to the Dunmore pottery, catching the 6.05 morning train to Falkirk and then a five mile drive. The prestigious pottery was set in beautiful farm land belonging to Lord and Lady Murray of Dunmore Park and Lady Murray took a great interest in it. The Gardner family had been making simple domestic pots for over a hundred years, but when Peter Gardner took over the pottery from his father, he had begun to import special clays from Dorset, and had branched out into finer work. Lady Murray, with her many aristocratic connections, including the Prince of Wales, constituted herself Peter Gardner's chief saleswoman, and an amazing range of vases, rose bowls, plaques and ornaments flowed South to the great houses of England. Lady Howard had several pieces, Lucy knew, and so she was intrigued to visit.

"Lucky it was such a model establishment," said Mary as they settled into the train for Glasgow. "It would have been most awkward if we had had to lay information for a prosecution."

In Glasgow Lucy bought two small ornamental porcelain driving cars, one for Hye and one for herself.

With Mary beside her in the evenings they were able to polish off a great deal of correspondence and paperwork, and at the end of the week they travelled back together to London and Mary came to stay with Lucy for the weekend.

32

Establishing the new office

More office help, but no let up; May's baby christened; a very social interlude; Maconochie Bros. have jam-making Complaints now; the mission to Northern Ireland gets under way.

A few days later there was a Grand Reunion of the Female Factory Inspectorate at the Great George Street office. Rose had reappeared from her time in Northampton. Adelaide had been bouncing from London to Northern Ireland; she had been sent to search up clues to illegalities in the Truck Acts over employees' wages. Lucy and Mary were back in London to write up the lead poisoning problems in the pottery industry.

Adelaide and Rose were to check on other infringements on other Dangerous Trades, fur trading, bookbinding, artificial flower making. There was great excitement as they all met together for the first time for two months, and Miss Palmer was sent out to buy pastries to celebrate. Miss Hardrough had arrived, employed to type up the reports for two days a week – welcoming applause – and the news that Miss Palmer was now employed full-time brought great general rejoicing.

However, while all of them were in the midst of their own time-consuming reports, many other day-to-day complaints relating to general factory and workshop life kept arriving on their desks; Dr Whitelegge needed to be kept informed; the Women's Associations were clamouring for attention; and the magistrates' courts across the country were as prickly as ever. There was no let up.

The first few days back together in London were very pleasant with a festive air about them. All four of them attended St Margaret's Westminster on July 13th for the Christening of Harold and May Tennant's first baby, a rare chance to dress up in airy summer afternoon attire, and not to run the risk of inky fingers smudging their fine muslins.

In the early evening of that day Rose and Lucy attended a Local Government Women's Association meeting, and spent a nostalgic hour with the Kensington Sanitary Inspectors; Matron, from the Chelsea Infirmary, was also there and Miss Lankester and friends from the National Health Society. Mary took the chance to go back to 100 Fulham Road and wash her hair.

Then, the next morning, after only a few hours in the office, they deserted it again for a social life, leaving only Miss Palmer to hold the fort. This time Lucy went to have her hair washed and dressed, and Hyacinth joined Mary Paterson on a shopping spree for long evening gloves. Mary had confessed she was nervous when buying anything for evening wear, and Hyacinth with her new found confidence was sympathetic to Mary's plight. Together they had a successful afternoon, and Lucy was wooed into buying three tiny rose quartz birds to set into her hair to accompany the pink evening gown. Everyone was out for the evening. Firstly, Mary and Lucy were invited to a women's Jubilee Soiree at the Grosvenor Galleries, when One Hundred Distinguished Women gave dinner to One Hundred Distinguished Men! Lucy enjoyed it and made the most of catching up with friends and acquaintances. All the Lady Factory Inspectors were there, including May Tennant, and they made sure to introduce and look after Mary Paterson, who was very suitably, if heavily, dressed in a high necked navy grosgrain, with a simple string of pearls and her dazzling new white gloves. At ten o'clock, Lucy took Mary back to Fulham Road, and then she and Hye, one tall and dark in pink silk and white gloves, and one small and fair in dark green silk and black gloves, went off to a Soiree at Kathleen's, Lady Falmouth's, London House, and enjoyed themselves tremendously with Granville and Roland Streatfeild, whom they had not expected to meet there.

From then on duty called, with the Pottery Report, and then Lucy travelled north for a day in court in Burton on Trent with three prosecutions of which she won two. Several more cases were in the pipeline for Derby and Walsall. "I really hope I can do each set in one day. I don't care for overnight stays in a hotel – like a commercial traveller – if it's three or four nights and I can settle in, it's quite different."

She went one Saturday morning to hear Adelaide read a paper about Women Factory Inspectors at the Victorian Exhibition Lecture Hall – 'Very good it was, too' – and a Miss Gray of Islington read a paper on Women Sanitary Inspectors – 'but what is the basis of her experience? It was FUTILE.' She lunched there with Mr Sprague Oram (she had to stop her tongue from calling him Chief) and Dr Dudfield and the other Kensington Women Sanitary Inspectors.

In the afternoon she and Hye took Mary to the Syon House Garden Party with Aunt Gertrude. The sun was hot and Mary's nose got burnt. Hye plied it with cucumber while Lucy and Mary worked on the Potteries Report in the evening, and by Sunday Mary's nose had completely cooled down.

As the Potteries Report neared completion so other queries and problems grew more numerous and pressing, almost as if they were crawling out of the woodwork. 'We have waited long enough,' they were saying, 'it is our turn now.' Lucy had to leave Mary to take the first part of the report to the new part-time secretary, Miss Hardrough. (Miss Mandrill had left for a full-time post elsewhere.) Lucy herself set off on the early train for Derby, and then crossed to Walsall for a conference with HMI Jackson, and a visit to two factories on Complaints.

A woman employee at Ralph and Jordan had complained to the local Women's League Association that the firm had refused to put doors on the women's WCs. Another woman in another factory had complained because she had been fined for staying in the convenience too long when she had had a stomach upset. Yet another had complained because no brooms or disinfectants were supplied to clean the conveniences or the floors. HMI Jackson implied that the factory owners were obstinate in not calming the situation. Lucy inspected both firms, found the sanitary provisions in both places dire, and returned to London very late.

Miss Hardrough had worked hard and sent back the first paper typed and copied that same day.

They had settled down in the morning to begin on the second section of the report when Lo! The next problem arrived in the post. Another Complaint about the troublesome Millwall firm Maconochies!

"Now what?" shouted the exasperated Lucy. This letter, again from Miss Price, found that Maconochies was, as usual, claiming exemption from time-keeping this year, in respect of EVERYTHING. All workers, even Young Persons, were working longer, boiling jam and so on until past eleven at night. Many casual workers, employed by the day, were employed on routine work, potting meat, packing rations until the normal closing time, and then went straight on to sort the carts of fruit, which had come in halfway through the afternoon, until midnight.

Mary and Lucy worked at their Enquiry Report and fashioned it into good order, and then after an early supper set off to the Isle of Dogs to make a late visit.

Sure enough, it was a hive of activity. It was quite dark when they climbed into their cab with lists of names and addresses. The foremen and women did not attempt to dissuade them and were civil, though taciturn. Lucy was very glad that Mary was with her, exuding solid calm and interest.

"You're so brave, Mary!"

"I am until I need to buy evening gloves."

Dr Whitelegge was too busy to see her the next morning when she rushed there early to seek advice. So they were able to do the weekly returns with Miss Palmer and finished the entire Report by lunchtime. They threw down their pens with triumph and placed it reverently on Miss Hardrough's desk. After lunch Miss Palmer returned with a pink rose stolen from a hedge in St James' Park to decorate the Report. Mary returned to Fulham Road to pack and go home to Scotland. Lucy stayed and wrote letters to all the people who had helped them with the Report. Now she could return to the day-to-day problems of other working people.

When she finally had her appointment with Dr Whitelegge she was able to report that the ventilation case and the shutter guards were all settled. He was genuinely astonished to hear that WCs were EVER provided without doors, and agreed it was debasing and irregular, but was alarmed at the idea of prosecutions. Lucy felt, that as a very experienced and recent Medical Officer of Health, he should have come across the situation before, as privies without doors discouraged 'time wasting.'

However he was cautiously sympathetic to court rulings to fine workers for non-compliance with the Factory Act, such as damage to goods or late attendance. In many cases he felt the owners were abused by workers through the women's carelessness. He acknowledge the problems caused by the recalcitrant Maconochies, but supported the blatant overtime to a great extent. "Fruit ripens when it chooses, raspberries and strawberries won't wait, fish swim in shoals into nets, and when they are out of water they won't keep! There has to be a considerable leeway."

He thanked her profusely for the work she had done on the Special Lead Poisoning Report.

Then he said, "Miss Anderson has told us of growing unrest among the flax, linen and embroidery workers in Northern Ireland. The Truck Act has been widely flouted so that workers in outlying rural areas are too frequently forced to receive goods in lieu of wages from their agents, and now women who work in mills are being laid off and only employed in small rural workshops. May Tennant had begun to investigate this but has been unable to further it, and now there seem to be rumours of a Petition for Embroiderer Women to be able to work in their own homes with their families. We hear of this Petition growing all over Northern Ireland. But Chief District Inspector Snape has been unable to establish any sure facts.

"I should like to send you immediately to Londonderry to assess the situation. But – don't tell HMI Snape to begin with that you know anything about any Petition. Wait and see what he says."

Lucy went home in a towering rage. "They think we are machines. Not twenty-four hours since we finish the Lead Poisoning Report and now I'm to be sent off to Ireland! And for what? For vague rumours of some non-existent uprising! When am I going to spend any time with you? When are WE getting a holiday?"

Hye let her rant around the house and was quiet and sympathetic. Then she said, "It sounds to me as if it won't be a non-existent uprising. It sounds very murky to me. Maybe May Tennant could have nipped it in the bud but whatever it is, it's rumbling around. You'll probably only be a week or so. I'll go down to Flammswood or the Boyce. We'll have all August to find a holiday, just the two of us. My new term isn't until September 8th."

33

Mrs Snape becomes an ally

Inspecting via a jaunting car; the Truck Acts are mainly flouted; Mrs Snape solves the problem; the perfect holiday at Glendore; the Belleek Pottery is a shock; a fifty mile bicycle ride to Carrick; Mrs Snape is very cross.

Lucy wrote to the MP for Londonderry and told Mr Snape she was coming over to make some final visits to Belleek, and other small pottery firms. She also wrote to several folk who had helped her on her previous trip two years ago. She settled in to the Grand Central Hotel with her latest bicycle, and was relieved to discover that Mr Snape was on holiday. This would give her more time to cook up a more convincing reason for her visit. She went to the Trades Council to find details of the rumoured Workers Petition. Mr McCarron was also on holiday and Mr Doherty his assistant knew nothing of it. She visited Father McMenahan who refused, very politely, to meet her, and she suspected him at once of wanting to keep information from her.

Over the next four days she revisited in a jaunting car the country areas from last year. All the women in the hand embroidery workshops and home workers shook their heads when she asked if they had 'signed a petition' and ominously, she found that though many women in textile mills had indeed signed it, they had no idea what they had signed. Therefore any signatures were practically bogus, thought Lucy. What have they signed? No one was able to say. No one knew around Belfast. She drove over the peninsula around Carrowkeel. Nobody knew.

The journeys themselves were pleasant. One night she slept in an enchanting tiny inn on the coast of Lough Swilly and then sailed down the Lough, drove over Morne gap to Malin Head, visited the outlying cottages at Clonmary and Ballylifton and slept in Cardonagh. The visits to linen mills and embroidery home workers there were met with the same blank looks and shakes of the head regarding the Petition.

Several of the shirt making factories in Londonderry and the large towns had outlets, called Stations, in the outlying rural districts where women not only collected bundles of ready cut shirts to sew at home but also hand-embroidered exquisite patterns on to the shirts and blouse fronts. When they returned the finished work to the Stations the agent there, usually a shopkeeper running a General Store, would check the work and pay the women. In many cases though, no money ever changed hands, and the women were obliged to take their wages in the form of overpriced goods from the General Store, if they were to be given more work. All of this was clearly illegal as a result of the 1893 Truck Act. The agent took care that the women were always in debt to the Store. Lucy asked about the Petition at Muirheads and Marlanes Stores; much shaking of heads, although in both of these places Lucy sensed that they had information they were definitely withholding.

The scenery was frequently breathtaking but the roads were rough and hard and Lucy was glad to return to the comforts of the hotel and Belfast. She found a full bag of letters and papers and an apologetic note from HMI Snape saying he would call on Sunday afternoon, which he did, suntanned from his holiday with his family.

In amongst the Home Office assortment were three letters from Hye suggesting they should holiday together in Ireland. 'North or South, it makes no difference to me; but it must be a tiny, remote, charming place – and it MUST be COMFORTABLE, Lucy – and away from anyone who might want you to do ANYTHING!'

Lucy wrote off to May Tennant, with her great knowledge of Ireland, and May wrote back with 'just the place', a small guest house on the coast in deepest Cork owned by Dublin friends of her family. She sent the address. She knew they would be made more than welcome. Lucy wrote to Hye. 'Come any day after the 8th of August.'

The backlog of correspondence took two days to deal with and Lucy was glad of them. The week of rough roads and long drives had taken their toll and on this occasion 'Office Days' were a comfort. She sent off revisions to the Pottery Report to Miss Hardrough. She wrote to Mary Paterson and Adelaide. She wrote to Dr Whitelegge saying her enquiries would take another week, and indicated she would be on holiday in Cork for two weeks after that. She wrote the first report on jam making at Maconochies.

At the beginning of the next week she made another excursion into the wilds of Derry to try to unravel the mysterious Workshop Petition, and found as many mistaken notions as to the Employees Petition as there were women who had signed it. In some areas there seemed to be no knowledge of it whatsoever, but she uncovered too many infringements of the Truck Act at the Muirhead Station; those she spoke to there were too frightened to give her any reliable particulars, although she tried hard to gain their confidence. It was definite that the agent there constantly supplied his own store's goods to his workers and deducted it from their pay, again infringing the Truck Act.

When she was driven back to Buncrama, a hard drive but with superb views, and caught the last train to Belfast, she was rewarded with a letter from Hye. 'I shall arrive in Dublin on Saturday and shall stay at the Shelbourne Hotel. Get there as soon as you can. I am bringing the small trunk with a few more of your summer clothes as well as mine.'

Lucy scurried round to Mr Snape's office to ask advice on the next few days. It was already the 5th August. Clearly she could not finish all the visits before Hye arrived in Ireland.

"What shall I do, Mr Snape? I was planning to visit several places in Tralee with Inspector Neeley and then come back to Derry to finish off there. I was expecting Hyacinth to come to Belfast. I don't want her alone in Dublin."

Mr Snape solved the problem instantly by sending a cab for Mrs Snape. She arrived in an hour or so, and over coffee rearranged and smoothed Lucy's way.

"Forget about Derry," said Mrs Snape. "Tralee is charming and your sister would love to see it. Meet her in Dublin – lovely shops and I approve of the hotel she has chosen. Mr Neeley can meet you in Dublin, take you round Tralee, and you can stay in Tralee on the Sunday night."

"He may not want to be out on a Sunday."

"Oh, nonsense! He's only a Junior Inspector, he'll do as he's bidden. And he'll be delighted to accompany a couple of attractive young women and show off his local knowledge. Then on Monday you can get back to Dublin and move down to your friends in Cork for your holiday whenever you choose after that."

"Mrs Snape, you are a magician. You wave your wand and everything falls into place."

"I have my uses," said Mrs Snape.

Lucy went off to send a wire to Hye, and Mr Neeley, and the hotels in Tralee and Dublin, and her coming whereabouts to the Home Office, and many other notes, and arrived in the Dublin hotel an hour after Hye.

The next morning they travelled to Tralee and met HMI Neeley. Hyacinth didn't go with them on the Saturday evening to the fishing harbour where the boats were unloading and the fisherwomen gutting, cleaning and packing with all their might by great kerosene lamps; but she accompanied them on the Sunday on the long hard drive through the spectacular scenery of Tralee. They stopped at many tiny hovels where the women were sewing and knitting, spinning and weaving, where the elder children were washing clothes and cooking, and the babies played about in the dust among the chickens and the thin wild looking cats. No sign of any menfolk or dogs. "Perhaps they have gone to church?" said Hye.

Mr Neeley laughed out loud. "No Sabbath day of rest for anyone here. And no chance of calculating the hours spent per garment. Only the pitiful rate for the job."

Back at the hotel Hye shook out her skirts and sat in the bedroom with her feet in a basin of warm water and salts. "I don't understand how you do this day after day."

"Not every day."

"Too many days."

"THESE women do it EVERY day."

The two weeks' holiday at Glendore was as perfect as they had been told.

The house was set back from the coast road in a garden sheltered from the sea winds, with large airy rooms and sea views. They were made welcome and comfortable and the house provided a carriage to bring them on the long scenic drive from Cork.

The weather was kind, and the rain was soft. The food was fresh from farm and garden and sea every day. Lucy and Hye walked far and slept deep and their tired town bodies absorbed the peace through the pores of their skin. A family of four with two young sons, aged ten and twelve, were also staying there. The boys were out with their father from breakfast until dusk swimming and rowing, while their mother sat contentedly in the garden with a book and her sewing, smiling and humming, and ready to talk and take tea with the sisters if they came back from a walk at teatime.

They travelled back to Dublin and on to Belfast together.

"My dears!" exclaimed Mrs Snape, as she and her husband alighted from the cab at the hotel where Lucy and Hye had invited them for a Thank You dinner. "You are both transformed!"

Lucy waved Hye off the morning after, and Mary Paterson arrived by the afternoon boat.

After a day of dealing with Lucy's copious correspondence they set off early taking bicycles on the train with them to Ballyshannon. They made several visits to outworkers around Omagh and Fintona, and found them complaining bitterly of their agents' infringements of the Truck Acts.

They visited the Belleek Pottery on the Castle Caldwell estate in the West near Ballyshannon. It was producing high quality feldspar pieces overseen by the owner of the estate, John Bloomfield. After the Great Famine he had started the factory to provide employment for local people. An amateur mineralogist, he had discovered his land contained feldspar and other minerals for producing fine china. Now he was an old man and had long since lost his interest in the business but still owned thousands of pieces. The pottery works had ceased making decorative ornaments. It bore little resemblance to the patrician decoration of the Scottish Dunsmore plant, most of the skilled artisans had left and the new owners were focusing on profitable earthenware tiles.

Lucy and Mary were dismayed at the state of the sheds and the morale of the workers. It was a far cry from the proud, much smaller establishment at Dunsmore.

From the pottery they remounted their bicycles and went to Ballyshannon, took an early lunch at an inn there and then rode to Donegal, visiting Broome Hall, the seat of the Hamiltons, on the way. Lucy thought it was a lovely old place. Mary thought it was on the edge of collapse and probably not before time.

In Donegal they made a friend, Miss Kee, a quiet unassuming middle-aged woman. She was now a companion to the wife of the local Church of Ireland Minister, but had been a sprigging outworker in the handkerchief industry in her earlier years. She was an exquisite needlewoman, and a thorn in the flesh of the local agents. She remembered May Tennant with respect and affection and promised to give them her advice and knowledge in their task of enforcing the Truck Acts. She told them of an isolated hamlet some miles away where the sprigging women were in thrall to a Gombeen agent named Mrs Boyle in Killiebegs, and they decided to visit there and then. The Church of Ireland Minister waved them off as they mounted their bicycles. "You are all dangerous women," he beamed cheerfully.

The road to Killiebegs took them alongside the sea with the delicious salt breeze on their left and the scent of hot heather on their right. Nestled amongst the heather were hundreds of rounded bee hives. As they rode through Killiebegs they passed a General Store, painted dark green with a corrugated iron roof. Mary wanted to stop but Lucy said, "No! We don't want them to recognise us on a future occasion."

Past the store the road became rutted and stony, at times fading into no more than a grassy track, and the scenery more and more wonderful. "What must this be like in winter with the wind and the wet!" Up and down they rode, frequently having to get off and push the bicycles over small rocks, until they came suddenly upon the tiny hamlet of Carrick, no more than five or six ramshackle one-roomed barn-like houses, with not a chimney nor a window amongst them. The entire female population, about nine women, was sitting on stools and boxes outside in the sun, their rough skirts covered with linen aprons to protect the precious handkerchief squares, their blouses open, and in some cases off entirely to get the warmth of the sun. The two ladies surprised them, and shawls were hurriedly pulled across for modesty.

Lucy and Mary asked to see the sewing and were sincerely impressed. It was difficult to talk to the women who were friendly enough, but they all spoke Gaelic, and, Mary guessed, their own dialect of Gaelic at that. Two of the younger women had some English. Lucy asked to buy some handkerchiefs, but the girls explained that they had to return the same number as they were given or their pay was docked.

With the sun still strong and warm it was an idyllic picture. "But come winter, how do they survive?" said Mary as they pedalled back along the tracks, passing two men balancing a small cart piled high with turf and pulled by an evil-looking donkey. The men looked at them with amusement. They bounced over the uneven ground, and were grateful for the smoother surfaces from Killiebegs to Donegal. A long, long way.

Mary went home to Glasgow on the Saturday and Lucy travelled to see her off to Stranraer, and then to visit outworkers at Ballygarry.

She stayed in bed on Sunday, VERY seedy, dizzy and sick, and on the Monday did not feel able to struggle round to the HMI's office for their planned conference. He came to the hotel instead and was worried about her. "What has happened to that golden girl we saw a week ago?" Mrs Snape was more direct when she heard, and visited Lucy as she rested on her bed in the afternoon.

"What were you thinking of, riding a bicycle fifty miles on rough ground just to meet a few handkerchief embroiderers? You and Miss Paterson need your heads examined! And you, with your particular history of illness! YOU shouldn't be riding a bicycle EVER!"

"Oh, I don't think—"

"No, that's just it! But I DO! Get rid of it!"

"But it was such a pleasant day. We really enjoyed it. And we needed to pack so much information in for our enquiry before Mary went home. There's so much to do. I admit my head does ache."

Mrs Snape snorted. "Headache! I say it's sunstroke."

Lucy looked woebegone, her head throbbed and the thought of another long journey across the sea to London tomorrow was disturbing.

Mrs Snape changed tack. "Lucy, I hope I may call you that when we are alone together. You must not push your body beyond endurance. You are too valuable to your profession. My husband was ready to resent you when you first arrived; now he respects your judgements and your determination, and he realises what a difference you are making on your visits – you and all the Lady Inspectors – even in such a short time. But everything you do is new. You cannot change the world in a few days. If you don't look after yourself, how can you look after all the others? Lie quiet for today. I will come back tomorrow morning and help you pack. You can have an hour or so with Mr Snape in the morning here to sort out your affairs and papers."

"Yes, you are right of course, Mrs Snape. And so kind to say you will help me pack. Such a load off my mind. I feel better already."

Mrs Snape pressed Lucy's hands. "It will be a pleasure. You will be glad to be home. And your friends in London will be happy to see you!"

34

Keeping their heads above water

The Home Office tries to curb the Female Department; climbing the mountains of paperwork; HMI Walmsley does not make life any easier; nor does HMI Arnold; but the London Girls' Clubs are a tonic.

The journey home went smoothly to Lucy's surprise and relief. Mrs Snape's mothering and concern had an extraordinarily soothing effect and it was true that Lucy did feel better for her visit. The conference with Mr Snape was positive. She showed him the lists of the places she and Mary had inspected, told him of her concerns for each place, and drew up with him a draft plan of how to proceed when she returned to Ireland in mid-October for her next inspection.

While she had been away Mrs Anstey had thoroughly cleaned the house and it shone and sparkled in the September sunshine, and smelt deliciously of beeswax and lavender polish. As Mrs Snape had predicted there were letters from friends wanting to meet up with her; Blanche came to supper with them both, and another night they dined with Granville and Roland Streatfeild in Eaton Place. Roland told them he wanted to become one of Her Majesty's Inspectors for Education. "You're mad!" cried Hyacinth. "It's killing Lucy!" But Lucy, a wiser Lucy, said it was not. She was not going to let it.

On the third of September, 1897, the Female Department of Factory Inspectors held their first Conference, after Adelaide Anderson had been officially appointed as May Tennant's successor. It was a disappointed group that met. May's title of Lady Superintending Inspector had been withdrawn and replaced by Principal Lady Inspector. Worse, Dr Whitelegge had removed her Department's power to authorise prosecutions in the courts; this meant that Adelaide was no longer on a par with the Male District Inspectors, and that therefore Dr Whitelegge's approval would be needed for any prosecutions they wished to bring. Nor were they allowed to order building alterations in ventilation and sanitation, but would have to apply to the relevant District for approval.

"Nothing will ever get done there then," raged Lucy. "The Male Inspectors won't want to upset their Employer cronies. If we have to depend upon the co-operation of the Male Inspectors, ninety per cent of our improvements will always be frustrated. Dr Whitelegge is frightened of the Inspectors, I always suspected it, May always said so, and now I believe it."

Adelaide was calm. "May is furious on our behalves, and the workers we are fighting for. She has written an article for *The Fortnightly*, and she is writing to the Home Secretary as well as to Dr Whitelegge. She says she will let us see the letters before they are sent. Meanwhile we need to go through the revised regulations as they have been set out and plan how to proceed under these circumstances."

The meeting began and Miss Palmer took the minutes. They agreed that the Male District Inspectors must bear their fair share of all the added worry of prosecutions and the extra clerical work that this would involve.

They questioned the definition of the term 'structural alteration'. What did it cover? Did it cover, for instance, that 'sashes of windows which have been jammed by dirt or layers of paint over many years must be made to open,' or 'doors must be affixed to WCs which have never had any doors before', and so on.

They minuted that they must be punctilious in keeping full notes of any conferences with every District Inspector, and keep filed copies of EVERYTHING safely in the Great George Street office.

They decided to use all possible means to publicise themselves and their work to the wider public. At the moment, almost any publicity was vital to their survival. The meeting ended in sombre mood.

They were still awaiting the Home Office reply to May Tennant's thunderous letter in August. They all seemed anxious, except for Mary, who presented her usual stolid exterior. She was looking forward to her weekend with a schoolfriend, she said, and then her visit to the Trades Union Congress in Birmingham. "As good as a real holiday. Nothing to do but sit and listen." Lucy wondered what her home was like in Scotland. As far as she knew, none of the other inspectors had ever visited her there. In their work together Lucy had found her unfailingly thoughtful and level headed. She was supportive. She was good tempered. She was dependable. She seemed to enjoy social events and the company of the other members of the Department; but there was an invisible door in her personality through which no one was invited. She was an enigma.

Lucy and Rose Squire stayed on at the Great George Street office until late afternoon on Saturday. They worked companionably in silence, each at her own table. Lucy sorted out her papers into geographical areas, Ireland, London, Hull, Stoke, noting dozens of untied ends and ongoing enquiries. Rose was doing the same. Every so often Rose sighed deeply, "I have no idea which of these tasks to finish first!"

Lucy smiled, "Oh, just toss a coin, Rose. My problem is that I thought we had come to the end of the Lead Special Enquiry. But now Dr Whitelegge is enquiring about points the Enquiry has raised! How am I ever to get back to Ireland next week?"

Dr Whitelegge was away on holiday, so she wrote to Sir John Gould, the Deputy Chief Inspector for Factories, for clarification of some of the safety rules for factories using lead in their processes. She also wrote to Mr Snape to ask him if he could prepare her a complete list of Scottish, Irish and English firms employing agents for the Handkerchief Sprigging Industry, and she wrote to Adelaide asking if she was permitted to send a circular to each firm asking them to tell their agents that they must keep a complete list of their outworkers.

She returned to the office on Sunday and worked peacefully alone all day sending dozens of notes and planning her diary for the months ahead. Hye was at home preparing for the new term and a month of training a new batch of Domestic Science students. They spent the evening packing, said goodbye to each other early on Monday morning and set off jauntily, both wearing new autumn hats.

Lucy and Mary and Adelaide travelled up to the Trade Union Congress with Lady Dilke and Gertrude Tuckwell and were fascinated by the range of subjects and speakers. Lucy wrote copious notes and, mindful of their recent decisions to attract publicity whenever possible, introduced herself to as many people as she could. Lady Dilke and Gertrude were invaluable on this score and Mary and Lucy and Adelaide smiled and shook hands and referred to pertinent details in various speeches. They met up each evening to compare notebooks and all found they had been asked to speak about the work of the Women's Inspectorate to several groups. Lucy had been sounded out to give a lecture to the Women's Industrial Council in November. Adelaide had been invited to the inauguration of the Congrèss International du Legislation de Travail in Brussels. "You will have to come as well, Lucy, you speak French. My French is fearfully schoolgirl. Just think of all the useful people we would meet there. It's in two weeks' time."

Lucy hesitated. "I'm planning to go back to Ireland next week. And I have a week's leave still to take. And I really need it, Adelaide."

"I really think Brussels must come first, Lucy. Besides I can't do it without you. Take your leave. Then come to Brussels. Then you'll be fit for the autumn onslaught in Ireland."

So Lucy wrote to Mr Snape postponing her enquiries until October and spent the next few days with Adelaide and Rose parcelling out the forms and complaints to be instigated all over the country; and then she had a pleasant week's leave, first with May Tennant in her new country house near Leominster with the new baby, a charming looking scrap when it wasn't puce with rage. May wanted to hear about the Department, but Violet and Cecil Asquith were staying in the house as well and it was difficult to find time to mull over all the details. The rest of the week was spent with the family at the Boyce, as tranquil and loving as ever; she had time to walk with Evelyn and Ethel in the dewy sharp mornings and the warm afternoons. Evenings were spent on replies to letters from Adelaide which arrived to all the Department members and had to be answered the same day.

Then she went back to work, feeling much stronger.

While she had been away a letter had arrived via Mary Paterson from Deputy Chief Inspector John Gould in answer to her queries about Cones Safety Rules for Mercury used in the hat making trade. She had wondered if they could be applied to the use of lead. Lucy considered Gould's letter fatuous and dismissive, and to add insult to injury he had sent it to Mary in mistake for her. She consulted May Tennant about the Pottery Report and the numerous extra queries and correspondence amassing. How was she to deal with the complaints and compensation procedures which had never before been broached? May was, as in the past, admirable. She approved strongly of Lucy's report and was infuriated by HMI Gould's letter.

"Those poor Mad Hatters!"

"I think he's just fobbing me off," said Lucy.

"He's patronising," said May. "Make a copy of it and then send it back to Mary and tell her to return it to him as 'not meant for her' etc. And THEN write to Dr Whitelegge about HIS reply and ask for HIS opinion."

Lucy left comforted, and yet cross with May – WHY did she have to marry and leave them when she was so gifted, knowledgeable and valuable to the work?

She rushed around Leeds and Hull for two days inspecting workshops on Complaints. The visit to Hull was particularly vexing as the Hull HMI was away, 'gone to Whitby for ten days', and it took a whole day to track down the Junior Inspector to answer her urgent requests for information of various major dressmaking businesses.

She had written to the HMI Office in Stoke three weeks before, and to all the large pottery firms of the workers affected by lead poisoning in the last five years. The circulars had been sent to the firms through HMI Walmsley, but only a trickle had come back to her at Great George Street. Lucy had asked at the Home Office itself, but the Head Clerk, Mr Peacock, seemed to know nothing about it. Lucy suspected the Stoke District Inspectors Office had never sent them out. So she sent them again herself, asking the firms personally for statistics of persons employed in lead procedures and asking them to send their replies to HMI Walmsley.

None refused except for a tiny firm in Burslem. All said, however, that they had only received the circular in the last few days and would send the numbers in the next few days.

She met with Dr Walmsley and asked him on what grounds the firms refused to give the statistics. He evaded and said that he had heard the facts from Peacock at the Home Office! She told him she had not found it so except in the one case. He said that he, Walmsley, could have easily got the information required if she had come directly to him, 'that a firm would give it to him though they wouldn't give it to Whitelegge whom they didn't know.' He then volunteered to get it for her from those places she would not have time to visit; so she gave him the names of Ridgeway, Plant and Gillmore, Bishop and Stonier, and asked him to send the statistics directly to the Home Office. He remarked that the Home Office staff were so careless that possibly some of the lists had been forwarded and then lost by the Home Office. Lucy looked non-committal. He instanced mistakes made in the Annual Returns. Lucy changed the subject to the Conference in Brussels. He said he had been to Brussels too, but had arrived just as the conference had finished, and read the report of it in the paper. His own reason for travelling was to visit a huge Dutch pottery, and he expatiated on the 'difficulty and depth of various types of glazes'. They took leave of each other with relief, and Lucy travelled back to London.

Early in the morning she took the train to Worcester for the day to check on a Complaint of a large tailoring establishment. HMI Arnold met her train and they talked for a few minutes on the platform before he boarded another train. He said he thought she had meant to come the Thursday before. She told him the name of the firm, Organ's, but not the nature of the Complaint. He said that he had visited the place recently and had found a room partitioned off, and was told that the tailor's daughter had been working, by herself, behind it. "If you had sent the Complaint to me directly, I could have attended to it and saved you the trouble." She thanked him warmly and dropped the subject. When she visited, she found that the one extra partition in Mr Organ's establishment had proliferated into several, very overcrowded and unhealthy spaces. She reported this to the Worcester Medical Officer of Health and then travelled straight home to London.

After all these scratchy encounters, it was a relief to spend Friday writing her speech at the office for her Club Leaders Lecture at the Women's Industrial Council in the evening. Representatives from eight London girls' clubs were there and she promised to go in the New Year and speak to three of them, Miss Bennett's 'Daisy' Club in Lambeth one Saturday evening, and Miss Neal's Club and Miss Child's Bethnal Green Recreation Society on Fridays. The sense of solidarity and common purpose in the room was like a tonic.

Hye and Lucy had scarcely seen each other for two weeks and were determined to have twenty-four hours together. They managed it. On Sunday afternoon Evelyn arrived to stay with Hye for a week or so, and they all three made quick work of Lucy's packing. They waved her off in Mr Rich's hired cab to catch the Night Mail from Stranraer and Larne to Belfast, with her trunk, and the latest trusty bicycle which she intended to keep well out of Mrs Snape's sight.

35

Lucy Deane Secret Agent

Mr Snape becomes an ally; the embroidery firms back Lucy; differing pay scales for embroiderers; 'I wish to be strictly anonymous'; Mr and Mrs Nellis in Ardara; Mr Gahan thinks the Embroidery Enquiry is a great lark; he punctures her front tyre; Miss Tierney and Miss Crummles; 'Bad Girl' Annie Mooney is the star.

Mr Snape was genuinely friendly when they met on Lucy's first morning in Belfast. 'Could it be that he has decided to trust me?' she wrote in her diary. He told her of the new Industrial Schools, bodies set up as a halfway house between normal schools and apprenticeships. They were Associations both for teaching and for making and selling the products of various home industries, and had been instituted and were maintained by the local District Board. There was one at Cirdath and one at Carrick.

He said he had visited the school at Cirdath. "Not officially you understand, but as a friend of the organisers. I'm pretty sure that the children and the Young Persons there were being employed irregularly but I shirked doing anything about it. They all seemed very contented, and were being taught well. However, I did inform Mr Cooke Taylor when he told me he was enquiring into Dublin Schools in the Dublin District."

Lucy laid out before him her proposed methods for the Enquiry and asked for any lists of outworkers that might be of use for her. Mr Snape looked horrified. "Lists of outworkers! I have no LISTS of outworkers. I told Cooke Taylor straight out I could never cope with all the work if I was required to obtain lists of outworkers AND keep them up to date!

You will have to get them from the specific linen mills themselves – if THEY have them – which I very much doubt."

Lucy looked at him and they both laughed.

"The Home Office think life is so simple and orderly," he said, "And WE know that every industry door we open has a bucket of worms that will be kicked over."

"Oh, yes," she agreed, "I found that when I went to visit Belleek Pottery. I thought I was going to visit a very high class works but it was very nasty indeed." She read some sentences from her tourist notebooks about Belleek and he nodded gravely and decided they would visit together as she would be working over in that area. "You go first," he said, "You know more than me. You instruct them. And if they object we will visit together."

He arranged for them to visit the head offices of some embroidered handkerchief firms so that she could find out from each the various rates of pay that each hand embroiderer could expect from her agent.

She found that the managers of the main offices were all extremely courteous and interested in the Enquiry and willing to co-operate in any way they could. All said they had persistent trouble with agents cheating, and one firm found it was worth their while to give the work out themselves, sending foremen especially to each district, because the agent would pocket a percentage of the price and only give the worker two thirds of it, with the result that the firms received inferior rushed work. "They have to rush it to make their money and that brings our trade into disrepute."

Different prices were paid for different embroideries. Very cheap handkerchiefs, on inferior linen with simple curls and sprigs, were paid 7d per dozen, while the finest linen, involving flowers, butterflies and cut stitch could be paid 3s 6d a dozen or more.

Initials were more complicated. A certain set price was paid for the whole range of the alphabet made in a certain style, but some letters took nearly twice as much time as others; for example 'I' was easy, 'P' was average, and 'M' was hard. Their system was to pay the same for each, but in giving it out to the women, they gave a percentage of easy and hard letters mixed in together, of 22 'hard' and 28 'easy'.

"We never give a dozen of the same letter only to the same girl, because if she delays it could keep back the whole of an order which has to go with a proper proportion of that letter to each order."

The objection seemed frivolous to Lucy. If a worker was told she would get no more work until she had brought in her remaining 'hard' letters she would probably do it. Still, she made a note to find out if agents paid different prices in different districts for the same work. Maybe Mary Paterson would know.

On her way back to the hotel a chilly wind was gusting the leaves off the trees and she was glad that Hye had made her pack her winter underwear and new galoshes and raincoat.

Mr Snape brought a Mr Walker, who had started up the Industrial Schools, to meet her at the hotel in the evening. Lucy was longing for a hot bath and an early night, but both men were obviously trying to be helpful and so they sat by a good fire and drank whiskey. Mr Walker directed her to the teacher of the Carrick school and gave her several helpful addresses. He said that the parish priest there, Father Heeley, would help her, but warned her that he would tell everyone about her, so she must be careful what she said. Both Mr Snape and Mr Walker were extremely doubtful if lists of outworkers could be legally asked for in this trade; both suggested that the only way to obtain them was by bluff; both implied she would be a much better spy than either of them.

When they had gone she wrote to Adelaide and to Peacock at the Home Office asking them to be sure not to send her any letters in Home Office or official envelopes. She wished to be strictly anonymous for the next few weeks.

Although she had asked Adelaide to send official letters to the hotel in Donegal she had wired to stay at Mr and Mrs Nellis' little inn in Ardara and they gave her a kindly welcome. "You've brought your bicycle!" exclaimed Mrs Nellis, "The weather won't be kind to you this time of year, not like the summer!" She shook her head as her husband wheeled it round to the stable block, and Lucy suspected she was right. She had hoped to meet the Junior HMI, Mr Townsend Gahan, at Donegal, but he was not there, so she sent a note to his home in Killiebegs, asking for his movements, and then spent a pleasant evening with the Nellises, and unpacked. The inn was fairly new with only four or five bedrooms on two floors, but her room, though small, was simply and neatly furnished and everywhere was warm and comfortable.

To her surprise a middle-aged American couple Robert and Margaret Hurley, and a son in his twenties, from New York State, were staying there as well. They were looking for traces of their grandparents who had managed to emigrate to America during the potato famine, one from Donegal, one from Galway. Mrs Hurley's mother had been pregnant with Margaret on the way over and her first husband had been too malnourished to survive the crossing; the young mother arrived as a widow and struggled to raise her little daughter. Robert's family were more fortunate and he now owned a handful of thriving hardware stores.

The next morning brought driving rain, so although the Hurleys, indefatigable, set off in a closed cab for the graveyard at Glencolumkille, Lucy stayed in her room writing many office letters. Mr Gahan called in the afternoon, a tall thin young man with an anxious expression which transformed into enthusiasm when Lucy explained her mission to him. He gave her names and information of people to contact and advised who were, and who were not, likely to be discreet. He appeared to regard the Embroidery Enquiry as 'a great lark' and wrote her an introductory note to the parish priest of Ardara, Father Arthur Hughes. Lucy went round in the afternoon and made great friends with him. He gave her many useful anecdotes and families to follow up and promised to keep his eyes and ears open for her. He implored her neither to betray her official position, nor to let any one know he was helping her. Lucy sneezed several times while she was with him and he insisted on accompanying her back to Mr and Mrs Nellis under the most enormous umbrella she had ever seen. "I wonder you don't get blown away with it!" she cried.

"Sure it's only for companionship," he replied. "If I'm by myself I trust to my cape."

The rain had gone when she woke, but her cold had developed into a sore throat and she was forced to stay all day on the sofa in the inn. She went for a short stroll in the evening and met the schoolmaster, one of the names on the list Mr Gahan had left her.

For the following two days she wrote letters and was given constant hot drinks by Mrs Nellis. Very few of the letters were to do with embroidery; nearly all were finishing up the loose ends of jam and pickling production, or pottery reports, or overcrowding in London tailors. She lent her bicycle to Mr Gahan to ride to Glenties, and he punctured the front tyre; full of self-reproach he sent it by train to John Griffiths in Londonderry who returned it the next day, pristine. Long letters from Adelaide and Hye and

Evelyn raised her spirits and by Saturday morning she felt restored enough to visit the Industrial School in Carrick.

She was taken to two workshops. The first was the 'Crochet School' with its diminutive teacher Miss Tierney, a green-eyed elf with a freckled face and blazing red hair. The room was very overcrowded and one child of twelve was employed full-time. The pay was fearfully poor and the girls were encouraged to take the work home and do it until ten or eleven o'clock at night. Yet, even with such frightful hours, they could only earn, as trainees, about 5s to 7s a week.

In the 'Drawn Thread' workshop the teacher was Miss Crummles, and there Lucy found a child of ten employed full-time. The room was not overcrowded and the class had only been started for two months. All the girls, very clean and neat, were being taught drawn work with a view to earning with it later on, but no one was earning anything yet. In order to compete fairly with the fraudulent 'sprigging' agents in the area, Miss Crummles had been given an agency from J.Shelton's Export Traders for ordinary sprigging work on condition that she paid with cash and not with goods to her young workers. They could make about 4d to 6d a day if they worked hard at the sprigging. "Shocking pay!" cried Lucy. Miss Crummles nodded. She recognised a friend and told Lucy many rumours about infringements of the Truck Acts – so many, that Lucy thought they must be exaggerated.

On the Saturday afternoon, when the half-holiday had begun, she went with Miss Tierney to see a girl called Annie Mooney who, though a 'bad girl' (why? wondered Lucy, but Miss Tierney would not elucidate), did beautiful quality sprigging for the local agent. Lucy was charmed with the work and promised a private order of work to her. Annie said she generally got half her pay, if not all, in goods, and often a docket, or 'ticket' to make up the value of the goods – not any money at all. She had just finished some work and promised to show Lucy the 'ticket' she would get. Annie was startlingly pretty, dark-brown wavy hair and huge violet blue eyes and a self-composed air. Lucy wondered if her looks had any bearing on her reputation as a 'bad girl.'

As she walked back to Ardara she called in on the Carrick parish priest, Father Heeley, as she saw him coming out of the church. She was very cautious and didn't tell him who she was. She mentioned she had been looking at some exquisite work and asked innocently what were 'tickets'. He promised to look out and tell her if he came across some tickets for value among the people.

Sunday morning, a perfect October sunny day, and the town filled with warmth and woodsmoke and cats sunning themselves on windowsills. She wrote several notes to folk on Mr Gahan's list, and a long letter to Adelaide about the irregularities of the workshop school in Carrick. 'This is NOT an official letter as I don't want to drag you into collusion with me in sanctioning the breaking of the law by these schools giving out "home work"; and yet I am of the opinion it would be foolish to check it just at this point.' She asked Adelaide to discuss it with May Tennant – in private. On her way back from the post box she called on one of Mr Gahan's names, Mrs Rowell of Woodhill. It was a mistake and Lucy was very sorry she had contacted her. Mrs Rowell was kind but talkative. She was also intensely curious and pressed questions on Lucy, why had she come to this tiny town, where had she come from, how long would she be staying. Lucy tried to fend off the barrage of interest without being disagreeable, but she feared she had been caught up with the town gossip, and having finally left Mrs Rowell waving at her door, tried hard to remember all the details she had inadvertently given. She worried her way to bed.

36

Collecting the evidence

Lucy sets eyes on her first 'ticket'; walking to the Tierneys' farm; word spreads about 'the English journalist lady'; she buys her first Boyle ticket for 2s 9d; "Why would I want such illegant boots?"; Father Kelly says he must be seen to be neutral; Lucy orders table cloths, hankies and handtowels; no one dare brave Mrs Boyle; Mrs Tierney's whiskey cake; Lucy lets the workshop schools lie for the present; "What to do, what to do?"

The new week began with the postman, head down against the wind and rain, delivering a letter from May Tennant with a charming photo of the baby, nicknamed Poupis, sitting on May's lap and both looking as if they had stolen the cream. Lucy propped it on the mantelpiece, next to a garish statuette of Mary and the infant Jesus. During breakfast Mrs Nellis brought her a bona fide ticket from Rose Kennedy of Carrick a Clare, whose aunt had received it from Mrs Boyle, the fraudulent agent nearby, about a month ago. It was a small rough piece of paper, undated and unsigned, in pencil, and it said:

To Goods 9 – 6

6 – 11

2 – 7

Mrs Nellis explained that Rose's aunt, Ellen Gavrahan, had brought in work done and worth 6s 11d. For this she had received no money, but goods such as tea and coffee and flour worth 9s 6d, and was to receive work worth 2s 7d to pay off her debt!

Lucy offered to pay the 2s 7d in order to keep the ticket but the girl wouldn't let her have it, so she settled to go and visit the aunt the next day. Before she had finished breakfast, Miss Tierney from the Crochet Workshop School sent across to say that a girl had just told her that she had taken in work to Mrs Boyle, and that Mrs Boyle had praised her and given her a 3d loaf and a ticket for her mother. So Lucy decided to go to their cottage at Thronkerrin tomorrow to visit the little girl and her family.

She took a walk out through the watery sun in the afternoon to the Industrial School and had a long talk with Miss Tierney about the conditions encountered by the women working at home, and she promised to collect particular details for Lucy. Miss Tierney lived with her parents on their small farm holding on the edge of Ardara. They walked to her home together through the gloaming. Miss Tierney threw an amazingly richly patterned crochet shawl over her plain brown jacket and skirt. It set off her blazing red hair. Farmer Tierney was away over the fields when they arrived, but the farm yard was meticulously swept, and a small field at one side had a group of six sheep that scuttered to the fence to greet Miss Tierney and be patted. On the other side of the path to the front door was a large chicken shed, as well kept as the summer house at the Boyce – better, thought Lucy. "The hens are Mother's," said Miss Tierney as they reached the gate, "She makes a tidy living with them." Certainly there were around two hundred of them stalking around, listening and pecking, and from the shed came the gentle chuckling and clucking of various gossipy hens. "She's got more than the usual just now, fattening a lot for Christmas. She sells eggs in Donegal market every Wednesday. Quite the business woman. And she spins the wool from the sheep and dyes it and sells that too." Mrs Tierney came to the door as they arrived, to shut up the hens for the night, a plumper, grey-haired version of her daughter and wearing another sumptuously crocheted thick shawl in moss green and black. She was very friendly and invited Lucy for supper the next evening.

The word seemed to be quietly spreading around the area that the English Lady was interested in women's work and living customs as well as in the beautiful countryside. As the year was so far advanced the consensus was that she was not the usual new fangled tourist lady on a bicycle; the local population was used to them, always in small groups, exclaiming over the idyllic simplicity of the Irish peasant; it was soon decided that she was some sort of feminist journalist collecting material for a smart London magazine, and this was strengthened by the number of letters which arrived for her and the number of fat letters she sent off. All this suited Lucy very well and her lists of people and families to visit began to grow very satisfactorily.

Over the next few days she was glad of her stout comfortable walking boots, particularly as the London-bred bike groaned and developed painful punctures on practically every outing. She visited the stunning Annie Mooney at Innaraghee and heard that one dozen of the letter 'D' worth 4s 6d was taken in by her the day before to Mrs Boyle, for a special order. She was given 1s 9d worth of goods and a ticket for 2s 9d. Lucy paid 2s 9d for the ticket and got it. Annie said Father Hughes had often spoken to her of the hardness of the system, but she was afraid to object. She was just embarking on a tablecloth, clearly a vastly superior standard of work than usual, but there was no indication marked anywhere on it, no price symbol, anyway. She hoped she would get 4s 0d for her work, "Just for the one piece."

At Thronkerrin she went to the Breslin cottage to see plain spinning and weaving. The father was weaving plain, undyed woollen cloth no more than two yards wide, his eldest daughter spinning the yarn alongside him. Mrs Breslin was discovered in the neighbouring cottage with two friends, sprigging. It was her little daughter from the Industrial School who had received the threepenny loaf the previous day. Lucy would have liked to have seen the ticket, but the three women seemed not to understand her, and she could hardly make out the few words they spoke. Half a mile further along the road were the Gallaghers of Duchel, a very different group. Four daughters, all producing wonderful embroidery. Lucy promised them some orders, she would supply the cloth and thread for handkerchiefs. They said they would be taking in their work, probably on Saturday, and would get goods and a ticket.

The supper with the Tierneys was delightful, a chicken stew and mashed potatoes and baked apples with cream. Farmer Tierney, small and wiry, with red hair going grey, was in good spirits; he had sold a cow at Donegal market for a good price, and was full of the news from his cronies in the inn there. And he made them all laugh with a piece of gossip about a young bank clerk, "that uppity one, too important to speak to you. He was wearing a red cravat to impress his lady love and Farmer Machin's young bull caught sight of it first and chased him round the square. He had to take refuge in the piglets' pens, while four of 'em managed to corral the bull. The piglets weren't polite to his trousers and his sweetheart laughed and laughed. His face was redder than his necktie!"

Miss Tierney walked back to the inn with Lucy and they called for a while on Mrs Lynn the Methodist minister's wife, who told them of a Mrs White at Demarel near the Point. And when she finally arrived back she discovered that Mrs Nellis had spoken to the schoolmaster about Lucy's bicycle puncture, and that he had taken it off to mend it, 'as a goodwill offering.'

It was a full moon on Thursday evening and a calm clear starry night. Farmer Tierney drove them to the Point to meet Thomas Boyd's wife and daughter. They were sitting in lamplight doing the most beautiful quilting, the best Lucy had ever seen. It had been specially sent to them from Belfast on Mrs Boyle's recommendation. But because of her patronage they were bound body and soul to her in gratitude; and though they owned that they rarely saw any 'money' and were expected to leave most of what they did get in her shop, there was no point in Lucy trying to win them over. They were late driving home, and she stayed up until the small hours writing a long report to Adelaide Anderson.

Nearly opposite the inn was a tiny one-roomed cottage with a young farm labourer and his even younger wife; their huge baby like a young cuckoo sat on the dirt floor gazing at her balefully. The sprigging tablecloth was prettily done and Lucy promised to provide her with material to make an order for her. The young father was very resentful of Mrs Boyle and said so volubly. The young mother said that last Saturday she had taken in 4s 6d worth of work and was given an elastic sided pair of boots, which she was pushed to take without wanting them. "What would I be wanting with such thin and illegant boots?" But she did not feel she could argue as Mrs Boyle always took her workers into the small back room to check the sewing and write out the tickets, and would then hand the tickets to one of her shop assistants who weighed out the articles that the customer wanted.

The next visit to Annie Mooney saw her working two dozen very fine handkerchiefs. On them was a ticket, '7 Pross – W – Lurgan'. She let Lucy take it temporarily. The Gallagher girls had a mound of fine lawn ladies' blouses, each one needing twenty-five tiny button-holes for minute buttons, they hoped they would get 3s- for each blouse. Also they had been given a sample linen shawl to embroider birds and flowers in each corner. They hoped for 4s 6d but had not indicated any price, and were stiffening themselves to bargain with her when they took the finished work in on Saturday.

Father Kelly from Carrick called on her in the early evening. Lucy voiced her dismay that they none of them had a spokesperson, or a union to speak up for them. He agreed, but was very clear that he was not going to take on such a role. He must be seen to be neutral, etc, etc.

"But there must be SOMEONE in the neighbourhood who would speak for them?" said Lucy. "I believe," she said innocently, "that the Truck Act which we have in England must be in force in Ireland?"

Father Kelly looked uncomfortable and allowed that it was probably so.

"It seems to me that if someone could stiffen their resolve to give evidence – someone professional, like you, in whom they have confidence…"

He smiled, a wintry smile.

She visited Miss Crummles who was certainly an excellent teacher in the Drawn Thread Workshop. The rows of little girls were producing high quality samplers under her patient, encouraging and exacting eye. Miss Crummles was excited as the Donegal National Schools Organiser wanted the Ardara Workshops to set up lacemaking there and was proposing a grant. It would mean a bigger classroom to be built next year and perhaps an extra assistant to help with the teaching. She had been given a ticket from one of her scholars, and she gave Lucy some facts about some of the companies for whom Mrs Boyle acted as agent – York Spinning Mills, Robinson and Chance, and J. Ireland and Sons. Lucy, silently jubilant, paid 1s- for the ticket and then another 1s 6d to Mrs Ellen Breslin who had just taken work in to Mrs Boyle. Mrs Breslin said 'they always had to accept goods, but Mrs Boyle might give money occasionally if asked, but never as a rule.' She confirmed that the 'prices' of goods bought at the shop with the tickets were dearer than those bought by cash.

That evening she wrote to Robinson and Cleaver in London for several plain linen tea cloths, and to Wakeford Bros for various patterns for sprigs, and a selection of coloured threads for embroidery recommended by Miss Tierney. She also wrote to the Belfast hotel asking them to take her warm dressing gown out of store and send it on to her.

Lucy realised that the hunt had to be on for an embroidery woman strong-minded enough to stand up to Mrs Boyle. Somewhere in the district there must be a spokeswoman willing to fight the Dragon Boyle. Her experience with the English courts had taught her that it was a hard and thankless task, with factory owners, business men and women, and local magistrates closing ranks and protecting their own interests. Here it was even more difficult, with the women so poor, and ill-educated, and isolated from each other, and no signs of any unions, or possibilities of local women's meetings or clubs.

The next morning she set off on the bicycle for Carrick a Clare to try and track down Rose Kennedy's aunt who had supplied the original ticket. She knocked on the battered door to which she had been directed, but no one answered, although she was certain someone was inside. She walked on down through the shabby row of houses to the tiny school, and on her way back saw a pale face at the Kennedy window. Another knock brought a reluctant wispy woman to the door who denied she was Rose Kennedy. Rose was out and she could not say when she would be back. She shut the door quickly. The next cottage door opened and the householder was more forthcoming. She was a weaver and her young daughter was in Miss Crummles Drawn Thread Workshop. She agreed that she resented Mrs Boyle's ticket system and over-pricing of goods – she was indignant, but weak and frightened. She confirmed that the aunt's name was Gavrahan, but did not know where she was.

Lucy cycled on asking for the name of Gavrahan and was directed to Lower Altenapple, but the track petered out and the bog threatened to engulf the bicycle. Luckily, while searching for another route to what she suspected was a non-existent place, she came upon Tullochlatay where a Biddy Keeney was on Miss Tierney's list. Biddy was a fine looking young woman, about sixteen, sitting sprigging in a large well-appointed warm kitchen with her two toddler brothers playing round her feet. Her mother had been driven to Killiebegs by a neighbour, her sister and brother were at school in Carrick. She was open and polite, but said firmly that she NEVER went to Ardara to Mrs Boyle, but to a Mrs Rae in Dentuly who came from Donegal every week to hand out and collect work. Mrs Rae mostly gave money but sometimes tickets for a store in Donegal; but as their neighbours frequently drove there to buy and sell animal stock, that was no problem.

Lucy's most helpful discovery was Margaret McGuire, a decisive looking woman on the edge of Killiebegs. She was a self-confident woman, her letter embroidery of fine standard. Lucy praised her work, promised her work to do 'to take back to my friends for Christmas' and felt that it would be well worth getting Mrs McGuire to speak freely. Margaret McGuire said that sometimes she INSISTED on Mrs Boyle paying her money. "She hates it, but she does it. I am one of her most useful needlewomen, and she knows it."

She cycled back into Ardara as the sun sank fiery red over the horizon. She was tired out and grateful for Mrs Nellis sending her up a small bath of hot water for her feet and more coals for her bedroom fire. There was a letter waiting for her from a Mr Walker. He was on the Board of the local National School Workshops and had heard something of her enquiries from Miss Tierney. He understood, he said, that these were confidential and so asked if he could visit her at Miss Tierney's home the next morning. With his letter came a note from Miss Tierney inviting her to lunch on Sunday.

Mr Walker was a thick set, florid faced man with Dundreary whiskers and a bright brown tweed suit. He sat by the roaring fire in the Tierney's small parlour and sweated profusely, while the late October sun poured in at the window, and now and then a sheep's inquisitive head bumped on the glass.

He was no fool and had put two and two together and, though he held no brief for Mrs Boyle and her like, he was concerned that a prosecution – or a strike, which he had grasped that she was likely to bring about – might cause heads of linen firms to refrain from sending work to agents throughout the Donegal area and so he begged her to consider undertaking a simultaneous enquiry in Down County so that they were not disadvantaged.

Lucy said this could only be undertaken if he could give her any information which would make it worth her while to go there. She decided to trust him with the Home Office Truck Act Enquiry, and her own plan as far as she had it, and begged him to speak to the priests and endeavour to influence them to stiffen the girls' resolve. However, she didn't think he would be of much use to her. His overriding concern was to support and strengthen the work of the new National Workshops. He was not the man to unite and fight the cause of ill-educated and isolated women miles from each other.

Mrs Tierney produced another feast, this time a lamb stew which smelt wonderful while they were waiting for it and tasted like ambrosia. Everyone praised it and Mrs Tierney was very pleased. She cleared the plates from the table, smiling, and then set out five small lustre plates. Farmer Tierney looked up. "Why, Mary, I believe I know what's to come." He beamed round the table. "Ladies and gentlemen, if I am right, we are in for a treat." Mrs Tierney came in from the larder with a dark fruit cake. "Mother, when did you cook this? You dark horse! How did you cook this and us not smell it?" It was a whiskey cake. She cut them thick slices. "Eat it slow. It's strong!" It was potent indeed, very moist with whiskey.

Lucy had intended to spend the evening writing a long letter to Hyacinth when she came back from the lunch. Instead, she was so replete with the whiskey that long before the letter was finished her eyes were closing; she was in her bed well before nine o'clock and slept dreamlessly until Mrs Nellis brought the morning jug of hot water at seven fifteen.

Monday was November the First and soft mist covered the town until mid-morning. It was Annual Fair Day, no school for the children and a holiday feel to the whole area. No fair was set up in Ardara, but there was a relaxed mood in the little town. Lucy finished Hye's letter and wrote one to Mr Gahan asking for an interview and then cycled off to Glenties to send off a long telegram to Adelaide. In the late afternoon Miss Tierney drove her to visit Father Hughes' other churches at Marins and Kildoney and when she returned there was a return wire from Adelaide and two letters both from her, an official looking one and an unofficial looking one. Both had been written before Adelaide had seen Doctor Whitelegge, and were far more satisfactory and positive than the subsequently sent wire which Lucy thought smelt of Home Office caution.

November the Second, and two packets of letters arrived, one sent on by Hyacinth from 100 Fulham Road, mostly domestic bills and family notes. Hye wrote of her Cookery College day-to-day affairs as usual, but finished in capital letters. 'WHAT ARE YOU DOING OUT THERE ON THE EDGE OF THE WORLD IN THE RAIN AND THE MUD? Your clothes must be filthy and if you stay much longer you will go round barefoot with a ragged shawl over your tangled locks. THREE WEEKS IS TOO LONG. COME HOME!'

The other packet contained twelve copies of the Truck Acts 1831 – 1887 which she had sent for from Eyre and Spottiswoode, and various letters from London stores requiring money for the teacloths, hand towels, handkerchiefs, thread and so on for the Christmas presents which she proposed to order from the embroidering families.

What was she doing? And what had she achieved in her three weeks of bicycling to inarticulate and frightened people? She had found some friends and followers, but they either would not, or could not, further her cause. She had established proof of blatant infringement of the Truck Act with just one agent. She had uncovered overcrowding and illegal working of underage young people working in one local National School Workshop – a firm case for prosecution – and yet the teachers were admirable and the pupils motivated and competent! What to do?

HMI Snape had left her severely alone as she requested, and was due a full report now. Young Mr Gahan had been obediently only a shadowy figure in the background. As far as the head offices of the linen firms were concerned no extra Factory Inspector existed in the Donegal neighbourhood.

Adelaide's letter had made it clear that Doctor Whitelegge did not wish her to bring any pressure on the large linen firms. In that case, it appeared to her that any prosecution of this particular agent – Mrs Boyle – would have to be abandoned. This did not suit Lucy one little bit.

Mr Gahan arrived in his smart little fly in the early afternoon bringing with him useful replies to all her queries, and also a list of Irish potteries which Peacock had sent via HMI Snape.

He told her that:

- Mr Micks was the practical officer, the Secretary of the Regional School Board;
- the Workshop Schools were, it appeared, under the Education Board, in so far as they were Schools (and should therefore teach some basic educational subjects – which the Ardara schools did not) but they were partially maintained by the Irish Lace and Linen Trading Company and their 'apprentices' should be receiving some remuneration – which they were not;

- the Education Board supplied the building, the rent, the teachers and a
  bonus for encouraging the girls' learning and good attendance;
- the Irish Lace Company supplied the materials, gave the work, paid the
  wages, and disposed of any produce at a profit.

Hmm! thought Mr Gahan.

Lucy told him of the two points she found fault with, the overcrowding
in Miss Tierney's room and the education infringements, children
constantly working overtime, but she was hazy as to hours of overtime.
Were they Schoolchildren, or were they Young Persons in Employment?
Whichever they were, he told her, he thought both matters were points
for the Secretary of the Board of Workshops to attend to. Lucy said she
hoped he would not mention it at present, and he promised. She said she
was determined to follow it through in a business-like way, and she would
communicate with the proper person now that she had discovered who the
proper person was.

He told her that a Mr Craven, an Englishman, had been appointed
as the Principal Magistrate in the District. He was quite new, said Mr
Gahan, with disarming indiscretion, and had surrounded himself with
a bunch of local fools and knaves as Justices of the Peace who protected
their businesses and their cronies first and administered the law second.

"Just like in England!" remarked Lucy.

She told him of the extreme difficulty to get the embroidery women to
speak freely and her distress that they had no one to speak up for them and
put their case. "Their priests should be their protectors and mediators," she
said. "They should bring their influence to bear on my witnesses to stiffen
their resolve and show them they are not alone."

Young Mr Gahan nodded thoughtfully. He suggested she could write
for an interview with the Bishop, Dr O' Donnell. He was a good man, said
Mr Gahan, and would be sure to be on the right side, he could soon stiffen
up the priests!

He drove off into the windy dusk. Lucy apologised to his smart pony
for having to wait so long. "We'll be home in no time," he said, "We've a
good tail wind, we shall fly like a little galleon."

Lucy did not get a good tail wind the next morning, and battled over
to Glencomkille to find that the Gildays and the Dohertys were working
on great quilts for 9s and 12s each, unbelievably low pay for all the work

in them. The Dohertys were sharing their quilt work with another family. Mrs Gilday had taken her last 12s-quilt to Mrs Boyle on Annual Fair Day and been given a ticket for it with which she had bought her son a pair of corduroy trousers and got a few pence given her in exchange. The other families would be taking in their quilt the next day.

She bicycled back in a temper, three-quarters composed of the bad treatment they were bent under and one-quarter composed of their lazy acquiescence. Adelaide's latest letter that awaited her didn't help either. 'The Home Office will approve any prosecution against fraudulent agents, but not against specific firms, and refuses to allow any compulsion if the agent refuses to give the names of the firms.'

It was all very unsatisfactory.

37

The plot thickens

Wild weather; an invitation from Canon and Mrs Sinclair; and from Major and Mrs Hamilton; "I am not cut out to be a spy"; Mrs Nellis is very impressed; Mary Paterson will come to help collect evidence; "I am not well versed in skullduggery"; "I am depressed and appalled by the feebleness and terrorism in this country."

She wrote a stiff official letter to Adelaide, asking that it should be filed, and then a private letter to her, slating the Home Office for its over-cautious attitude. 'I feel we are little Cecil Rhodes in our approach – we feel we must exploit the cheap slave labour that is available!'

She wrote to Hye and asked her to send her second pair of winter boots. She wrote to Mary Paterson to ask if she could come to help her out – 'with some skullduggery, so don't tell Adelaide or any one yet.' She wrote to Bishop O'Donnell setting out her credentials and asking for an interview.

The weather next morning was atrocious, stormy winds and driving needles of rain. Lucy gave in and spent the day finally writing up the report on the Belleek Pottery and the Belfast potteries and sent them off for Mary to sign. The postman brought her two sodden letters sent on by Hye. He apologised. He said they were quite dry until he had taken them out of his bag ten seconds before. One was from the Boscawen aunts; they had remembered an old schoolfriend who had married a Church of Ireland clergyman and now lived in retirement in Inver, a few miles south of Ardara. The second came from Lady Howard who had remembered Major and Mrs Hamilton, and that he was now Lord Lieutenant of Donegal, at Broome Hall, Ballintra, and she had written to tell them of Lucy. The third was a scribbled note from Hyacinth. 'Lady Howard knows EVERYONE, remember. If Mrs Hamilton invites you, you are NOT to accept unless your dress – and you – are CLEAN, which I very much doubt. And you are not to smell of peat smoke.'

Lucy sighed. It would be nice to visit these folk. She must overhaul her wardrobe, certainly. It was imperative to buy new stockings. She sent a note to the Reverend and Mrs Sinclair, at Bonny Glen, Inver, to ask if she could call, but decided to leave the more exalted Hamiltons until she could find out more about them.

The next day was calmer and softer. She rode to Glenties on the bicycle to see Mrs Dewitt, a small hosiery and embroidery agent whom Mrs Lyons, the Methodist minister's wife, had recommended she should visit and who paid cash. However, she was misdirected and sent to another shopkeeper agent who did give tickets to the women embroiderers. Luckily Lucy was now so cautious that no harm was done. When she found Mrs Dewitt she bought 4s worth of stockings and had a good conversation with her. Calling in on a Mr and Mrs Shovelin she discovered they had been given a capital ticket from Mrs Boyle two days after the Annual Fair Day. 1s 3d was to be paid for work, and of this 1s was taken for snuff, and a ticket given for the remaining 3d. Mrs Shovelin was too nervous to give it to Lucy, though Lucy begged her for it. She said she would consult her husband about it.

On Sunday she received a most unsatisfactory letter from Bishop O'Donnell, making it clear he was not going to instruct any of his priests to intervene, and regretting he could not meet her; and although she had a long and apparently amiable conversation with Father Kelly about a possible Enquiry, he flatly refused to help her at all, as it 'would risk his popularity with an influential parishioner.' He did give her the names of various magistrates.

The Reverend and Mrs Lyons were much more interested and involved. They invited her to tea and suggested she should meet a Miss McAvoy who they felt would be a suitable person to take up the sprigging agency if Mrs Boyle should ever be turned out. Miss McAvoy agreed she would be willing, but told them clearly she could take no initiative on this. If the firms themselves asked her to take the post Miss McAvoy would refer them to Mr and Mrs Lyons, and she was sure it was essential to have an honest and capable person who did NOT keep a shop.

Lucy perceived trouble ahead here, as she spoke, for she knew that the Orange Party, as represented here by the Protestant Lyons couple, meant to get an influential business into their own hands, and she was sure that the priests would fight it. She asked them if they knew of any responsible person who would go to Mrs Boyle's store and actually see how she paid for the work brought in, someone who would be willing and capable to give witness. They pondered for a while and Mrs Lyons finally proposed a Johnnie MacHarron. She urged them to be very careful when sounding him out and went back to Mr and Mrs Nellis at the hotel anxious and unsure of the best way to proceed. "I am just not cut out to be a spy," she said to herself, "it is altogether too stressful."

While she had been out messengers had come from the Hamiltons at Broome Hall Ballintra, and the Sinclairs at Bonny Glen, Inver, both with invitations to stay. The Hamilton letter had a very imposing envelope with a crest on it, and Mrs Nellis was taut with curiosity. Lucy knew she would have to remark on it. "Oh my goodness, I think I may know something about this. How very grand!" She read it through and was genuinely surprised. "Why, this is from Mrs Hamilton whose daughter I met at a women's conference in London. (this was not true). She has invited me to stay for a night to talk about my enquiries here – and it also appears that she too acts as an agent for the sprigging on her own estate through a firm in Londonderry! That seems extraordinary."

"'Tis a very large estate," said Mrs Nellis, "she will likely have many cottagers making their money that way."

"Well, I sincerely hope she is a good agent," said Lucy, "and pays them the proper money. Do you think I should go? Will it be very grand? I have no smart dresses with me."

Mrs Nellis was shocked. "Oh, of course you must go – they won't expect grand dresses. And if her daughter knows you."

Lucy warmed to the deception. "Not well, though. We only met for two days at the conference. And then there's this lady, Mrs Sinclair at Inver, Bonny Glen. Do you know of that family? My aunts were friends in their youth and have written to her. She wants me to stay the night as well."

"Oh, that's a very nice house, not nearly so grand, but big, you know."

"Well, if you think it would be all right—"

"Do, do," said Mrs Nellis "but be sure to come back and tell us all about it."

So Lucy accepted the invitations and over the next few days Mrs Nellis and her maid and Lucy washed and brushed and sponged Lucy's coats and skirts, and Lucy washed her hair, and Mrs Nellis was as excited as if she was going to stay with the Lord Lieutenant herself.

Lucy spent the days before setting off for Inver visiting as many women as she could. Mr and Mrs Shovelin had decided not to give her the snuff ticket. He said violently that HE wasn't afraid of Mrs Boyle, but would not for a hundred pounds want that the neighbours should point at him for an informer. "One would think that I was the illegal conspirator," she cried to Annette Tierney, "instead of Mrs Boyle!"

She had a chance meeting with Mr Lyons whom she met in the road, and he suggested importing a worker from outside the area to visit Mrs Boyle's store incognito and give evidence of what she saw. She visited Annie Mooney to take her a set of personal work. She visited Miss Tierney to say she was off on a visit. She posted official reports to Adelaide. She wrote to Hye assuring her she would be scrupulously clean and tidy.

She hired a fly to drive her to Bonny Glen, a small handsome manor house on the bay at Inver, sheltered by a wooded slope from the sea winds, and next to the most beautiful church. The house was luxurious and warm and the old Canon and his wife spoilt her and pampered her and reminisced about old times with Aunt Florrie and Aunt Gertrude. They listened gravely to her tales of tickets, but were sure that the Truck Act was not often flouted in their own small area. Mrs Sinclair had sent a message to two 'spriggers' to come the next morning to make sure. Neither the Canon nor his wife could think of anyone discreet or suitable enough to visit Mrs Boyle, but they promised to keep it 'in the forefront of their minds.'

They told her they were impressed by Mr Gahan – and by Mrs Gahan and their two tiny boys – but were less impressed by Mr Mick, Secretary of the Education Board. "I should think he could be easily knocked off course," observed the Canon, in his commonsense way.

"We go to bed early, as old people do," said Mrs Sinclair. "You will find a small fire in your room and the maid will bring your breakfast and your hot water, and we will see you in the morning room about nine o'clock. Sleep well my dear, no bicycling required in the morning, give yourself a true rest. You look very dark under your eyes, a sign of fatigue." She kissed Lucy on the cheek, and Lucy went across the charming shadowy hall, and up the curved gracious staircase with its polished shallow treads.

She undressed slowly, turning herself to warm by the fireplace. Everything in the room was lovely to look at, from the long faded curtains to the blue soap dish, everything was cared for and valued. As soon as she turned down the lamp and laid her head on the pillows she was asleep, until a knock on the door brought her breakfast.

Lucy knew the dark rings round her eyes heralded her monthlies, but the gentle evening and her calm sleep had left her quite relaxed. The morning with Mrs Sinclair and the two young embroiderers was useful. Carrie Handy and Bella Ford brought their work to show her. It was not in the same league as 'bad' Annie Mooney, but workmanlike and neat, and she ordered half a dozen handkerchiefs each from them, with HD and LD and a shamrock in the corner.

She asked them if they were paid cash or with tickets, and she saw that they gave each other warning glances; they said, "mostly cash, Madam," and one went pink. Lucy did not press the subject.

After lunch the cab arrived to drive her into Donegal to Smellins Hotel, a pleasant drive over surprisingly smooth roads. Mrs Hamilton was sending a carriage for her at four, and so she was able to rest in the hotel and order herself a pot of tea before it arrived to take her to Ballintra. The elegant carriage came punctually and had vastly superior springs from any other carriage Lucy had taken in Ireland. Only Lady Howard's carriage in Malvern ran so smoothly.

Broome Hall was a very large mansion indeed within a great park and extremely imposing. Its furniture, pictures, floors and ornaments were all on the grand scale. Its fires were large and burnt more noisily in huge fireplaces, its chandeliers tinkled in the warmth from their candle lights, it had more bedrooms, more Persian rugs, more draughts, and various quite unnerving portions of decay, rainwater stains and flaking plaster. Mrs Hamilton seemed too small a lady to inhabit such a mighty building; but she seemed genuinely pleased to greet her good friend's godchild, and was very well informed about Lucy's work as a Factory Inspector. She had a sharp twinkle in the eyes as Lucy recounted various adventures with the bicycle and the struggle to obtain tickets.

Major Hamilton was not much taller than his wife. He was a kind and clever man, eager to put her at her ease. They were all surprised to find that they had met Lucy's mother and father when they had gone to Ireland for the Nailboro Relief Fund in the 1870's.

The only other guest for dinner was Mr Craven, the Principal Magistrate in the region, he of whom Mr Gahan had been so dismissive. Lucy found him open and intelligent and was very glad to meet him. She gave him the history of her Truck Act Enquiry to date and found him clear-headed and sympathetic. It made her hopeful that he would do well for her when the case came to a hearing. The Hamiltons' son slipped into his seat at dinner, set for them cosily in the morning room, a silent young man in his early twenties. He barely spoke but gazed at Lucy as she talked with Mr Craven as if she was some strange creature. At the end of the meal he smiled vaguely and disappeared like a wraith.

Her bedroom at Broome Hall was too large, too chilly, and the bed cold despite the two stone hot water bottles. Lucy put on her stockings at some time in the night and felt herself getting very Seedy. She longed to return to Bonny Glen, or the snug little room at the inn at Ardara.

She slept badly. Mrs Hamilton was hospitable and kindly, and distressed that she did not want any breakfast. She had amassed a selection of wonderful linen and lace embroidery, locally made, to show to Lucy, and explained that she too was 'an amateur agent,' for the spriggers on her estate, but was too afraid of unpopularity, "James' position in the County, you know," to be of any use to Lucy. The crab pincers of pain scuttled around her stomach and hot and cold waves of dizziness rippled round her head; and she longed for her bed in Ardara and was thankful when the smooth springed carriage came at the end of a thankfully light lunch to take her back to Donegal and deposit her at Smellins Hotel. It had been an uncomfortable visit, but she considered it well worthwhile for the sake of meeting Mr Craven.

Young Mr Gahan was waiting for her at Smellins, as they had arranged, but Lucy was desperate to lie down and the hotel gave her a room for a few hours. Gallantly, Mr Gahan waited for her, they collected a large packet of official London letters that had been gathering for a couple of weeks, and drove her home to Ardara. It was a long drive for him, as he then had to drive on to his family in Killiebegs.

"Oh, I am so glad to be back here!" cried Lucy as Mr Nellis unloaded her bags and Mrs Nellis bustled for hot water bottles. "This is MUCH the nicest place of all." A night and a morning in bed and a quiet afternoon writing up her business diary and reports and expenses, and Lucy was ready to recount her visits to Mrs Nellis and Rose, the maid of all work, over cups of tea and applecake.

"It's real story land, Miss Deane."

A letter from Mary Paterson had arrived, agreeing to come and help to collect evidence. 'Though how to do it Lucy? I am not well versed in skullduggery. We must be quite certain of our means and our procedures.' She sent a list of dates when she would be available to travel. A letter from Hye was peevish. 'You have been in the Depths of Beyond TOO LONG. Come home now.' A letter from Adelaide at the Home Office feared that the matter was perhaps too intractable at the moment, and that other routine work and the Dangerous Trades Enquiry needed attention. Lucy despaired.

A few days later she cycled over to lunch to a young Mrs Stewart of Drummebeg near Inver. She was the Sinclairs' daughter and had recently married Mr Stewart – Mrs Hamilton of Broome Hall's youngest brother! She and her husband showed her some perfect lace work that the girls in the village brought to her. Lucy ordered some. Mrs Stewart acknowledged that she often heard her girls say they were never given money from the agents but she too, with her husband, were too frightened of their position and friends in the community to be of any use to Lucy.

Pedalling back to Ardara she made up her mind that she and Mary Paterson would have to cut this Gordian knot themselves and give evidence. She could find no single person in the County to stand up bravely to witness.

She wrote in her diary, 'I am depressed and appalled at the extraordinary feebleness and terrorism in the country, the want of truth and independence, the terror of all, high and low, of appearing or being unpopular, the utter disregard for law and justice, the terrible tales of the corruption of the magistrates.'

38

Setting the trap

Lucy becomes Mother Christmas; she distributes the work she has ordered; Mary Paterson agrees to come in disguise; how to put off Adelaide; the Carrick lacemaking school; Miss Tierney's sister has a one-roomed cottage for Mary; staying the night at the Gahans; renowned work in gale-swept Martinby; 'he thought you was a witch'; Mr Gallagher advises a visit to Maccullins.

Three sizeable parcels arrived from Robinson and Cleaver in London, and as it was a bitterly cold day and the Atlantic wind threw driving sleet across Donegal, Lucy set to work to sort them out and prepare them into separate packets for the women to whom she had promised work. She borrowed Mrs Nellis' dining table, and by the afternoon it was covered with neat brown paper parcels tied up with string, each with its own clear label.

Mrs Nellis and Rose were charmed. "'Tis like Christmas. And you're Mother Christmas."

By tea time the rain had paused so she took the first sets of work to the National Schools Workshop where she found Miss Crummles in her two-room apartment at the side, entertaining Miss Tierney and Miss Tierney's sister, married to a farm agent towards Glenties, and old Mr Crummles, her grandfather, the petty sessions clerk, who gave her, unwittingly, much information of dodgy dealings and characters in the neighbourhood.

The next day she went by bicycle to Miss McCullough on the Glenties

Road and gave her a nightdress case to embroider. She took the wives and daughters of Con and Pat Gilday a teatime tablecloth each. The mothers were too scared to speak out at all, but Rose, Anne and Biddy were more communicative; they said she could see the tickets being given any day in the shop, and complained of them bitterly. Mary Gilday had been given a 'poke' of meal for her last quilt, worth 5s 6d, but they feared for their work chances if they complained openly. On her way home from them she gave Ellen Doherty a nightdress case to decorate for Lucy's personal use, and paid her sister 2s for a pair of knitted white gloves. She paid Bernadette Morrow 2s for four yards of sprigged lawn edging. Bernie said she had tickets from Mrs Boyle and would sell them to Lucy, and so did the Gallaghers, though they were only for a few pence.

She was tired but exhilarated with the purchases of these few dirty little scraps of paper and wrote to Mary Paterson asking her to come from November 24th to December 1st. Queries and questions immediately pushed forward. Where should they meet? Where should Mary stay? Not with Lucy, obviously. Should Mary go to Mrs Boyle in her business clothes? Or as a peasant working woman? Mary was taller, better fed and more confident than the average working woman in Donegal. What were the legal pitfalls to be avoided? Who could be trusted to give them confidential advice? She thought she would write to May Tennant to suggest someone in Dublin. Many other hazy queries began to bubble up in her head. "I am really not cut out to lead a double life, or to play act like this." She thought of Mary. "And nor is Mary!" and laughed out loud as she addressed the envelope. Mrs Nellis looked up from her sewing, but Lucy did not explain.

She could not even give the 'Hunting of Mrs Boyle' her undivided attention. The letters she had collected from the Donegal Hotel came from the Chief and from various District Inspectors around Britain, reporting Complaints, following up instructions, asking for extra information on lead poisoning and fur pulling, lists from hospitals and girls' clubs, requests to speak at conferences.

Lucy was exasperated. "How do they think I am to complete this task if I have to keep breaking off to cope with all these loose ends? Anyone would think it was my own idea, and not something the Chief had expressly required to be done urgently!"

Then, to turn the screw further, a letter came from Hye saying she had a few days of holiday due to her and had decided to go to Antwerp for a week with Ethel. 'I had much rather go with you, as Ethel is so dull and respectable, but you have DESERTED me. We are staying with an old school friend of Ethel, now married, just outside Antwerp. I do hope it will be cold enough to skate.'

Finally, to her dismay, the postman brought a letter from Adelaide, proposing to come herself and help Lucy. What to do? What to do? How to put her off tactfully? She composed and recomposed the letter as she bicycled on her rounds with the packages of orders.

Rose Gavrahan seemed braver than the others. They had a long talk and she gave Lucy another ticket for which Lucy paid. Lucy implied Rose could be helped if she gave witness and was 'boycotted' for it. Rose said she had decided she would stand firm, and cheered Lucy up by her courage, and was pleased to be given another nightdress bag to embroider. 'Bad Girl' Annie Mooney, the star embroiderer, was working on complex initials spaced with shamrock leaves. Her work had been specially requested by Rose and Co. of Lurgan. She had made Lucy a star pincushion. Lucy paid her 3s. "It is quite perfect, Annie, and nobody shall EVER put a pin in it. I will keep it upon my dressing table and treasure it."

Mr Gahan called by the inn and told her of the new lacemaking workshop that had been opened north of Carrick, which would sadden Miss Crummles who had hoped to include it in Ardara. He also told her about the collection of embroiderers scratching a living in the wilds of Martinby, and wondered if she thought it worth her while to visit them for the purposes of the Enquiry. If she did, he said, he would advise staying in Carrick or Killiebegs for one or two nights, as the terrain was rocky and a bicycle unsafe to ride except in the daytime. And it would soon be December. Lucy talked to Miss Tierney and Miss Crummles who were keen for her to visit the new little School Workshop. "I can't imagine what possessed them to place it out there on the edge of the world," said Miss Crummles. "I wouldn't like to be a lone woman teaching there. I don't think I would do it for twice the salary. But they do say there are some wonderful lacemakers and knitters way out there, and I daresay the teacher there would be the agent."

Lucy decided she would make the trek up there, and so Mr Gahan invited her to stay with him and his wife and little family, starting the next day and staying for two nights.

She thought that she would never be able to set off, though, as among the post that day came another letter from Adelaide, determined to come and help with the Truck Agency Enquiry, and saying that she had sent a letter to Mary Paterson saying that she wanted to come herself. So then there was an urgent wire from Mary saying should she not come then? So then Lucy had to send Mary a wire saying 'Come, for heaven's sake,' and a wire to Adelaide saying 'Don't come! Explanatory letter follows.' And then she had to write two letters to Adelaide – detailed letters explaining the difficulties and objections to Adelaide's coming.

But THEN, before she had posted these, Miss Tierney arrived to say that there was a one-roomed cottage next to her married sister's farm on the outskirts of Glenties which could be available for Mary to lodge in when she arrived dressed as a poor country girl looking for work in the district! It had stood empty for some months but it was dry and would be possible, "It has had hay stored in it but my sister says we can sweep it all over to one side and that will make it warmer for your friend!" said Miss Tierney. Lucy thanked them all.

She stayed up most of the night sorting her papers, tidying loose ends, and details of past problems in England, mending her bicycle light and packing her warmest clothes for the short stay at Killiebegs.

Mr Gahan kindly drove over at breakfast time and put her case and bicycle into the fly. The west wind was at their side all the way to Killiebegs, buffeting the carriage sideways. Twice Mr Gahan got down to lead the good little horse in a particularly gusty interlude. He and his very pretty wife looked anxious when Lucy insisted on setting off to the lacemaking workshop on her bicycle, through Carrick and almost to Glencolmkille. The stony road twisted up and down and up and down the hills; in the lee of the wind Lucy enjoyed the calm and quiet, and braced herself for the tops of the hills where she knew the cold fresh gusts awaited her. As she approached Carrick she saw it all spread out before her, the one main street ruled straight through the village, looking surprisingly neat with the low white houses, each with its smoke wagging like a grey flag, and with the small thatched church at the end of the village. A scatter of outlying farms ringed the village and in the distance on the far end, almost at the ridge of the next hill, was a minute white building with a thatched roof and a long sign painted across the front. This was the very new Carrick District National School Lace Workshop, the name nearly as long as the building.

Lucy introduced herself to the young teacher, Miss Callan, in the very overcrowded dark stuffy room. Fifteen young girls, all between twelve and fourteen, and all looking several years younger, were sitting at a long trestle table covered with a black cloth, their long hair pulled severely back and their heads bent over their lacemaking cushions and pins. This was the Morning Group who came from 9.30 to 12.30. Lucy examined the work and was startled by the standard reached in so short a time. Miss Callan, with black hair, a sharp nose, and small darting eyes, looking very like a blackbird, sat at a small table, and each girl came out in turn to have individual attention.

Though the school had only been open just over two weeks, the little girls had made extraordinary progress. They were very quiet and orderly and when Miss Callan called the morning to a halt, they gently wrapped their pieces of work each in its own linen bag and placed it in the 'Morning Box'. But when they got outside the door they leapt and skipped and shouted all the way down into the village. Another group of fifteen would come for teaching from 2p.m. to 5 p.m.

Lucy had a cup of tea with Miss Callan who lived during the week in the small bed sitting room through from the main classroom, and went home to her mother and father on Saturday afternoon, walking on to Glencolmkille with her washing in a sack! She said she was not lonely as she had friends in the village, and her aunt 'kept an eye on her' and her cousins often came to sleep with her. She was extremely self-composed and was just turned eighteen years old. Lucy marvelled.

She called on the priest but he was out, so she braced herself for the ride back to Killiebegs, and found that with the wind behind her, she bounced back in record time, to Jenny Gahan's relief, and spent an interesting evening talking to John Gahan. A day or two before she had received an interesting letter from a Doctor Edmunds, a Junior Education Inspector in Cardiff, asking for information on Irish Home Industries which the Welsh Education Board wished to start up in Wales. She pumped Mr Gahan about the Irish Home Industries and went through all the relevant books he owned on the subject.

The next day the wind had dropped and she set out on her trusty two-wheeled steed armed with a lunch of bread rolls and ham and cheese packed by Jenny Gahan. She called in on the morning class of the Lace School and then rode on to the romantic wild village of Martinby. Fishermen on the strand stared at her, but no one spoke English and the wind coming in off the sea whipped her cheeks, though the sun shone brightly. She struggled over the cliff path to Martinmore with its spectacular view, and then, with Miss Callan's instructions, to Martinby itself, a wild uncivilised hamlet of wretched cabins. On the road she passed a little posse of girls waving at her. They were part of the Lace School's Afternoon group, on their long walk to school. But she noticed that they took a short cut from her stony path, cutting across a hillside and then plunging down a deep ravine in a direction she estimated would bring them out on the Glencolmkille to Carrick Road.

There was one very small store at Martinby run by a Mrs Craig, who had reasonable English. She was an agent, handing out mostly simple handkerchiefs with initials and sprigging. She told Lucy she worked exclusively for Malers firm in Belfast. Any special orders for first class knitting or lacemaking were sent exclusively to Martinby by Malers, as there were five or six women there renowned for their fine work. Lucy supposed this was why the standard in the new school was so high. The girls from Martinby had watched their mothers working from babyhood. The special orders were rare though, and mostly the work was given out in small packages each with its label of price on each dozen articles of work – so that the agent couldn't cheat on price. Mrs Craig always paid in money; but being the only shop in the area she always got all the custom.

Back in Carrick she visited the Paterson Agency, and was shown elaborate and lovely knitting, plain and fancy, from work jerseys to children's party socks and lacy bootikins and shawls. All for sale was at very low prices, paid for with money, no tickets, as far as she could tell. She took the details of several patterns and bought socks for the Gahan boys. On Martinmore her hat pins had succumbed to the wind and she had had to scramble down a slope to retrieve the hat although she had firmly tied it on with an extra scarf.

She arrived back in Killiebegs, after her round trip of 28 miles, her cheeks and nose red and raw from the wind, her hair streaming like a Maenad and several inches of mud on the hem of her skirt. The Gahan toddlers retreated to the corner of the kitchen in terror at the sight of her, and Jenny Gahan had to lend her a skirt while the young nursemaid scrubbed at the brown serge skirt in the scullery and Lucy recounted the day's adventures at the kitchen table drinking strong sweet tea. "I called on the priest again in Carrick on my way home. His housekeeper said he was out again. But I don't think he was. I saw a face at the window. He just wouldn't answer the door!"

"He thought you was a witch," said the older Gahan child.

After a good night's sleep and a good breakfast Mr Gahan deposited her and the muddy bicycle back at the Ardara Inn. Later in the morning the Ardara police inspector had called, on his sturdy vehicle, and looked at hers with disfavour. They sat and had a cup of coffee together and exchanged local gossip with Mr and Mrs Nellis. He was sorry, he said, that he had not been to make her acquaintance before but he had been to a conference in the very north of Donegal and when he got back he found one of his constables had broken his leg chasing a pig in Glenties, so he had had to do all the work himself. Lucy sympathised and said she too was sorry they had not met and that her time was drawing to a close and her report on the home embroidery workers was nearly completed. She told him of her misgivings about Mrs Boyle and the Truck Act and he pushed his lips out very far and very slowly, and then gave her – apparently quite unconsciously – the argument which the dishonest agents would use against her in a prosecution, for which she was very grateful; she told him she considered their meeting to have been both timely and important.

During her two days away a small mountain of letters had gathered to await her. She opened the letter from Mary Paterson first which said she was arriving the next afternoon in Belfast. Where were they to meet? She had, she said, her dressing up clothes ready.

Lucy drew in a long breath. Suddenly all the plans were going to materialise. All the visiting, making friends, questioning, all the strands of friendship, deceit, trust, all the people she needed to help, all had to merge together to finish the task.

She sent a wire to Mary to come to Strabane.

She wired to the hotel in Strabane for rooms for two nights.

She sent a wire to Adelaide to alert her to the situation.

She wrote to Mr Hugh Gallagher, whose name John Gahan had given her as the only honest agent he knew of in Donegal, suggesting a meeting in Donegal the next morning.

He wired back that would be fine. He would meet her at the Smellins Hotel.

She sent a short letter to Hyacinth, just returned from Antwerp, to say that she was moving into the final stage of her secret agent life, and hoped to be home in a week or so.

She went through all her papers, meetings, checked her diary entries, and packed away all her reports except the most recent.

She gave Mrs Nellis a bundle of washing and asked her to sponge and brush all her outdoor clothes, polish her shoes, and clean her bicycle as well as possible.

She felt sad at leaving Mr and Mrs Nellis, Rosie and Joe the pot boy for two days. They had cared for her admirably but she could give them no ideas about where she would be for the foreseeable future.

November 25th 1897. Mary would arrive in Ireland that afternoon. Lucy took the early train to Donegal and met the virtuous Hugh Gallagher, the linen agent for John Ireland and Co at Smellins Hotel. He travelled around the whole of Donegal for this firm visiting the many local agents. A small elderly man with a dry manner and a quiet voice, he welcomed her, saying he greatly respected Mr Gahan, and always found him a transparently honest and hardworking young man. Lucy agreed.

"I hear you have found many irregularities in the trade," he began.

"They weren't hard to find," said Lucy.

"Not if you take the trouble to keep your eyes and ears open," he said. "The problem lies mostly with the agents who run stores in isolated areas. The country is fortunate in having John Ireland and Co. agent's offices all over the North of Ireland. But if you are a small firm with home workers strung out in lonely spots, your agents and your embroiderers are dependent on one another. If either is damaged the entire firm may founder. The firm may occasionally have to turn a blind eye."

"But the breaking of the law becomes brazen and blatant. I have seen it time and again."

"When that is so of course it must be redressed," he replied. "And have you collected enough evidence to prosecute?"

"Plenty of material evidence – mainly relating to one miscreant. But we need one or two persons to stand up bravely in court and speak for all the downtrodden ones."

Mr Gallagher brought his stick to his mouth and rubbed it against his lips for a moment. "Only one miscreant – you would need more; you would need there to be at least three or four to be sure of a satisfactory outcome. I see why Mr Gahan is anxious to help you! You are indeed a brave woman, I have brought you a list of agents for various firms, in a twelve-mile radius of Donegal that it would be worth your while to visit for your enquiries." Lucy thanked him and they ate lunch together before he left. "There is one agent in particular I have heard it would be very much worth your while to visit if you could get there. Mr Campbell at Drunamore, near Inver. His store is open especially on Sundays to receive and hand out work, I gather."

After he had taken his leave she consulted his list and saw a Mr McAllner, in Donegal city, quite close to the hotel, so she walked along there; but the address was simply a small office building, and there was no reply when she rang the bell.

39

Mary and Lucy win the day

Mary arrives in Strabane with dressing up clothes; they plan their strategies; Lucy gives Mary a lift; Lucy bicycles to the Sinclairs at Inver; stormy weather; storms on Sunday in Drunamore; Mr Maccullins gives out tickets; Lucy is recognised, but by friends; the bicycle crashes; the Sinclairs shelter her; Mary is successful but exhausted; 'now I can come home.'

She returned to the hotel and took lunch, and wrote to Adelaide to report progress before catching the afternoon train to Strabane. There she waited impatiently until the Belfast train arrived; and there was Mary Paterson, business-like and imperturbable, straight-backed and severe looking as usual like an earnest Sunday school teacher. Lucy feared no one would ever believe she was a poor countrywoman searching for work. However, it was too late now.

At the Strabane hotel they talked and talked, and Lucy realised what a relief it was to have a trusted colleague beside her and to be put in touch with the latest news from the Female Inspectors Department, and to know how the Dangerous Trades Enquiry was progressing and how the Lead Report was rumbling on. Even Mary's precise Scottish lilt sounded refreshingly English. After an early evening meal they sat in Mary's bedroom and finalised the plans for the Great Truck Shop Deception.

Mary showed Lucy her proposed disguise costume – a stout plain clean grey serge skirt above ankle length, bulked out with warm grey flannel petticoats, thick black woollen stockings and old but serviceable black boots, two grey jerseys, and a black grey and white checked thick shawl, neatly darned in several places, a small grey elderly felt hat with a small cockade of black and white feathers from some long-dead bird, a small red and white scarf round her neck, a strip of thin black flannel to tie the hat firmly on her head, 'in case of wind', an old Gladstone bag and a capacious old leather handbag held in her neatly darned woollen gloved hand. She changed her business-like expression to an anxious half smile and dropped her shoulders imperceptibly, and stood before Lucy as a respectable brave working-class young woman looking for work.

Lucy was enchanted. "Mary, you are perfect!"

Mary, too, was pleased with the effect. "Maybe I have missed my vocation. I could get a living on the Halls. If I could sing."

The next morning they constructed a model prosecution report to see if the definition of Mrs Boyle's offence would suit the Home Office, and sent it off to Adelaide. Lucy wrote a note to Mrs Sinclair at Inver asking if she might stay at Bonny Glen on the Saturday night, in order to visit Mr Maccullins at Drunamore on the Sunday. They hoped he would prove to be suitably recalcitrant so that he could be added to the 'miscreant' list.

Then they took third class tickets from Strabane and travelled to Glenties where they alighted separately. Lucy went to hire a cab to take her to Ardara. Mary stood, looking irresolute at the front of the station. She really is extraordinarily good at this, thought Lucy. As she came back from the stables and was waiting for the horse to be harnessed to the cab, Mary came shyly forward and said, in the hearing of several bystanders,

"Excuse me, Madam, can you tell me how far it is to Ardara?"

"Just about six miles," said Lucy, "That way."

Mary's face fell. "Oh!" she said. "Thank you."

The cab drove up. "Do you know of Sly's farm, this side of Ardara?"

"I do," said the man.

"Is it on the main road?"

"It is, about three miles down the road."

Mary thanked him impassively and turned to begin walking.

Lucy watched a moment, and then said, "You're not from round here?"

"Indeed not. I'm from Scotland."

"Are the Slys relatives of yours?"

"Well, not exactly. They know I'm coming. I'm hoping to find work in the area."

Just at that moment, providentially, a drop of rain hit Lucy's head. "I would be willing to give this lady a lift to the farm or near to it."

The man nodded.

Mary looked astonished. "Are you sure?"

"Get in," said Lucy, climbing in first.

They sat in near silence as the cab jogged through the darkening afternoon, peering out of the small windows at the black heathland with the long-dead bleached grasses swept by the breeze. Mary shivered.

"You'll be glad to be in the warmth."

"I could certainly do with a warm bed."

"Miss Tierney's sister said she would be looking out for you?"

"Let's hope so."

The driver rapped on the window with his whip as they approached the homestead.

"I'll go to Glenties tomorrow to the store," said Mary gathering her shawl about her, and her bags.

"Good luck. And I'll come to see you here at Sly's on Sunday afternoon after I've been to the agent's shop in Inver."

"And let's hope that will be it," said Mary.

Mary stepped down onto the road and stood looking down the farm track. A lamp hovered outside the farm door.

"They're looking out for you," said the driver comfortingly. "They'll be glad you've arrived safely."

"That's nice," said Mary bravely. She began to pick her way down the track and the small light began to move waveringly towards her.

The cab waited a moment. The driver called, "I see them greeting her. She's all right now." And the horse moved swiftly on to Ardara.

Outside the hotel she paid the driver – he would not accept any fare for the extra passenger.

"That is kind."

"No, no, poor woman in a strange place."

"Yes. I saw her on the train, she looked very tired then."

"Well, sure, she'll be fine now."

He went on to the stables in the village, and Lucy went in to a warm fire and a hot meal and friends. She worried over Mary, waking up several times in the night.

May Abraham Tennant had sent the name of Mr Quirt, a solicitor in Dublin, and Lucy wrote to him at once to ask if he would give her legal advice on the Truck Act.

She wrote to May to thank her.

She wrote to Mr Child at the bank to send her £20 as she had been spending money like water these last weeks.

A note from Mrs Sinclair at Inver looked forward to welcoming her that evening.

Lucy was on edge, thinking of Mary all the time. What if she could not get any first-hand evidence at Mrs Boyle's store? What if the women turned against her, a stranger? What if Mrs Boyle realised she was being investigated?

Mrs Nellis sensed her anxiety and became anxious on her behalf; she knew better than to ask for the reason, but was infected by the tension. Miss Tierney came down from the School Workshop as soon as it had closed on the Saturday afternoon. She was surprised to see Lucy tucking her overnight bag for Inver into her bicycle basket. Lucy told her of the safe arrival.

"But I shan't be able to hear how she got on at the store until tomorrow afternoon."

Miss Tierney promised to visit her sister on the Sunday morning. She cautioned Lucy. "The weather will be stormy, they say. You'll have to be wary on that machine, or you'll be blown into the ditch."

Lucy promised to be careful and rode off to Bonny Glen.

"Did you ever know such a stubborn, obstinate young woman?" said Mrs Nellis in exasperation. "If she wasn't so nice I'd be glad she was going!"

Miss Tierney and Mrs Nellis crossed themselves and clasped hands.

Canon and Mrs Sinclair were their usual kindly and hospitable selves. Lucy told them everything that had been going on, and that she felt she was now very close to a prosecution and a court case. She told of her impending visit to Mr Maccullins store the next morning. To her surprise Mrs Sinclair clapped her hands. "Such an unpleasant man. We rarely go there and I did not think he was anybody's agent. I have never heard of any embroidery being given out from there. He has a large store and two or three others between here and Donegal."

Canon Sinclair's face was grave. "But he has many contacts with other businesses in the area. He will be much more slippery to pin down than Mrs Boyle of Glenties."

During the night the wind grew into a gale, rattling the windows, making all the lamps flicker as they were carried along the corridors in the house. By first light the rain was sleeting in noisy gusts.

"You cannot go out in this!" cried Mrs Sinclair in horror.

"I must," said Lucy. "It's my one and only chance. If I could get evidence here it would be worth much more than the other smaller agents."

She set off against everyone's advice, from the Sinclairs to the stable man, on her bicycle. The building in Drunamore stood dripping and apparently closed. Lucy sheltered in a barn doorway with the rain and wind slapping her rain cape around her legs woefully, and then realised occasional groups of women were struggling down the village street with shawls tied over their baskets, and turning down an alley leading to the back of the store. She risked leaving the bicycle in the lee of the barn, and followed a couple who knocked firmly on the back door. She heard bolts being drawn back and slipped in with the two women. Eight or ten women were already inside unwrapping their precious cargoes of finished work, from layers of oiled brown paper, brown paper, cloth bag, white linen, and tissue paper, and then finally waiting in line for the agent, Mr Maccullins, to inspect their work and allot them their wages.

Sure enough, though he did give some coins to every woman he also gave them a ticket, while a young assistant wrote the transaction down in a large ledger.

The women looked at Lucy, who was as bedraggled as they were. One of them said, "Have you brought work in?"

Lucy said she had not, but did the man give work out to new people, she had brought some samples she had done when she was up Strabane way.

They nodded and went on chatting among themselves. She saw the women who had been in the line before her going into a separate cubicle and coming out with new packages of work to do, and then ranging around the shelves for their household purchases.

Lucy noticed a young woman staring at her and speaking to her neighbour who also stared. She could feel other eyes turning and the mood changing and suspicion rising. She was next in line to speak to Mr Maccullins, there was no escape.

"Do you give out work to new folk? I've just come into the district, used to work for Mr Gallagher, north of Donegal."

He appraised her. "Show me your work."

"I've only been able to bring a few pieces," said Lucy, unwrapping half a dozen samples brought from Miss Tierney's and Miss Crummles' classes.

"I could only give you basic work," he said. "Start you on simple initials, simple sprigging. This work is very uneven in quality."

Lucy looked crestfallen.

"Wait over there until I've seen these girls. Then I'll make my mind up."

Lucy meekly stood aside, aware of the whispering. The small thin girl came and stood beside her.

"We've seen you around here," she said in a low voice. "You're not from Donegal."

Lucy looked at her.

"Why are you here?" whispered the girl.

"I think he should be paying you with proper money, never with illegal tickets," whispered Lucy.

"We need to get food for ourselves, somehow," whispered the girl sharply.

"Of course!" whispered Lucy, "I'm on your side."

"If you are you'll get out of here fast," said the girl, raising her voice. "You'll not come here and take our work from this store. Go back to your own place."

Lucy drew back. The girl laughed in her face.

Mr Maccullins looked up. "I'll have no bad temper in my store. Biddy Gillespie, shut your mouth. Or I'll tip you out."

Lucy shrugged her shoulders and moved away.

Biddy Gillespie erupted. "It's not me causing trouble, it's this one." She turned to her friend. "We'll see she goes, won't we?" She whispered to Lucy, "Come to the door – it's all right, we're friends."

The two girls escorted her to the door. "We know you," they whispered, "we live in Inver. We've heard about you."

"I'm staying at Bonny Glen."

They grinned. "We know. My sister's the kitchen maid. We'll sell you our tickets. Go home out of the wet." They gave her two radiant smiles, changed their expressions to thunder, and slammed the door shut.

She made her way back to the bicycle and began to go back on the long road to Ardara, but long before she had even reached Killiebegs she was wet to the skin and the bicycle had been blown over twice grazing her hands and tearing her stocking. The road was deserted, and she could hardly catch her breath; she had to turn her back on the wind to seek shelter with the Sinclairs. They took her in with true Christian compassion, found her dry clothes, gave her a hot bath, and a calm afternoon in the graceful sitting room by the warm fire while she told them her story.

When she reached the name of Biddy Gillespie, old Mrs Sinclair clapped her hands over her head and whooped, and Canon Sinclair banged his fists on the arms of his chair.

"They are a SPLENDID family. Biddy's sister Betty is our kitchen maid. We must go and tell her right away." They trooped through the baize door into the kitchen where Cook and Betty were preparing supper, and Lucy told her news. Betty, a younger version of Biddy, reddened with pleasure, but seemed speechless, looking down at the floor. Cook took command of the situation. She was sure Betty was very obliged to Miss Deane for taking the time to come and tell her, and she would pass Miss Deane's thanks on to Biddy when next she saw her, wouldn't she, Betty?

But during the evening, Lucy grew more and more worried about Mary Paterson. "I should have gone to see her this afternoon. How am I to get to her? She will be expecting me."

"She certainly won't be expecting you in this weather and she is not alone. Mrs Sly will look after her. The Ardara hotel will guess you are safe with us, and this is where you will stay until the storm blows itself out. Be patient, Lucy, all will be well."

Lucy tried to be patient, but the strain of not knowing any details at all, the thought of Mary alone in a bare cottage, in such a storm, even with, as Mrs Sinclair was sure, a fire and plenty of food, was very troubling. Practical Canon Sinclair made up a list of possible local JPs who might be on the bench at a future court case and went through them all with her methodically as to their personalities, their interests, their trades and their professions. Lucy made careful notes about them all, while the storm battered the landscape and rattled the shutters and the dark clouds swept over the skies outside.

She slept fitfully, waking every hour or so to hear the racket and the gale howling in the chimney until, at about five o'clock, the wind died down, and growing pockets of stillness gradually seemed to smooth themselves over the walls of the old house. Then she slept until the maid knocked on her door with tea and a jug of hot water, and her own clothes, washed and dried and ironed and aired, were brought back to her.

After an early breakfast – and Mrs Sinclair insisted that she ate a good one – the Bonny Glen fly drove her all the way to Ardara with the brave bruised bicycle resting in the back. The sky was leaden but there was no rain, the trees dripped into the puddles, and the rivers of water that ran along the road spurted like fountains as the fly bowled along, arriving at Ardara just after ten o'clock.

She paused at the hotel just long enough to read the letter from Adelaide wishing them luck on their venture and asking when they would be back in London. Then she dusted off the bicycle and rode with great care to the Slys' farmhouse.

"I'm so sorry I could not come before."

"Oh, we knew nothing could face that storm. Your friend was out in it on Saturday and she says she has had a successful day at Mrs Boyle's store. She has a fearful cold and we think she has a fever. But she is warm in her bed. I said she was to stay there until you came, and we are giving her hot drinks."

Lucy entered the tiny cottage. A cheerful fire burned on the hearth and the truckle bed had been pulled close to the fire. Mary lay in this, swathed in shawls, propped up with cushions and pillows.

"Oh, Mary, what have I done to you?" cried Lucy, pulling up a stool beside her.

"You have given me a great adventure and a sore throat," croaked Mary, "But I accomplished everything we need! I've got plenty of evidence, and the names of several women who were given tickets. A splendid young woman called Rose Gavrahan was in the shop and talking to the women outside. And I bought a jar of honey, paid for it myself, doing wonders for my throat. Last night Mr and Mrs Sly made me stay in their house as this one hadn't properly warmed through. But now it's warm and cosy and my wet clothes have dried. And all I want to do is sleep!"

Lucy's eyes welled up and she wanted to sob.

"Don't be silly, Lucy," said Mary. "We are victorious. We have won!"

"We must get you to the hotel and a doctor as soon as we can."

"Don't need a doctor. I need to go to sleep. Mrs Sly is looking after me."

Mrs Sly was a sensible young woman. "It would be best to get her to the hotel soon, and for the doctor to look her over, but I'm sure she will recover quickly. She is just exhausted. I'll look after her until you can collect her."

So Lucy cycled back to the hotel and Mrs Nellis rose once again to the challenge and prepared a room for Mary while Mr Nellis went to hire a cab to collect her.

By early evening Mary, dressed in her business clothes, was helped into the cab and ensconced in the cheerful firelit bedroom next to Lucy's room. Lucy sat in the firelight while Mary snoozed, and wrote out four Prosecution reports to send to Adelaide in the morning at Great George Street.

She wrote to John Gahan to send the Complaints book for the District.

She wrote to Hyacinth. "We've done it. Now I can come home."

She looked up and saw Mary was fast asleep.

A Few Mini Biographies

MAY ABRAHAM (TENNANT) 1869–1946

May Abraham was born in Dublin, the daughter of George Whiteley Abraham, a Commissioner of Lunacy, a medical doctor and member of the Irish bar. She was educated at home, but her father died when she was a very young woman, having lost his fortune, and so she had to earn her living. She came to London and worked as a secretary and the treasurer for Lady Emilia Dilke's Women's Trade Union League; in 1891 she was appointed as one of the Lady Assistant Commissioners on the Royal Commission for Women's Labour, and this led directly on to her being appointed, in 1892, with Mary Muirhead Paterson, as the first two Women Factory Inspectors. She married Harold 'Jack' Tennant MP in 1896 and resigned from the Inspectorate in 1897.

However, she continued to be a member of the Dangerous Trades Committee, and was the Chief Adviser to the Women's Welfare Labour Department.

During World War One she was on the Central Committee on Divorce, various other committees such as the Committee for the Prevention of Tuberculosis and for the promotion of maternal health; she was also a Governor of Bedford College.

MRS CECIL FRANCES ALEXANDER 1818 – 1895

Mrs Alexander was born Cecil Humphreys in Dublin, Ireland and began writing religious verse in her childhood. She was strongly influenced by Dr Walter Hook, Dean of Chichester, and by the Church of England Oxford movement, in particular by John Keble who edited one of her anthologies.

She became one of the best known and best loved of the Victorian hymn writers, and her hymns, 'All things bright and beautiful,' 'There is a green hill far away,' 'Once in Royal David's City,' and many others are still sung and loved today.

She married in 1850 to William Alexander who became both the Bishop of Derry and the Archbishop of Armagh, and the couple lived in Milton House, Strabane, when they were not in the Bishop's official Palace in Derry. She was involved in countless charitable organisations all her life.

ADELAIDE ANDERSON 1863 – 1936

Adelaide was born in Melbourne, Australia, to a Scottish ship broker and his wife, but educated in London, firstly at home by governesses, then at schools in France and Germany, and then at Queen's College, Harley Street. She enrolled at Girton College Cambridge, where she graduated in the Moral Sciences Tripos (but of course, with no degree awarded) in 1887.

She lectured on philosophy and economics for the women's Co-operative Guild and was active for women's suffrage. In 1892 she joined the Royal Commission of Woman's Labour as a clerk, and was made a Factory Inspector in 1894, becoming the Principal Woman Inspector in 1897, on May Abraham's marriage.

She held the post until 1921. She was given a DBE in 1921. After she had retired she went on several visits to China over eight years, firstly as a member of the Commission of Child Labour at the International Settlement in Shanghai, then as a member of the Committee on China Indemnity, and in 1931 on a mission for the International Labour Office regarding the setting up of a Factory Inspectorate for China.

HERBERT HENRY ASQUITH 1852 – 1928

Herbert Asquith's parents, Joseph Asquith, a woollen mill owner, and his wife Emily Willans were a middle class, Congregational family in Morley, the West Riding of Yorkshire. His father died when he was seven and the family moved to Huddersfield to Emily's father's home. In 1863 Herbert was sent to his uncle in London and went to the City of London School, winning a scholarship to Balliol College, Oxford in 1870.

He became the President of the Oxford Union in 1874. He was called to the bar in 1876 and was appointed QC in 1890.

He married twice; his first wife gave him four sons and a daughter before dying of typhoid fever in 1891. His second wife, Margot Tennant, gave him five children also, but sadly only two survived, Elizabeth and Anthony, the film director.

He became the Liberal MP for East Fife in 1886 and Home Secretary in 1892, but when the Liberal Party lost power in the 1895 election he spent 10 years in Opposition. When the Liberals were returned to power in 1905 he became Prime Minister and again Prime Minister in 1908.

He died after a stroke, at his home in Sutton Courtenay near Oxford in 1928, aged 75.

MARGOT ASQUITH (nee Tennant) 1864 – 1945

Margot was born at Glen in Peebleshire in 1864, the daughter of Sir Charles Tennant, a wealthy industrialist. She was the eleventh child and sixth daughter. She and her sister Laura grew up wild, uninhibited and venturesome. Her brother Harold married May Abraham. The two sisters grew up inseparable socialites, but also worked tirelessly in the East End of London on independent charitable and philanthropic works, running lunchtime clubs for women factory workers in Whitechapel for eight years, alongside her celebrity social life and writings, and her role as a political hostess when she married Herbert Asquith in 1894. She brought him into a glittering social world he had never experienced, but her outspoken and incautious behaviour brought a distinctly negative response from the political world and the general public alike.

After her husband died in 1928 she moved from the family home in Sutton Courteney, from house to house, living for some time in rooms at the Savoy Hotel, and finally in Thurlow Place, South Kensington.

SIR CHARLES DILKE 1843 – 1911

Sir Charles Wentworth Dilke Bart came from a radical family. His father was the editor of the *Athenaeum* from 1830 to 1846.

He became the MP for Chelsea at the age of 25 from 1868. His

Republicanism gained him notoriety. By 1880 he was the acknowledged leader of the Liberal Radicals, when he became an Under Secretary of State at the Foreign Office, and in 1882 he entered the Cabinet as the President of the Local Government Boards. But in 1886 a scandalous indiscretion cut short his future when he was cited as co-respondent in divorce proceedings. Although the case against him failed he withdrew from parliamentary life until 1892 when he became the MP for the Forest of Dean. He fought for women's suffrage, labour and trade unions, factory reforms, and compulsory education.

LADY EMILIA DILKE 1840 – 1904

Emilia Francis Strong was brought up in Oxford where her father was a bank manager who was friendly with many of the leaders of the Victorian art world. She was schooled at home by governesses. She studied at the School for Design in South Kensington and became an art critic and historian.

In 1861 she married Mark Pattison, the Rector of Lincoln College Oxford, a man many years older than herself, and after his death she married Sir Charles Dilke in 1885. She turned their house into a hub of hospitality for all types of Liberal reforms, and supported all his causes; her patronage and political influence was essential for many women Liberal and Labour activists, including Gertrude Tuckwell, May Abraham, Lucy Deane and countless others. She became the President of the Women's Trade Union League and attended the Trade Union Congress annually until her death in 1904.

DOCTOR THOM ORME DUDFIELD 1833 – 1912

Doctor Dudfield was born in Gloucestershire, and became Medical Officer of Health for Kensington in London in 1871, remaining there for the rest of his working life. He gained the title of 'the model of a Medical Officer of Health' working tirelessly to reform the problems of dirt and filth in his area. Though Kensington had some of the wealthiest streets in the city, the area of North Kensington was as squalid as anywhere in the country, known as 'the Potteries' and the 'Piggeries'. In 1871 the sanitary requirements were handed over to District Councils. Dr

Dudfield complained that the consequent inspections of the countless small outworkers' laundry and dressmakers' businesses took up too much time and so he pressured his council of Kensington Vestrymen, a very reactionary, Conservative group of men, to take the great leap of appointing not one but two Women Sanitary Inspectors, Lucy Deane and Rose Squire. They took on the task of listing and reporting on the firms in the area, faced down the hostility of proprietors and forewomen, and checked on ventilation, overtime, hygienic meal rooms and sanitary arrangements, giving advice. In their first six months they had visited 450 premises across Kensington – four workplaces a day each, and then writing their reports in the evenings. Plenty of unpaid overtime for them!

ELIZABETH GARRETT ANDERSON 1836 – 1917

Elizabeth was born Elizabeth Garrett, the second of twelve children, in Whitechapel where her father was a silversmith. When she was three years old the family moved to Long Acre and then moved back to her father's home town of Aldeburgh, Suffolk, where he became a prosperous barley and coal merchant. In due course he built the handsome Snape Maltings, now the home for Benjamin Britten's Music Festival.

All the Garrett children were encouraged to become achievers and Elizabeth's parents, especially her father, did all they could to support her struggles to gain a medical education, first as a surgery nurse at the Middlesex Hospital, living with her married sister Louie in London in 1860. She was finally allowed in to the dissecting room and the chemistry lectures, but the male students tried to block her studies.

She applied to all the medical schools. All refused her. She studied privately with various professors, and was admitted to the Society of Apothecaries but not allowed to practise in any hospital. In 1865 she opened her own private practice in 20 Upper Berkeley Street, London, and some years later her own New Hospital for Women, which became the Elizabeth Garrett Anderson Hospital. She married James Skelton Anderson, of the Orient Steamship Company. In her later life she returned to Aldeburgh and became very active in local politics, becoming the first woman in the country to be elected Mayor, as Mayor of Aldeburgh.

LADY HOWARD DE WALDEN 1806 – 1899

The Dowager Lady Howard de Walden was Lady Lucy Joan Cavendish Scott Bentinck the daughter of the 4th Duke of Portland. Their country seat was Audley End. She used her great wealth for many charitable enterprises, one of the largest being the Dental Hospital and College in Great Portland Street, and she donated to dozens of charities working for better conditions for women's employment, living conditions and education.

In her last years she built a great mansion in Malvern called St James, which became the famous St. James School after her death.

She had been best friends with Lucy and Hyacinth's grandmother Lady Falmouth, and supported the two young girls after their parents died, until they were settled in their careers. She died at the age of 93, having been a widow for 31 years.

MISS FAY LANKESTER 184? – 1924

Fay Lankester was one of the eight children of Edwin Lankester, biologist, doctor and social reformer; of her siblings, Owen was a doctor in Wimpole Street, Ray was one of the founders of modern British biology, Nina became one of the first women clerks in the Post Office, Marion married an East End clergyman and worked in Poor Relief in Stepney.

From an early age Fay took an interest in the study of hygiene, and was well known in London Society as 'a lady of quiet gentle manners and artistic taste.'

The National Health Society was founded in 1871 by Dr Elizabeth Blackwell, the first woman doctor – who donated both time and money to it. It trained middle class women for voluntary work amongst the poor and issued certificates to qualify them to give lectures to guide poor women to manage healthy households. The training lectures were given by eminent physicians at the Society's premises in Berners Street, off Oxford Street, but the day-to-day administration rested in the hands of Fay Lankester from the beginning.

THE NATIONAL HEALTH SOCIETY

Miss Lankester expanded the courses to include elementary physiology, first aid, home nursing, infectious diseases, diet and hygiene. The Society would provide the lecturers, diagrams, books and bandages. Each class had examinations and those passing three or more examinations were qualified to lecture for the Society. The courses were very popular. In 1890 2,500 ladies attended. The examinations were not compulsory, but 450 women received certificates and 10 (one of whom was Lucy) received the Silver Medal.

In 1892 the Society had to expand its training programme. Those wishing to enter had to be 'educated gentlefolk over 25 years of age.' The Fee was 10 guineas for each course including the exam. In 1892 the Society had 500 applicants.

A few women were attracted by the much more rigorous course for Sanitary Inspectors, especially those who were interested in municipal reforms, such as the very few women attached to Local Vestries; they were required to have knowledge of sewage, sanitation, drain pipes, road surfaces, finance and law. Lucy Deane studied with them in her spare time.

When the Home Secretary and Medical Officers required the first women to join the ranks of Sanitary Inspectors they went first to Miss Fay Lankester at the National Health Society to ask her to recommend outstanding candidates. Lucy Deane and Rose Squire were the two to be immediately selected.

ELIZA ORME 1848 – 1937

Eliza Orme was the daughter of a wealthy distiller, educated at home and then went on to study at Bedford College and the University of London. She was refused admission to many courses because of her sex but finally graduated in Law in 1888, the first woman to do so.

She had been interested since her youth in industrial disputes and the growth of women's trades unions, and in 1886 was active in organising the deputations and protests of the women pitbrow workers. She opened a private law practice, and wrote on feminist issues, suffrage and educational opportunities. She held that women should not be excluded from any workplaces.

In 1892 she headed the work of the Royal Commission into women's labour with Clare Collet, Margaret Irwin, May Abraham (and Mary Paterson as a clerk and précis writer). This group travelled widely to report on such diverse industries as the linen trades in Ireland, the Black Country's iron industry, and London's public houses. They investigated differential wage rates between men and women, and the effects of women's industrial employment on health, morality and home and illustrated numerous concerns around the health and welfare of both factory workers, home workers, and 'sweated' labour.

The quality of work produced by the Royal Commission, and the abuses and grievances which they highlighted, were vital in affirming both the need for Women Inspectors, and the capacity of educated ladies to undertake such researches.

MARY MUIRHEAD PATERSON 1864 – 1941

Mary Paterson was the daughter of a prosperous boat builder, Gavin Paterson and his wife Annie, nee Muirhead. The Muirhead family had endowed Queen Margaret College for Girls in Glasgow, and Mary became one of the first pupils there. The family was committed to the education of women, and as a young woman Mary travelled extensively in the USA and Canada with her uncle Henry Muirhead. He was a socialist, and went to survey industrial conditions, and later became a member of the Independent Labour Party.

Mary began her career as a schoolteacher in London in 1892, and in 1892 was appointed as a clerk and précis writer for the Royal Commission of Labour. In 1893 she and May Abraham were appointed the first Women Factory Inspectors by Herbert Asquith and the Chief Inspector of Factories, Mr Richard Sprague Oram. May was based in London, and Mary in Scotland. Mary became Deputy Principal Inspector in 1908, but in 1911 became one of the first National Health Insurance Commissioners for Scotland, and was awarded a CBE in 1920.

RICHARD SPRAGUE ORAM 1830 – 1909

He was born in Devon, the son of a Superintendent Registrar from a strong non-conformist background. He was a Customs Officer as a young man, but joined the Factory Inspectorate in 1861 and became a Superintendent from 1881. As Chief Inspector of Factories he presided over major changes especially during the period when the Liberal Herbert Asquith was Home Secretary, 1892 – 1895. He was a strongly committed social reformer with other influential Liberals, and a strong supporter of the new Women Inspectors, effectively establishing their position within the Home Office. He retired after five years when the new Conservative Government took over in 1896, but he steered through many reforms in the Factory Inspectorate in that time. He was regarded as kindly and eccentric.

ROSE ELIZABETH SQUIRE 1861 – 1938

She was born in London, the daughter of William Squire, a Harley Street surgeon, and his wife Martha Wilkinson. She received home education, but at the age of 32 found she needed to earn a living and gained a diploma from Miss Lankester's National Health Society in 1892. She gained her Sanitary Inspectors Certificate in 1893 and was appointed by Dr Thom Dudfield with Lucy Deane as Sanitary Inspectors for Kensington.

In 1895 she became the fifth Lady Inspector of Factories.

In 1906 – 1907 she was the Special Investigator to the Royal Commission on Poor Laws.

From 1908 to 1912 she was based in Manchester, living with her sister and inspecting factories in the northern Districts. She thoroughly enjoyed her life there, but 1912 found her back in London, inspecting the health of munitions workers during World War One.

In 1918 she was appointed the Director of the women's welfare department of the Ministry of Munitions.

In 1920 she was the first woman to hold an administrative post in the Home Office.

She retired in 1926, and lived until her death at a little village called Fryerning in Essex.

HAROLD TENNANT MP 1865 – 1935

Harold 'Jack' Tennant was born at the Glen, Inverleithen, Peebles, the son of Sir Charles Tennant, a wealthy land owner. He went to Eton and Cambridge. In 1894 he became the Liberal MP for Berwickshire and then the Parliamentary Secretary to the Board of Trade.

He became the Private Secretary to H.H. Asquith when he was the Home Secretary in 1892 – 1895. He was a radical Liberal, supporting workers' compensation, minimum wage provisions, factory inspections, and unemployment insurance. He married his second wife, May Abraham, the first Woman Factory Inspector, in July 1897.

His socialite sister, Margot, married Herbert Henry Asquith.

GERTRUDE TUCKWELL 1861 – 1951

She was born in Oxford to William Tuckwell, master of New College School and Chaplain to New College Oxford. She was home schooled in her family's Christian Socialist tradition – her father was widely known as 'the radical parson' – trained as a teacher and taught at Bishop Otter College in Chichester and then at a working-class infant school in Chelsea.

She was always interested in trade unionism and became a trades union organiser campaigning for women's rights. In 1891 she became involved with the Women's Trades Union League when she came to London to act as secretary to her aunt, Lady Emilia Dilke, who was President of the League. From 1898 until 1905 she became the secretary of the Christian Social Union Research Committee. She took over as President of the Women's Trades Union League in 1905 until her retirement in 1918. Her sister Marian was a journalist.

She shared a flat in Chelsea with May Abraham until the latter married Harold Tennant MP in 1897.

She was one of the first seven women to be appointed as Justices of the Peace in 1919. She was the first woman magistrate in London, and a founder member of the Magistrates' Association in 1920. In 1930 she was inducted into the Order of the Companions of Honour.

She was interested and active in the world of social reforms to the end of her life. She lived in Surrey and died aged ninety in Guildford.

DOCTOR SIR ARTHUR WHITELEGGE 1852 – 1933

Arthur Whitelegge came from Manchester. He trained in medicine in London and Cambridge where he took a diploma in Public Health and became the Medical Officer of Health in Nottingham and then in Yorkshire.

He was appointed Chief Inspector of Factories after Richard Sprague Oram in 1896 because of his knowledge of public health in industrial districts.

Initially his appointment was unpopular amongst the existing Factory Inspectors, but he greatly reorganised the inspectorate into districts which would work more closely with the local Sanitary Authorities, and expanded the use of statistics. He appointed Dr Thomas Legge in 1898 to be the first Medical Inspector of Factories.

He was knighted in 1911 and retired in 1917.

Acknowledgments

Many folk have assisted me over the years to write this account about Lucy Deane.

She was my husband's grandmother's cousin, and she was first appointed in 1893, aged twenty eight, as one of the first Female Factory Inspectors. She was sent for advice to Miss Eliza Orme, who had become the first British woman lawyer some years previously. Miss Orme told her to keep records of EVERYTHING – "but not to buy smart leather bound note books, but soft cheap 3d school exercise books and indelible pencils; to keep one in her private handbag at all times, and to write immediately after any meeting, in cabs, hotels, trains,factories; and to keep a record of everyone and everything and everywhere she travelled; and to record her opinions and descriptions of everyone she met."

Lucy took this to heart and so across 125 years I thank Miss Orme for making the book possible.

Next, I want to thank those unknown relations of earlier generations who salvaged the diaries and papers, and squirreled them away in a small tin trunk and sent them on their journeys down the years until they reached our basement in the 1960's. I suspect Great Aunt Evelyn Deane, Lucy's cousin and best friend, who figures largely in this book, had plenty to do with it; and I thank God that the family mania for never throwing anything away has come in so useful.

Warwick University housed them for several years and then turned them over to the L.S.E. In the 1980's an American social historian, Mary Drake McFeelywrote her book "The Lady Inspectors, and asked us for photographs, and this rekindled our interest in Lucy. Thanks to her.

Thanks to the archive department at LSE for making me comfortable over the 18 months that I spent copying out the 23 small shabby exercise books, and helping me to sharpen my pencils – not indelible ones.

And thanks to Isabel Ryan for her invaluable help in deciphering Lucy's illegible handwriting. The book would have foundered without Isobel.

Thanks to cousin Susan Harland, who wrote many letters to the various branches of the Deane family, tracking down family friends and houses which Lucy mentions,

Ann Morisy and Vivian Wright took immense trouble proof –reading the book in its early stages and made many suggestions and improvements. And as I was incapable of steering my computer to track down suitable pictures from Picture Libraries, Vivian sorted out the collecting of illustrations with infinite patience and resourcefulness.

John Brown of the Streatham Society kindly trawled his extensive archives for late Victorian family and working conditions, and allowed me to choose several.

I am grateful to the Mary Evans Picture Library, National Portrait Gallery, Black Country Living Museum, Gladstone Pottery Museum and The National Library of Ireland for permitting me to use illustrations.

Close family and friends have been unfailingly positive, and Edward, James, Will, Ellie, Rory and Gary have put up with my one track mind for several years.

The Book Guild Publishers have nursemaided me through the final organisation, particularly Jack Wedgbury, Hannah Virk, Philippa Iliffe with patience. I am truly grateful.

Lastly, love and thanks to Martin who has suffered much extra household neglect over the past few years, and was always ready to help when I needed him.